C000058016

# THE abc OF
# BRITISH RAILWAYS
# LOCOMOTIVES

## COMBINED VOLUME
### PARTS 1—4
### Nos. 1-99999
#### ALSO DIESEL AND ELECTRIC LOCOMOTIVES AND MULTIPLE UNITS

SUMMER
1961
EDITION

LONDON :

Ian Allan Ltd

# NOTES ON THE USE OF THIS BOOK

THE following notes are a guide to the system of reference marks and other details given in the lists of dimensions shown for each class.

1. Many of the classes listed are sub-divided by reason of mechanical or constructional differences (on the Eastern and North Eastern Regions the sub-divisions are denoted in some cases by "Parts," shown thus: D16/3). At the head of each class will be found a list of such sub-divisions, if any, usually arranged in order of introduction. Each part is given there a reference mark by which its relevant dimensions, if differing from those of other parts, and the locomotives included in this sub-division, or part, may be indentified. Any other differences between locomotives are also indicated, with reference marks, below the details of the class's introduction.

2. The lists of dimensions at the head of each class show locomotives fitted with two inside cylinders, Stephenson valve gear and slide valves, unless otherwise stated, e.g. (O) = two outside cylinders, P.V. = piston valves.

3. The following method is used to denote superheated locomotives, the letters being inserted, where applicable, after the boiler pressure details : Su = All engines superheated.
SS = Some engines superheated.

4. The date on which the first locomotive of a class was built or modified is denoted by "Introduced."

5. S. denotes Service (Departmental) locomotive still carrying B.R. number. This reference letter is introduced only for the reader's guidance and is not borne by the locomotive concerned.

*Note :* On the Southern Region the letters "DS" preceding a number indicate a Service Locomotive. On the S.R. (only) this marking appears on the locomotive.

6. Full details of the following will be found in the books named :—

- Diesel and Electric locomotives in *ABC of British Railways Locomotives, Part 5 Diesel and Electric Locomotives.*

- Diesel Multiple-units in *ABC of British Railways Locomotives, Part 6 Diesel Multiple-units.*

- Electric Multiple-units in *ABC of British Railways Locomotives, Part 7 Electric Multiple-units.*

# BRITISH RAILWAYS LOCOMOTIVE
# SHEDS AND SHED CODES
## AND PRINCIPAL SIGNING-ON POINTS

ALL B.R. LOCOMOTIVES CARRY THE CODE OF THEIR HOME DEPOT
ON A SMALL PLATE AFFIXED TO THE SMOKEBOX DOOR.

## LONDON MIDLAND REGION

**LMW Western A.C. Lines**

| | |
|---|---|
| 1A | **Willesden** |
| 1B | Camden |
| 1C | Watford |
| 1D | Devons Road (Bow) |
| 1E | Bletchley |
| | Leighton Buzzard |

| | |
|---|---|
| 2A | **Rugby** |
| 2B | Nuneaton |
| 2E | Northampton |
| 2F | Woodford Halse |

| | |
|---|---|
| 5A | **Crewe North** |
| 5B | Crewe South |
| 5C | Stafford |
| 5D | Stoke |
| 5E | Alsager |
| 5F | Uttoxeter |

| | |
|---|---|
| 6A | **Chester (Midland)** |
| 6B | Mold Junction |
| 6C | Birkenhead |
| 6F | Bidston |
| 6G | Llandudno Junction |
| 6H | Bangor |
| 6J | Holyhead |
| 6K | Rhyl |

| | |
|---|---|
| 8A | **Edge Hill** |
| 8B | Warrington (Dallam) |
| 8C | Speke Junction |
| 8D | Widnes |
| 8E | Northwich |
| 8F | Springs Branch (Wigan) |
| 8G | Sutton Oak |

| | |
|---|---|
| 9A | **Longsight (Manchester)** |
| 9B | Stockport (Edgeley) |
| 9C | Macclesfield |
| 9D | Buxton |
| 9E | Trafford Park |
| | Glazebrook |
| 9F | Heaton Mersey |
| | Gowhole |
| 9G | Gorton |
| | Dinting |
| | Reddish |

| | |
|---|---|
| 12A | **Carlisle (Kingmoor)** |
| 12B | Carlisle (Upperby) |
| | Penrith |
| 12C | Carlisle (Canal) |
| 12D | Kirkby Stephen |
| 12E | Barrow |
| 12F | Workington |
| 12G | Oxenholme |
| 12H | Tebay |

| | |
|---|---|
| 14A | **Cricklewood** |
| 14B | Kentish Town |
| 14D | Neasden |
| | Aylesbury |
| 14E | Bedford |

| | |
|---|---|
| 15A | **Wellingborough** |
| 15B | Kettering |
| 15C | Leicester (Midland) |
| 15D | Coalville |
| 15E | Leicester (Central) |
| 15F | Market Harborough |

| | |
|---|---|
| 16A | **Nottingham** |
| 16B | Kirkby-in-Ashfield |
| 16D | Annesley |

| 17A | **Derby** | | 24D | Lower Darwen |
|---|---|---|---|---|
| 17B | Burton | | 24E | Blackpool |
| | Overseal | | 24F | Fleetwood |
| 17C | Rowsley | | 24G | Skipton |
| | Cromford | | 24H | Hellifield |
| | Middleton | | 24J | Lancaster (Green Ayre) |
| | Sheep Pasture | | 24K | Preston |
| | | | 24L | Carnforth |
| 18A | **Toton (Stapleford &** | | | |
| | **Sandiacre)** | | | |
| 18B | Westhouses | | 26A | **Newton Heath** |
| 18C | Hasland | | 26B | Agecroft |
| | | | 26C | Bolton |
| | | | 26D | Bury |
| 21A | **Saltley** | | 26E | Lees (Oldham) |
| 21B | Bescot | | 26F | Patricroft |
| 21C | Bushbury | | | |
| 21D | Aston | | | |
| 21E | **Monument Lane** | | 27A | **Bank Hall** |
| 21F | Walsall | | 27B | Aintree |
| | | | 27C | Southport |
| | | | 27D | Wigan |
| 24A | **Accrington** | | 27E | Walton-on-the-Hill |
| 24B | Rose Grove | | 27F | Brunswick (Liverpool) |
| 24C | Lostock Hall | | | Warrington (Central) |

## EASTERN REGION

| 30A | **Stratford** | | 34A | **Kings Cross** |
|---|---|---|---|---|
| | Bishops Stortford | | 34B | Hornsey |
| | Chelmsford | | 34D | Hitchin |
| | Enfield Town | | 34E | New England |
| | Hertford East | | 34F | Grantham |
| | Southend (Victoria) | | 34G | Finsbury Park |
| | Wood St. (Walthamstow) | | | |
| 30E | Colchester | | | |
| | Clacton | | | |
| | Maldon | | 36A | **Doncaster** |
| | Walton-on-Naze | | 36C | Frodingham |
| 30F | Parkeston | | 36E | Retford |
| | | | | |
| 31A | **Cambridge** | | 40A | **Lincoln** |
| | Ely | | 40B | Immingham |
| 31B | Whitemoor | | | Grimsby |
| 31C | Kings Lynn | | | New Holland |
| | | | 40E | Colwick |
| | | | 40F | Boston |
| 32A | **Norwich (Thorpe)** | | | Sleaford |
| | Cromer Beach | | | |
| 32B | Ipswich | | | |
| 32C | Lowestoft Central | | 41A | **Sheffield (Darnall)** |
| 32D | Yarmouth South Town | | 41B | Sheffield (Grimesthorpe) |
| | | | 41C | Millhouses |
| | | | 41D | Canklow |
| 33B | Tilbury | | 41E | Staveley (Barrow Hill) |
| 33C | Shoeburyness | | 41F | Mexborough |
| | | | 41H | Staveley (ex-G.C.) |
| | | | 41J | Langwith |

4

# NORTH EASTERN REGION

| | | | |
|---|---|---|---|
| 50A | **York** | 52H | Tyne Dock |
| 50B | Hull (Dairycoates) | | Pelton Level |
| | Hull (Alexandra Dock) | 52K | Consett |
| 50C | Hull (Botanic Gardens) | | |
| 50D | Goole | | |
| 50E | Scarborough | | |
| 50F | Malton | 55A | **Leeds (Holbeck)** |
| | | 55B | Stourton |
| | | 55C | Farnley |
| 51A | **Darlington** | 55D | Royston |
| 51C | West Hartlepool | 55E | Normanton |
| 51F | West Auckland | 55F | Bradford (Manningham) |
| 51J | Northallerton | | Keighley |
| 51L | Thornaby | 55G | Huddersfield |
| | | 55H | Leeds (Neville Hill) |
| | | | |
| 52A | **Gateshead** | 56A | **Wakefield** |
| | Bowes Bridge | | Knottingley |
| 52B | Heaton | 56B | Ardsley |
| 52C | Blaydon | 56C | Copley Hill |
| | Alston | 56D | Mirfield |
| 52D | Tweedmouth | 56E | Sowerby Bridge |
| | Alnmouth | 56F | Low Moor |
| 52E | Percy Main | 56G | Bradford (Hammerton St.) |
| 52F | North and South Blyth | | |
| 52G | Sunderland | | |

# SCOTTISH REGION

| | | | |
|---|---|---|---|
| 60A | **Inverness** | 62C | Dunfermline |
| | Dingwall | | Alloa |
| | Kyle of Lochalsh | | Kelty |
| 60B | Aviemore | | |
| | Boat of Garten | 63A | **Perth** |
| 60C | Helmsdale | | Aberfeldy |
| | Tain | | Blair Atholl |
| 60D | Wick | | Crieff |
| | Thurso | | Forfar |
| | | 63B | Fort William |
| 61A | **Kittybrewster** | | Mallaig |
| | Ballater | 63C | Oban |
| | Fraserburgh | | **Ballachulish** |
| | Inverurie | | |
| | Peterhead | | |
| 61B | Aberdeen (Ferryhill) | 64A | **St. Margarets** |
| 61C | Keith | | **(Edinburgh)** |
| | Banff | | Dunbar |
| | Elgin | | Galashiels |
| | | | Hardengreen |
| 62A | **Thornton** | | Longniddry |
| | Anstruther | | North Berwick |
| | Burntisland | | Seafield |
| | Kirkcaldy | | South Leith |
| | Ladybank | 64B | Haymarket |
| | Methil | 64C | Dalry Road |
| | | 64F | Bathgate |
| 62B | Dundee (Tay Bridge) | | |
| | Arbroath | | |
| | Montrose | 64G | Hawick |
| | St. Andrews | 64H | Leith Central |

| 65A | **Eastfield (Glasgow)** | | 66A | **Polmadie (Glasgow)** |
| | Arrochar | | 66B | Motherwell |
| 65B | St. Rollox | | 66C | Hamilton |
| 65C | Parkhead | | 66D | Greenock (Ladyburn) |
| 65D | Dawsholm | | 66E | Carstairs |
| | Dumbarton | | | |
| 65E | Kipps | | | |
| 65F | Grangemouth | | 67A | **Corkerhill (Glasgow)** |
| 65G | Yoker | | 67B | Hurlford |
| 65H | Helensburgh | | | Beith |
| 65I | Balloch | | | Muirkirk |
| 65J | Stirling | | 67C | Ayr |
| | Killin | | 67D | Ardrossan |
| 65K | Polmont | | | |
| | | | 68B | Dumfries |
| | | | 68C | Stranraer |
| | | | 68D | Beattock |

## SOUTHERN REGION

| 70A | **Nine Elms** | | 72B | Salisbury |
| 70B | Feltham | | 72C | Yeovil |
| 70C | Guildford | | 72E | Barnstaple Junction |
| | Reading South | | | Ilfracombe |
| 70D | Basingstoke | | | Torrington |
| 70H | Ryde (I.O.W.) | | 72F | Wadebridge |
| | | | | |
| 71A | **Eastleigh** | | 73A | **Stewarts Lane** |
| | Andover Junction | | 73B | Bricklayers Arms |
| | Lymington | | 73C | Hither Green |
| | Southampton Terminus | | 73E | Faversham |
| | Winchester | | 73F | Ashford (Kent) |
| 71B | Bournemouth | | | Gillingham (Kent) |
| | Branksome | | | Ramsgate |
| 71G | Weymouth | | 73H | Dover |
| | Bridport | | | Folkestone |
| 71I | Southampton Docks | | 73J | Tonbridge |
| | | | | |
| 72A | **Exmouth Junction** | | 75A | **Brighton** |
| | Bude | | 75B | Redhill |
| | Callington | | 75C | Norwood Junction |
| | Exmouth | | 75E | Three Bridges |
| | Lyme Regis | | | Horsham |
| | Okehampton | | 75F | Tunbridge Wells West |
| | Seaton | | | |

## WESTERN REGION

| CED | **Cardiff East Dock** | | 81F | Oxford |
| | | | | Fairford |
| DG | **Danygraig Diesel Depot** | | | |
| | | | | |
| 81A | **Old Oak Common** | | 82A | **Bristol (Bath Road)** |
| 81B | Slough | | 82B | St. Philip's Marsh |
| 81C | Southall | | | Bath |
| 81D | Reading | | | Wells |
| 81E | Didcot | | | Weston-super-Mare |

6

| | | | | |
|---|---|---|---|---|
| 82C | Swindon | | 86E | Severn Tunnel Junction |
| | Chippenham | | 86F | Aberbeeg |
| 82D | Westbury | | 86G | Pontypool Road |
| | Frome | | | |
| 82E | Bristol (Barrow Road) | | | |
| 82F | Bath (Green Park) | | 87A | **Neath** |
| | Radstock West | | | Glyn Neath |
| 82G | Templecombe | | | Neath (N. & B.) |
| | | | 87B | Duffryn Yard |
| | | | 87D | Swansea East Dock |
| | | | | Gurnos |
| 83A | **Newton Abbot** | | | Upper Bank |
| | Kingsbridge | | 87E | Landore |
| 83B | Taunton | | 87F | Llanelly |
| 83C | Exeter | | | Burry Port |
| | Tiverton Junction | | | Llandovery |
| 83D | Laira (Plymouth) | | | Pantyffynnon |
| | Launceston | | 87G | Carmarthen |
| 83E | St. Blazey | | | Aberayron |
| | Bodmin | | 87H | Neyland |
| | Moorswater | | | Cardigan |
| 83F | Truro | | | Milford Haven |
| 83G | Penzance | | | Pembroke Dock |
| | Helston | | | Whitland |
| | St. Ives | | 87J | Goodwick |
| 83H | Plymouth (Friary) | | | |
| | | | | |
| 84A | **Wolverhampton** | | 88A | **Cardiff (Canton)** |
| | **(Stafford Road)** | | 88B | Cardiff (Radyr) |
| 84B | Oxley | | | Cathays |
| 84C | Banbury | | 88C | Barry |
| 84D | Leamington Spa | | 88D | Merthyr |
| 84E | Tyseley | | | Dowlais Cae Harris |
| | Stratford-on-Avon | | | Rhymney |
| 84F | Stourbridge | | 88E | Abercynon |
| 84G | Kidderminster | | 88F | Treherbert |
| 84H | Wellington (Salop) | | | Ferndale |
| | | | 88G | Llantrisant |
| | | | 88H | Tondu |
| 85A | **Worcester** | | 88J | Aberdare |
| | Evesham | | 88K | Brecon |
| | Honeybourne | | | |
| | Kingham | | | |
| | Ledbury | | 89A | **Shrewsbury** |
| 85B | Gloucester (Horton Road) | | | Builth Road |
| | Brimscombe | | | Craven Arms |
| | Cheltenham (Malvern Rd.) | | | Knighton |
| | Lydney | | | Leominster |
| | Ross-on-Wye | | 89B | Croes Newydd |
| 85C | Gloucester (Barnwood) | | | Bala |
| | Dursley | | | Penmaenpool |
| | Tewkesbury | | | Trawsfynydd |
| 85D | Bromsgrove | | 89C | Machynlleth |
| | Redditch | | | Aberystwyth |
| | | | | Aberystwyth (V. of R.) |
| | | | | Portmadoc |
| 86A | **Newport** | | | Pwllheli |
| | **(Ebbw Junction)** | | 89D | Oswestry |
| 86B | Newport (Pill) | | | Llanidloes |
| 86C | Hereford | | | Moat Lane |

7

# SUMMARY OF WESTERN REGION
# STEAM LOCOMOTIVE CLASSES
## WITH HISTORICAL NOTES AND DIMENSIONS

The code given in smaller bold type at the head of each Class,
e.g. " 6MT " denotes its British Railways power classification.

The numbers of locomotives in service have been checked in the W.R. to January
28th, 1961, S.R. to February 10th, 1961, and L.M.R. to January 28th, 1961.

**4-6-0**   **6MT**   **1000 Class**
## " County "

Introduced 1945. Hawksworth design
with 280 lb. boiler pressure since
reduced to 250 lb. per sq. in.
Fitted with double chimney.
Weight: Loco.   76 tons 17 cwt.
          Tender 49 tons 0 cwt.
Pressure: 250 lb. Su.
Cyls.: (O) 18½" × 30".
Driving Wheels: 6' 3".
T.E.: 28,241 lb.  P.V.

1000–29               **Total 30**

**4-6-0**   **7P**   **4073 Class**
## " Castle "

*Introduced 1923. Collett design,
developed from " Star " (4037,
5083–92 converted from " Star ").
†Introduced 1946. Fitted with 3-row
superheater.
‡Introduced 1947. Fitted with 4-row
superheater.
¶Introduced 1956. Fitted with double
chimney.
Weight: Loco.  79 tons 17 cwt.
          Tender 46 tons 14 cwt.
Pressure: 225 lb. Su.
Cyls.: (4) 16" × 26".
Driving Wheels: 6' 8½".
T.E.: 31,625 lb.
Inside Walschaerts valve gear and
rocking shafts.  P.V.

*4037/75/6/9/81–3/5/6/9/92/4–6/
8/9, 5001–4/6/8/11–20/2–5/7/
9–32/4/5/8–42/4–7/51–5/8–60/
2/6–70/6/80/4/5/7/9–92
†4077, 5000/7/21/37/48/50/63/5/
72/4/5/7/8/81/2/93/6–9, 7000/
2/5/7–9/11/2/5–7/20/1/5–8/31/
3/5/7

‡4074/8, 5026/36/49/71/3/94/5,
7019/24/9/30/4
*¶5056
†¶7001/3/6/10/4/23/32
‡¶4080/7/8/90/3, 5033/43/57/61/
4/88, 7004/13/8/22/36
.
                     **Total 155**

**4-6-0**   **5MT**   **4900 Class**
## " Hall "

Introduced 1928. Modified design of
Collett rebuild with 6' 0" driving
wheels of " Saint " (built 1907) for
new construction, with higher-
pitched boiler, modified footplating
and detail differences.
Weight: Loco. 75 tons 0 cwt.
          Tender 46 tons 14 cwt.
Pressure: 225 lb. Su.
Cyls.: (O) 18½" × 30".
Driving Wheels: 6' 0".
T.E.: 27,275 lb.
P.V.

4902–10/2–39/41–99, 5900–14/6–
99, 6900–58      **Total 254**

**4-6-0**   **8P**   **6000 Class**
## " King "

Introduced 1927. Collett design.
All engines modified since 1947 with
4-row superheater and since 1955
with double chimney.
Weight: Loco.  89 tons 0 cwt.
          Tender 46 tons 14 cwt.
Pressure: 250 lb. Su.
Cyls.: (4) 16¼" × 28".
Driving Wheels: 6' 6".
T.E.: 40,285 lb.
Inside Walschaerts valve gear and
rocking shafts.  P.V.

6000–29               **Total 30**

## 4-6-0   5MT   6800 Class
### " Grange "

Introduced 1936. Collett design, variation of " Hall " with smaller wheels, incorporating certain parts of withdrawn 4300 2-6-0 locos.
Weight: Loco.  74 tons 0 cwt.
       Tender 40 tons 0 cwt.
Pressure: 225 lb. Su.
Cyls.: (O) 18½″ × 30″.
Driving Wheels: 5′ 8″.
T.E.: 28,875 lb.
P.V.

6800/2–79                **Total 79**

## 4-6-0   5MT   6959 Class
### " Modified Hall "

Introduced 1944. Hawksworth development of " Hall," with larger superheater, "one-piece" main frames and plate-framed bogie.
Weight:  Loco. 75 tons 16 cwt.
        Tender 46 tons 14 cwt.
Pressure: 225 lb. Su.
Cyls.: (O) 18½″ × 30″.
Driving Wheels: 6′ 0″.
T.E.: 27,275 lb.
P.V

6959–99, 7900–29        **Total 71**

## 4-6-0   5MT   7800 Class
### " Manor "

Introduced 1938. Collett design for secondary lines, incorporating certain parts of withdrawn 4300 2-6-0 locos.
Weight: Loco.  68 tons 18 cwt.
       Tender 40 tons 0 cwt.
Pressure: 225 lb. Su.
Cyls.: (O) 18″ × 30″.
Driving Wheels: 5′ 8″.
T.E.: 27,340 lb.
P.V.

7800–29                **Total 30**

## 4-4-0      " City " Class

Introduced 1903. Churchward design.
Weight: Loco.  55 tons 6 cwt.
       Tender 36 tons 15 cwt.
Pressure: 200 lb. Su.
Cyls.: 18″ × 26″.
Driving Wheels: 6′ 8½″.
T.E.: 17,790 lb.

3440
**Withdrawn 1931 and preserved in York Museum. Returned to service 1957.**

                 **Total 1**

## 2-8-0   8F   2800 Class

*Introduced 1903. Churchward design, earlier locos. subsequently fitted with new boiler and superheater.
†Introduced 1938. Collett locos., with side-window cab and detail alterations.
Weight: Loco.  { 75 tons 10 cwt.*
              { 76 tons  5 cwt.†
       Tender 40 tons 0 cwt.
Pressure: 225 lb. Su.
Cyls.: (O) 18½″ × 30″.
Driving Wheels: 4′ 7½″.
T.E.: 35,380 lb.
P.V.

*2807/18/22/34/6/9/41/2/5/9/51–
  62/5–7/71–6/9/82/3

†2884–99, 3800–66    **Total 117**

## 2-8-0   7F   4700 Class

Introduced 1919. Churchward mixed traffic design (4700 built with smaller boiler and later rebuilt).
Weight: Loco.  82 tons 0 cwt.
       Tender 46 tons 14 cwt.
Pressure: 225 lb. Su.
Cyls.: (O) 19″ × 30″.
Driving Wheels: 5′ 8″.
T.E.: 30,460 lb.
P.V.

4700–8                **Total 9**

## 2-6-0   4MT   4300 Class

*Introduced 1911. Churchward design.
†Introduced 1925. Locos. with detail alteration affecting weight.
‡Introduced 1932. Locos. with side window cab and detail alterations.
Weight: Loco.  { 62 tons 0 cwt.*
              { 64 tons 0 cwt.†
              { 65 tons 6 cwt.‡
       Tender 40 tons 0 cwt.

Pressure: 200 lb. Su.
Cyls.: (O) 18½″ × 30″.
T.E.: 25,670 lb.
P.V.

*5306/18/22/6/30/2/6/51/7/8/69/
76/80/5/99, 6301/2/4/6/9/10/
2–4/6/7/9/20/4/6/7/9/30/5–42/
/4–50/3/6/7/61–70/2–6/8–81/
4–8/90–2/4/5, 7305–21

†7300–4

‡7322–41 **Total 122**


## 0-6-0  3MT  2251 Class

Introduced 1930. Collett design.
Weight:
    Loco.    43 tons 8 cwt.
    Tender { 36 tons 15 cwt.
            47 tons 6 cwt. (ex-R.O.D.
            tender from 3000 Class
            2-8-0).
Pressure: 200 lb. Su.
Cyls.: 17½″ × 24″.
Driving Wheels: 5′ 2″.
T.E.: 20,155 lb.

2200/1/4/6/9–12/4–24/9–34/6/9
–51/3/5–7/60/1/7/8/71/3/6/7/
83/6–9/91/2/4/5/8,
3200/1/3–19 **Total 80**


## 2-8-2T  8F  7200 Class

Introduced 1934. Collett rebuild, with
extended bunker and trailing wheels,
of Churchward 4200 class 2-8-0T.
Weight: 92 tons 2 cwt.
Pressure: 200 lb. Su.
Cyls.: (O) 19″ × 30″.
Driving Wheels: 4′ 7½″.
T.E.: 33,170 lb.
P.V.

7200–53 **Total 54**


## 2-8-0T  {7F* / 8F†}  4200 Class

*Introduced 1910. Churchward design.
†5205 class. Introduced 1923. With
enlarged cyls. and detail alterations.
Weight: { 81 tons 12 cwt.*
          82 tons 2 cwt.†

Pressure: 200 lb. Su.
Cyls.: { (O) 18½″ × 30″*.
      { (O) 19″ × 30″†.
Driving Wheels: 4′ 7½″.
T.E.: { 31,450 lb.*
      { 33,170 lb.†
P.V.

*420/7/13/4/8/22/5/7–30/2/3/5–8/
41–3/6–8/50–9/62–80/2–6/9–
99, 5200–4

†5205/6/8–64 **Total 131**


## 2-6-2T  4MT  4500 Class

*Introduced 1906. Churchward design
for light branches, developed from
4400 class with larger wheels, earlier
locos. subsequently fitted with superheater.

†4575 class. Introduced 1927. With
detail alterations and increased
weight.

‡Introduced 1953. Push-and-pull fitted.

Weight: { 57 tons 0 cwt.*
        { 61 tons 0 cwt.†‡
Pressure: 200 lb. Su.
Cyls.: (O) 17″ × 24″.
Driving Wheels: 4′ 7½″.
T.E.: 21,250 lb.
P.V.

*4507/49/52/5/7/8/61/3–7/9–71/
3/4

†4588/91/3, 5503/8/9/15/6/8/20/1/
5/6/31/2/7–9/41/2/4/7–50/3/4/
62–4/9–71/3

‡5511/45/55/60/8/72

**Total 57**


## 2-6-2T  4MT  5101 & 6100 Classes

*5101 class. Introduced 1929. Modified
design for new construction of Collett
rebuild, with detail alterations and
increased weight, of Churchward 3100
class (introduced 1903 and subsequently fitted with superheater).

**†6100 class.** Introduced 1931. Locos. for London suburban area with increased boiler pressure.
Weight: 78 tons 9 cwt.
Pressure: $\begin{cases} 200 \text{ lb. Su.*} \\ 225 \text{ lb. Su.†} \end{cases}$
Cyls.: (O) 18″ × 30″.
Driving Wheels: 5′ 8″
T.E.: $\begin{cases} 24,300 \text{ lb.*} \\ 27,340 \text{ lb.†} \end{cases}$
P.V.

*4100–37/40–61/3/5–9/71–9, 5101/51–4/8/64/6/7/73–5/7/80–4/7/8/90–5/8/9

†6101/3/6–20/2–69 **Total 168**

---

**2-6-2T** 4MT **8100 Class**

Introduced 1938. Collett rebuild, with higher pressure and smaller wheels, of Churchward locos. in 5100 class.
Weight: 76 tons 11 cwt.
Pressure: 225 lb. Su.
Cyls.: (O) 18″ × 30″.
Driving Wheels: 5′ 6″.
T.E.: 28,165 lb.
P.V.

8100–4/6–9 **Total 9**

---

NOTE

The following abbreviations are used to indicate the pre-grouping owners of certain Western Region locomotives:

Car.R.    Cardiff Railway.
P. & M.   Powlesland & Mason (Contractor).
V. of R.  Cambrian Railways (Vale of Rheidol).
W. & L.   Cambrian Railways (Welshpool & Llanfair).

---

**2-6-2T** unclass. **V. of R.**

*Introduced 1902. Davies and Metcalfe design for V. of R. 1′ 11½″ gauge.
†Introduced 1923. G.W. development of V. of R. design.
Weight: 25 tons 0 cwt.
Gauge: 1′ 11½″.
Pressure: 165 lb.
Cyls.: (O) $\begin{cases} 11″ \times 17″.* \\ 11½″ \times 17″.† \end{cases}$
Driving Wheels: 2′ 6″.
T.E.: $\begin{cases} 9,615 \text{ lb.*} \\ 10,510 \text{ lb.†} \end{cases}$
Walschaerts valve gear.

*9  †7/8 **Total 3**

---

**0-6-2T** 5MT **5600 Class**

*Introduced 1924. Collett design for service in Welsh valleys.
†Introduced 1927. Locos. with detail alterations.
Weight: $\begin{cases} 68 \text{ tons 12 cwt.*} \\ 69 \text{ tons 7 cwt.†} \end{cases}$
Pressure: 200 lb. Su.
Cyls.: 18″ × 26″.
Driving Wheels: 4′ 7½″.
T.E.: 25,800 lb.
P.V

*5600–99

†6600–99 **Total 200**

---

**0-6-0ST** 0F **1361 Class**

Introduced 1910. Churchward design for dock shunting.
Weight: 35 tons 4 cwt.
Pressure: 150 lb.
Cyls.: (O) 16″ × 20″.
Driving Wheels: 3′ 8″.
T.E.: 14,835 lb.

1361–5 **Total 5**

---

**0-6-0PT** 1F **1366 Class**

Introduced 1934. Collett development of 1361 class, with pannier tanks.
Weight: 35 tons 15 cwt.
Pressure: 165 lb.
Cyls.: (O) 16″ × 20″.
Driving Wheels: 3′ 8″.
T.E.: 16,320 lb.

1367–9 **Total 3**

## 0-6-0PT 4F 1500 Class

Introduced 1949. Hawksworth short-wheelbase heavy shunting design.
Weight: 58 tons 4 cwt.
Pressure: 200 lb.
Cyls.: (O) 17½″ × 24″.
Driving Wheels: 4′ 7½″.
T.E.: 22,515 lb.
Walschaerts valve gear. P.V.

1500/3–8 **Total 7**

## 0-6-0PT 2F 1600 Class

Introduced 1949. Hawksworth light branch line and shunting design.
Weight: 41 tons 12 cwt.
Pressure: 165 lb.
Cyls.: 16½″ × 24″.
Driving Wheels: 4′ 1½″.
T.E.: 18,515 lb.

1605–9/11–5/7–9, 21–4/6–8/30–
4/6/8–43/5–51/3–8/60–9
**Total 55**

## 0-6-0PT 1P 5400 Class

Introduced 1931. Collett design for light passenger work, push-and-pull fitted.
Weight: 46 tons 12 cwt.
Pressure: 165 lb.
Cyls.: 16½″ × 24″.
Driving Wheels: 5′ 2″.
T.E.: 14,780 lb.

5410/2/6/20/1 **Total 5**

## 0-6-0PT 3F 5700 Class

*Introduced 1929. Collett design for shunting and light goods work developed from 2021 class.
†Introduced 1930. Locos. with steam brake and no A.T.C. fittings, for shunting only.
§Introduced 1933. Locos. with detail alterations, modified cab (except 8700) and increased weight.
‡Introduced 1933. Locos. with condensing apparatus for working over L.T. Metropolitan line.
¶Introduced 1948. Steam brake locos. with increased weight.

Weight: { 47 tons 10 cwt.*†
{ 50 tons 15 cwt.‡
{ 49 tons 0 cwt.§¶
Pressure: 200 lb.
Cyls.: 17½″ × 24″.
Driving Wheels: 4′ 7½″.
T.E.: 22,515 lb.

*5706/20/8/44/6/9/56/8/61/6/8/
70/1/3–5/8–80/3/7/9/91/3/8,
7700/13/5/8/20/1/4/9/32,6/9/
41/4/5,7–9/53/5/6/6012/4/5/
71/2/80/2–8/90/6,8/9, 8701/2/
5–7/9–49
†6700/14/20/4/38/9/41/2/9
§3600–8/10–37/9–48/50–3703/5–
39/41–92/4–8, 4600–85/7–99,
8700/50–3/6/7/9–77/9–99,
9600–72/4–82, 9711–36/8–48/
50–71/3–94/6–9
‡9700/2–7/9/10
¶6754/5/7/60/2–5/7–70/2/7/8
**Total 648**

## 0-6-0PT 2P* 2F† 6400 & 7400 Classes

*6400 class. Introduced 1932. Collett design for light passenger work, variation of 5400 class with smaller wheels, push-and-pull fitted.
†7400 class. Introduced 1936. Non-push-and-pull fitted locos.
Weight: { 45 tons 12 cwt.*
{ 45 tons 9 cwt.†
Pressure: 180 lb.
Cyls.: 16½″ × 24″.
Driving Wheels: 4′ 7½″.
T.E.: 18,010 lb.

*6400/3/8/10–3/5/6/8/9/21/2/4/
6/9–31/3–8
†7402–9/12–4/7/8/21–37/9–46/
8/9

**Total : 6400 Class 24**
**7400 Class 40**

## 0-6-0PT 4F 9400 Class

*Introduced 1947. Hawksworth taper boiler design for heavy shunting.
†Introduced 1949. Locos. with non-superheated boiler.
Weight: 55 tons 7 cwt.
Pressure: 200 lb. SS.
Cyls.: 17½" × 24".
Driving Wheels: 4' 7½".
T.E.: 22,515 lb.

*9401/4-9

†3400-9, 8400-5/7/9,14-6/8/20/
2/5/6/8/30/1/3/5-41/4-6/9/51-3
6/8/9/61/4-7/9-72/4/5/7-84/6-
91/3-9, 9410-3/5/6/8-26/9-31/
3/5/7/40-2/4/6/8/50-7/60/1/3-
7/9-80/2-90/3-5/7/8

Total 154

## 0-6-0T Unclass. W. & L.

(Line closed: locos. stored.)
Introduced 1902. Beyer Peacock design for 2' 6" gauge W. & L. Section, Cambrian Railways.
Weight: 19 tons 18 cwt.
Gauge: 2' 6".
Pressure: 150 lb.
Cyls.: (O) 11½" × 16".
Driving Wheels: 2' 9".
T.E.: 8,175 lb.
Walschaerts valve gear.

822/3                          Total 2

## 0-4-2T 1P 1400 & 5800 Classes

*1400 class introduced 1932. Collett design for light branch work (originally designated 4800 class). Push-and-pull fitted.
†5800 class introduced 1933. Non-push-and-pull fitted locos.
Weight: 41 tons 6 cwt.
Pressure: 165 lb.
Cyls.: 16" × 24".
Driving Wheels: 5' 2".
T.E.: 13,900 lb.

*1409/10/9-21/4/6/31/2/4/5/8/40/
2/4/5/7/50/1/3/5/8/62/3/6/8/
70-4

†5815                          Total 32

## 0-4-0ST 0F Cardiff Rly.

Introduced 1893. Kitson design for Cardiff Railway.
Weight: 25 tons 10 cwt.
Pressure: 160 lb.
Cyls.: (O) 14" × 21".
Driving Wheels: 3' 2½".
T.E.: 14,540 lb.
Hawthorn Kitson valve gear.

1338                           Total 1

## 0-4-0ST 0F P. & M.

Introduced 1907. Peckett design for P. & M.
Weight: 33 tons 10 cwt.
Pressure: 150 lb.
Cyls.: (O) 15" × 21".
Driving Wheels: 3' 7".
T.E.: 14,010 lb.

1151/2                         Total 2

## HISTORIC LOCOMOTIVES PRESERVED IN STORE

| Type | Originating Company | Pre-Grouping No. | G.W.R. No. | Name | Place of Preservation |
|------|---------------------|------------------|------------|------|----------------------|
| 0-6-0 | G.W.R. | 2516 | 2516 | — | Swindon |
| 4-6-0 | G.W.R. | 4003 | 4003 | Lode Star | Swindon |
| 4-6-0 | G.W.R. | 4073 | 4073 | Caerphilly Castle | Swindon |

# NUMERICAL LIST OF WESTERN REGION
## STEAM LOCOMOTIVES

Locomotives are of G.W. origin except where
indicated by other initials

### 2-6-2T     V. of R.

- 7   Owain Glyndŵr
- 8   Llywelyn
- 9   Prince of Wales

### 0-6-0T     W. & L.

822     823

(Line closed : locos. stored.)

### 4-6-0     1000 Class
#### "County"

| | |
|---|---|
| 1000 | County of Middlesex |
| 1001 | County of Bucks |
| 1002 | County of Berks |
| 1003 | County of Wilts |
| 1004 | County of Somerset |
| 1005 | County of Devon |
| 1006 | County of Cornwall |
| 1007 | County of Brecknock |
| 1008 | County of Cardigan |
| 1009 | County of Carmarthen |
| 1010 | County of Caernarvon |
| 1011 | County of Chester |
| 1012 | County of Denbigh |
| 1013 | County of Dorset |
| 1014 | County of Glamorgan |
| 1015 | County of Gloucester |
| 1016 | County of Hants |
| 1017 | County of Hereford |
| 1018 | County of Leicester |
| 1019 | County of Merioneth |
| 1020 | County of Monmouth |
| 1021 | County of Montgomery |
| 1022 | County of Northampton |
| 1023 | County of Oxford |
| 1024 | County of Pembroke |
| 1025 | County of Radnor |
| 1026 | County of Salop |
| 1027 | County of Stafford |
| 1028 | County of Warwick |
| 1029 | County of Worcester |

### 0-4-0ST     P. & M.

1151     1152

### 0-4-0ST     Car. R.

1338

### 0-6-0ST     1361 Class

| 1361 | 1363 | 1365 |
|------|------|------|
| 1362 | 1364 | |

### 0-6-0PT     1366 Class

1367  |  1368  |  1369

## 0-4-2T       1400 Class

| | | | |
|------|------|------|------|
| 1409 | 1432 | 1447 | 1466 |
| 1410 | 1434 | 1450 | 1468 |
| 1419 | 1435 | 1451 | 1470 |
| 1420 | 1438 | 1453 | 1471 |
| 1421 | 1440 | 1455 | 1472 |
| 1424 | 1442 | 1458 | 1473 |
| 1426 | 1444 | 1462 | 1474 |
| 1431 | 1445 | 1463 | |

## 0-6-0PT       1500 Class

| | | | |
|------|------|------|------|
| 1500 | 1504 | 1506 | 1508 |
| 1503 | 1505 | 1507 | |

## 0-6-0PT       1600 Class

| | | | |
|------|------|------|------|
| 1605 | 1622 | 1640 | 1656 |
| 1606 | 1623 | 1641 | 1657 |
| 1607 | 1624 | 1642 | 1658 |
| 1608 | 1626 | 1643 | 1660 |
| 1609 | 1627 | 1645 | 1661 |
| 1611 | 1628 | 1646 | 1662 |
| 1612 | 1630 | 1647 | 1663 |
| 1613 | 1631 | 1648 | 1664 |
| 1614 | 1632 | 1649 | 1665 |
| 1615 | 1633 | 1650 | 1666 |
| 1617 | 1634 | 1651 | 1667 |
| 1618 | 1636 | 1653 | 1668 |
| 1619 | 1638 | 1654 | 1669 |
| 1621 | 1639 | 1655 | |

## 0-6-0       2251 Class

| | | | |
|------|------|------|------|
| 2200 | 2211 | 2218 | 2224 |
| 2201 | 2212 | 2219 | 2229 |
| 2204 | 2214 | 2220 | 2230 |
| 2206 | 2215 | 2221 | 2231 |
| 2209 | 2216 | 2222 | 2232 |
| 2210 | 2217 | 2223 | 2233 |

| | | | |
|------|------|------|------|
| 2234 | 2247 | 2260 | 2286 |
| 2236 | 2248 | 2261 | 2287 |
| 2239 | 2249 | 2267 | 2288 |
| 2240 | 2250 | 2268 | 2289 |
| 2241 | 2251 | 2271 | 2291 |
| 2242 | 2253 | 2273 | 2292 |
| 2243 | 2255 | 2276 | 2294 |
| 2244 | 2256 | 2277 | 2295 |
| 2245 | 2257 | 2283 | 2298 |
| 2246 | | | |

## 2-8-0       2800 Class

| | | | |
|------|------|------|------|
| 2807 | 2854 | 2872 | 2888 |
| 2818 | 2855 | 2873 | 2889 |
| 2822 | 2856 | 2874 | 2890 |
| 2834 | 2857 | 2875 | 2891 |
| 2836 | 2858 | 2876 | 2892 |
| 2839 | 2859 | 2879 | 2893 |
| 2841 | 2860 | 2882 | 2894 |
| 2842 | 2861 | 2883 | 2895 |
| 2845 | 2862 | 2884 | 2896 |
| 2849 | 2865 | 2885 | 2897 |
| 2851 | 2866 | 2886 | 2898 |
| 2852 | 2867 | 2887 | 2899 |
| 2853 | 2871 | | |

## 0-6-0       2251 Class

| | | | |
|------|------|------|------|
| 3200 | 3206 | 3211 | 3216 |
| 3201 | 3207 | 3212 | 3217 |
| 3203 | 3208 | 3213 | 3218 |
| 3204 | 3209 | 3214 | 3219 |
| 3205 | 3210 | 3215 | |

## 0-6-0PT       9400 Class

| | | | |
|------|------|------|------|
| 3400 | 3403 | 3406 | 3408 |
| 3401 | 3404 | 3407 | 3409 |
| 3402 | 3405 | | |

## 4-4-0       " City " Class

3440    City of Truro

15

## 0-6-0PT

| | |
|---|---|
| 3600 | 3647 |
| 3601 | 3648 |
| 3602 | 3650 |
| 3603 | 3651 |
| 3604 | 3652 |
| 3605 | 3653 |
| 3606 | 3654 |
| 3607 | 3655 |
| 3608 | 3656 |
| 3610 | 3657 |
| 3611 | 3658 |
| 3612 | 3659 |
| 3613 | 3660 |
| 3614 | 3661 |
| 3615 | 3662 |
| 3616 | 3663 |
| 3617 | 3664 |
| 3618 | 3665 |
| 3619 | 3666 |
| 3620 | 3667 |
| 3621 | 3668 |
| 3622 | 3669 |
| 3623 | 3670 |
| 3624 | 3671 |
| 3625 | 3672 |
| 3626 | 3673 |
| 3627 | 3674 |
| 3628 | 3675 |
| 3629 | 3676 |
| 3630 | 3677 |
| 3631 | 3678 |
| 3632 | 3679 |
| 3633 | 3680 |
| 3634 | 3681 |
| 3635 | 3682 |
| 3636 | 3683 |
| 3637 | 3684 |
| 3639 | 3685 |
| 3640 | 3686 |
| 3641 | 3687 |
| 3642 | 3688 |
| 3643 | 3689 |
| 3644 | 3690 |
| 3645 | 3691 |
| 3646 | 3692 |

## 5700 Class

| | | | |
|---|---|---|---|
| 3693 | 3739 | 3785 | 3789 |
| 3694 | 3741 | 3786 | 3790 |
| 3695 | 3742 | 3787 | 3791 |
| 3696 | 3743 | 3788 | |
| 3697 | 3744 | | |
| 3698 | 3745 | | |
| 3699 | 3746 | | |
| 3700 | 3747 | | |
| 3701 | 3748 | | |
| 3702 | 3749 | | |
| 3703 | 3750 | | |
| 3705 | 3751 | | |
| 3706 | 3752 | | |
| 3707 | 3753 | | |
| 3708 | 3754 | | |
| 3709 | 3755 | | |
| 3710 | 3756 | | |
| 3711 | 3757 | | |
| 3712 | 3758 | | |
| 3713 | 3759 | | |
| 3714 | 3760 | | |
| 3715 | 3761 | | |
| 3716 | 3762 | | |
| 3717 | 3763 | | |
| 3718 | 3764 | | |
| 3719 | 3765 | | |
| 3720 | 3766 | | |
| 3721 | 3767 | | |
| 3722 | 3768 | | |
| 3723 | 3769 | | |
| 3724 | 3770 | | |
| 3725 | 3771 | | |
| 3726 | 3772 | | |
| 3727 | 3773 | | |
| 3728 | 3774 | | |
| 3729 | 3775 | | |
| 3730 | 3776 | | |
| 3731 | 3777 | | |
| 3732 | 3778 | | |
| 3733 | 3779 | | |
| 3734 | 3780 | | |
| 3735 | 3781 | | |
| 3736 | 3782 | | |
| 3737 | 3783 | | |
| 3738 | 3784 | | |

Additional 5700 Class numbers (top right):

| | | | |
|---|---|---|---|
| 3785 | 3789 | 3792 | 3796 |
| 3786 | 3790 | 3794 | 3797 |
| 3787 | 3791 | 3795 | 3798 |
| 3788 | | | |

## 2-8-0    2800 Class

| | | | |
|---|---|---|---|
| 3800 | 3817 | 3834 | 3851 |
| 3801 | 3818 | 3835 | 3852 |
| 3802 | 3819 | 3836 | 3853 |
| 3803 | 3820 | 3837 | 3854 |
| 3804 | 3821 | 3838 | 3855 |
| 3805 | 3822 | 3839 | 3856 |
| 3806 | 3823 | 3840 | 3857 |
| 3807 | 3824 | 3841 | 3858 |
| 3808 | 3825 | 3842 | 3859 |
| 3809 | 3826 | 3843 | 3860 |
| 3810 | 3827 | 3844 | 3861 |
| 3811 | 3828 | 3845 | 3862 |
| 3812 | 3829 | 3846 | 3863 |
| 3813 | 3830 | 3847 | 3864 |
| 3814 | 3831 | 3848 | 3865 |
| 3815 | 3832 | 3849 | 3866 |
| 3816 | 3833 | 3850 | |

## 4-6-0    4073 Class

### " Castle "

| | |
|---|---|
| 4037 | The South Wales Borderers |
| 4074 | Caldicot Castle |
| 4075 | Cardiff Castle |
| 4076 | Carmarthen Castle |
| 4077 | Chepstow Castle |
| 4078 | Pembroke Castle |
| 4079 | Pendennis Castle |
| 4080 | Powderham Castle |
| 4081 | Warwick Castle |
| 4082 | Windsor Castle |
| 4083 | Abbotsbury Castle |
| 4085 | Berkeley Castle |
| 4086 | Builth Castle |
| 4087 | Cardigan Castle |

| | | | | |
|---|---|---|---|---|
| 4088 | Dartmouth Castle | 4266 | 4274 | 4283 | 4293 |
| 4089 | Donnington Castle | 4267 | 4275 | 4284 | 4294 |
| 4090 | Dorchester Castle | 4268 | 4276 | 4285 | 4295 |
| 4092 | Dunraven Castle | 4269 | 4277 | 4286 | 4296 |
| 4093 | Dunster Castle | 4270 | 4278 | 4289 | 4297 |
| 4094 | Dynevor Castle | 4271 | 4279 | 4290 | 4298 |
| 4095 | Harlech Castle | 4272 | 4280 | 4291 | 4299 |
| 4096 | Highclere Castle | 4273 | 4282 | 4292 | |
| 4098 | Kidwelly Castle | | | | |
| 4099 | Kilgerran Castle | | | | |

## 2-6-2T      5101 Class

| | | | |
|---|---|---|---|
| 4100 | 4119 | 4140 | 4159 |
| 4101 | 4120 | 4141 | 4160 |
| 4102 | 4121 | 4142 | 4161 |
| 4103 | 4122 | 4143 | 4163 |
| 4104 | 4123 | 4144 | 4165 |
| 4105 | 4124 | 4145 | 4166 |
| 4106 | 4125 | 4146 | 4167 |
| 4107 | 4126 | 4147 | 4168 |
| 4108 | 4127 | 4148 | 4169 |
| 4109 | 4128 | 4149 | 4171 |
| 4110 | 4129 | 4150 | 4172 |
| 4111 | 4130 | 4151 | 4173 |
| 4112 | 4131 | 4152 | 4174 |
| 4113 | 4132 | 4153 | 4175 |
| 4114 | 4133 | 4154 | 4176 |
| 4115 | 4134 | 4155 | 4177 |
| 4116 | 4135 | 4156 | 4178 |
| 4117 | 4136 | 4157 | 4179 |
| 4118 | 4137 | 4158 | |

## 2-6-2T      4500 Class

| | | | |
|---|---|---|---|
| 4507 | 4558 | 4566 | 4573 |
| 4549 | 4561 | 4567 | 4574 |
| 4552 | 4563 | 4569 | 4588 |
| 4555 | 4564 | 4570 | 4591 |
| 4557 | 4565 | 4571 | 4593 |

## 0-6-0PT      5700 Class

| | | | |
|---|---|---|---|
| 4600 | 4621 | 4642 | 4663 |
| 4601 | 4622 | 4643 | 4664 |
| 4602 | 4623 | 4644 | 4665 |
| 4603 | 4624 | 4645 | 4666 |
| 4604 | 4625 | 4646 | 4667 |
| 4605 | 4626 | 4647 | 4668 |
| 4606 | 4627 | 4648 | 4669 |
| 4607 | 4628 | 4649 | 4670 |
| 4608 | 4629 | 4650 | 4671 |
| 4609 | 4630 | 4651 | 4672 |
| 4610 | 4631 | 4652 | 4673 |
| 4611 | 4632 | 4653 | 4674 |
| 4612 | 4633 | 4654 | 4675 |
| 4613 | 4634 | 4655 | 4676 |
| 4614 | 4635 | 4656 | 4677 |
| 4615 | 4636 | 4657 | 4678 |
| 4616 | 4637 | 4658 | 4679 |
| 4617 | 4638 | 4659 | 4680 |
| 4618 | 4639 | 4660 | 4681 |
| 4619 | 4640 | 4661 | 4682 |
| 4620 | 4641 | 4662 | 4683 |

## 2-8-0T      4200 Class

| | | | |
|---|---|---|---|
| 4207 | 4230 | 4243 | 4255 |
| 4213 | 4232 | 4246 | 4256 |
| 4214 | 4233 | 4247 | 4257 |
| 4218 | 4235 | 4248 | 4258 |
| 4222 | 4236 | 4250 | 4259 |
| 4225 | 4237 | 4251 | 4262 |
| 4227 | 4238 | 4252 | 4263 |
| 4228 | 4241 | 4253 | 4264 |
| 4229 | 4242 | 4254 | 4265 |

| 4684 | 4689 | 4693 | 4697 |
|------|------|------|------|
| 4685 | 4690 | 4694 | 4698 |
| 4687 | 4691 | 4695 | 4699 |
| 4688 | 4692 | 4696 |      |

## 2-8-0        4700 Class

| 4700 | 4703 | 4705 | 4707 |
|------|------|------|------|
| 4701 | 4704 | 4706 | 4708 |
| 4702 |      |      |      |

## 4-6-0 " Hall " 4900 Class

| 4902 | Aldenham Hall |
| 4903 | Astley Hall |
| 4904 | Binnegar Hall |
| 4905 | Barton Hall |
| 4906 | Bradfield Hall |
| 4907 | Broughton Hall |
| 4908 | Broome Hall |
| 4909 | Blakesley Hall |
| 4910 | Blaisdon Hall |
| 4912 | Berrington Hall |
| 4913 | Baglan Hall |
| 4914 | Cranmore Hall |
| 4915 | Condover Hall |
| 4916 | Crumlin Hall |
| 4917 | Crosswood Hall |
| 4918 | Dartington Hall |
| 4919 | Donnington Hall |
| 4920 | Dumbleton Hall |
| 4921 | Eaton Hall |
| 4922 | Enville Hall |
| 4923 | Evenley Hall |
| 4924 | Eydon Hall |
| 4925 | Eynsham Hall |
| 4926 | Fairleigh Hall |
| 4927 | Farnborough Hall |
| 4928 | Gatacre Hall |
| 4929 | Goytrey Hall |
| 4930 | Hagley Hall |
| 4931 | Hanbury Hall |
| 4932 | Hatherton Hall |
| 4933 | Himley Hall |
| 4934 | Hindlip Hall |
| 4935 | Ketley Hall |
| 4936 | Kinlet Hall |
| 4937 | Lanelay Hall |
| 4938 | Liddington Hall |
| 4939 | Littleton Hall |
| 4941 | Llangedwyn Hall |
| 4942 | Maindy Hall |
| 4943 | Marrington Hall |
| 4944 | Middleton Hall |
| 4945 | Milligan Hall |
| 4946 | Moseley Hall |
| 4947 | Nanhoran Hall |
| 4948 | Northwick Hall |
| 4949 | Packwood Hall |
| 4950 | Patshull Hall |
| 4951 | Pendeford Hall |
| 4952 | Peplow Hall |
| 4953 | Pitchford Hall |
| 4954 | Plaish Hall |
| 4955 | Plaspower Hall |
| 4956 | Plowden Hall |
| 4957 | Postlip Hall |
| 4958 | Priory Hall |
| 4959 | Purley Hall |
| 4960 | Pyle Hall |
| 4961 | Pyrland Hall |
| 4962 | Ragley Hall |
| 4963 | Rignall Hall |
| 4964 | Rodwell Hall |
| 4965 | Rood Ashton Hall |
| 4966 | Shakenhurst Hall |
| 4967 | Shirenewton Hall |
| 4968 | Shotton Hall |
| 4969 | Shrugborough Hall |
| 4970 | Sketty Hall |
| 4971 | Stanway Hall |
| 4972 | Saint Brides Hall |
| 4973 | Sweeney Hall |
| 4974 | Talgarth Hall |
| 4975 | Umberslade Hall |
| 4976 | Warfield Hall |
| 4977 | Watcombe Hall |
| 4978 | Westwood Hall |
| 4979 | Wootton Hall |
| 4980 | Wrottesley Hall |
| 4981 | Abberley Hall |
| 4982 | Acton Hall |
| 4983 | Albert Hall |

| | |
|---|---|
| 4984 | Albrighton Hall |
| 4985 | Allesley Hall |
| 4986 | Aston Hall |
| 4987 | Brockley Hall |
| 4988 | Bulwell Hall |
| 4989 | Cherwell Hall |
| 4990 | Clifton Hall |
| 4991 | Cobham Hall |
| 4992 | Crosby Hall |
| 4993 | Dalton Hall |
| 4994 | Downton Hall |
| 4995 | Easton Hall |
| 4996 | Eden Hall |
| 4997 | Elton Hall |
| 4998 | Eyton Hall |
| 4999 | Gopsal Hall |

## 4-6-0        4073 Class
## " Castle "

| | |
|---|---|
| 5000 | Launceston Castle |
| 5001 | Llandovery Castle |
| 5002 | Ludlow Castle |
| 5003 | Lulworth Castle |
| 5004 | Llanstephan Castle |
| 5006 | Tregenna Castle |
| 5007 | Rougemont Castle |
| 5008 | Raglan Castle |
| 5011 | Tintagel Castle |
| 5012 | Berry Pomeroy Castle |
| 5013 | Abergavenny Castle |
| 5014 | Goodrich Castle |
| 5015 | Kingswear Castle |
| 5016 | Montgomery Castle |
| 5017 | The Gloucestershire Regiment 28th, 61st |
| 5018 | St. Mawes Castle |
| 5019 | Treago Castle |
| 5020 | Trematon Castle |
| 5021 | Whittington Castle |
| 5022 | Wigmore Castle |
| 5023 | Brecon Castle |
| 5024 | Carew Castle |
| 5025 | Chirk Castle |
| 5026 | Criccieth Castle |

| | |
|---|---|
| 5027 | Farleigh Castle |
| 5029 | Nunney Castle |
| 5030 | Shirburn Castle |
| 5031 | Totnes Castle |
| 5032 | Usk Castle |
| 5033 | Broughton Castle |
| 5034 | Corfe Castle |
| 5035 | Coity Castle |
| 5036 | Lyonshall Castle |
| 5037 | Monmouth Castle |
| 5038 | Morlais Castle |
| 5039 | Rhuddlan Castle |
| 5040 | Stokesay Castle |
| 5041 | Tiverton Castle |
| 5042 | Winchester Castle |
| 5043 | Earl of Mount Edgcumbe |
| 5044 | Earl of Dunraven |
| 5045 | Earl of Dudley |
| 5046 | Earl Cawdor |
| 5047 | Earl of Dartmouth |
| 5048 | Earl of Devon |
| 5049 | Earl of Plymouth |
| 5050 | Earl of St. Germans |
| 5051 | Earl Bathurst |
| 5052 | Earl of Radnor |
| 5053 | Earl Cairns |
| 5054 | Earl of Ducie |
| 5055 | Earl of Eldon |
| 5056 | Earl of Powis |
| 5057 | Earl Waldegrave |
| 5058 | Earl of Clancarty |
| 5059 | Earl St. Aldwyn |
| 5060 | Earl of Berkeley |
| 5061 | Earl of Birkenhead |
| 5062 | Earl of Shaftesbury |
| 5063 | Earl Baldwin |
| 5064 | Bishop's Castle |
| 5065 | Newport Castle |
| 5066 | Sir Felix Pole |
| 5067 | St. Fagans Castle |
| 5068 | Beverston Castle |
| 5069 | Isambard Kingdom Brunel |
| 5070 | Sir Daniel Gooch |
| 5071 | Spitfire |
| 5072 | Hurricane |
| 5073 | Blenheim |
| 5074 | Hampden |

| | |
|---|---|
| 5075 | Wellington |
| 5076 | Gladiator |
| 5077 | Fairey Battle |
| 5078 | Beaufort |
| 5080 | Defiant |
| 5081 | Lockheed Hudson |
| 5082 | Swordfish |
| 5084 | Reading Abbey |
| 5085 | Evesham Abbey |
| 5087 | Tintern Abbey |
| 5088 | Llanthony Abbey |
| 5089 | Westminster Abbey |
| 5090 | Neath Abbey |
| 5091 | Cleeve Abbey |
| 5092 | Tresco Abbey |
| 5093 | Upton Castle |
| 5094 | Tretower Castle |
| 5095 | Barbury Castle |
| 5096 | Bridgwater Castle |
| 5097 | Sarum Castle |
| 5098 | Clifford Castle |
| 5099 | Compton Castle |

| 5225 | 5235 | 5245 | 5255 |
|------|------|------|------|
| 5226 | 5236 | 5246 | 5256 |
| 5227 | 5237 | 5247 | 5257 |
| 5228 | 5238 | 5248 | 5258 |
| 5229 | 5239 | 5249 | 5259 |
| 5230 | 5240 | 5250 | 5260 |
| 5231 | 5241 | 5251 | 5261 |
| 5232 | 5242 | 5252 | 5262 |
| 5233 | 5243 | 5253 | 5263 |
| 5234 | 5244 | 5254 | 5264 |

## 2-6-0    4300 Class

| 5306 | 5330 | 5357 | 5380 |
|------|------|------|------|
| 5318 | 5332 | 5358 | 5385 |
| 5322 | 5336 | 5369 | 5399 |
| 5326 | 5351 | 5376 | |

## 0-6-0PT    5400 Class

| 5410 | 5416 | 5420 | 5421 |
|------|------|------|------|
| 5412 | | | |

## 2-6-2T    5101 Class

| 5101 | 5166 | 5181 | 5191 |
|------|------|------|------|
| 5151 | 5167 | 5182 | 5192 |
| 5152 | 5173 | 5183 | 5193 |
| 5153 | 5174 | 5184 | 5194 |
| 5154 | 5175 | 5187 | 5195 |
| 5158 | 5177 | 5188 | 5198 |
| 5164 | 5180 | 5190 | 5199 |

## 2-6-2T    4500 Class

| 5503 | 5526 | 5545 | 5562 |
|------|------|------|------|
| 5508 | 5531 | 5547 | 5563 |
| 5509 | 5532 | 5548 | 5564 |
| 5511 | 5537 | 5549 | 5568 |
| 5515 | 5538 | 5550 | 5569 |
| 5516 | 5539 | 5553 | 5570 |
| 5518 | 5541 | 5554 | 5571 |
| 5520 | 5542 | 5555 | 5572 |
| 5521 | 5544 | 5560 | 5573 |
| 5525 | | | |

## 2-8-0T    4200 Class

| 5200 | 5206 | 5213 | 5219 |
|------|------|------|------|
| 5201 | 5208 | 5214 | 5220 |
| 5202 | 5209 | 5215 | 5221 |
| 5203 | 5210 | 5216 | 5222 |
| 5204 | 5211 | 5217 | 5223 |
| 5205 | 5212 | 5218 | 5224 |

## 0-6-2T    5600 Class

| 5600 | 5606 | 5612 | 5618 |
|------|------|------|------|
| 5601 | 5607 | 5613 | 5619 |
| 5602 | 5608 | 5614 | 5620 |
| 5603 | 5609 | 5615 | 5621 |
| 5604 | 5610 | 5616 | 5622 |
| 5605 | 5611 | 5617 | 5623 |

| | | | | | |
|---|---|---|---|---|---|
| 5624 | 5643 | 5662 | 5681 | 5902 | Howick Hall |
| 5625 | 5644 | 5663 | 5682 | 5903 | Keele Hall |
| 5626 | 5645 | 5664 | 5683 | 5904 | Kelham Hall |
| 5627 | 5646 | 5665 | 5684 | 5905 | Knowsley Hall |
| 5628 | 5647 | 5666 | 5685 | 5906 | Lawton Hall |
| 5629 | 5648 | 5667 | 5686 | 5907 | Marble Hall |
| 5630 | 5649 | 5668 | 5687 | 5908 | Moreton Hall |
| 5631 | 5650 | 5669 | 5688 | 5909 | Newton Hall |
| 5632 | 5651 | 5670 | 5689 | 5910 | Park Hall |
| 5633 | 5652 | 5671 | 5690 | 5911 | Preston Hall |
| 5634 | 5653 | 5672 | 5691 | 5912 | Queen's Hall |
| 5635 | 5654 | 5673 | 5692 | 5913 | Rushton Hall |
| 5636 | 5655 | 5674 | 5693 | 5914 | Ripon Hall |
| 5637 | 5656 | 5675 | 5694 | 5916 | Trinity Hall |
| 5638 | 5657 | 5676 | 5695 | 5917 | Westminster Hall |
| 5639 | 5658 | 5677 | 5696 | 5918 | Walton Hall |
| 5640 | 5659 | 5678 | 5697 | 5919 | Worsley Hall |
| 5641 | 5660 | 5679 | 5698 | 5920 | Wycliffe Hall |
| 5642 | 5661 | 5680 | 5699 | 5921 | Bingley Hall |
| | | | | 5922 | Caxton Hall |
| | | | | 5923 | Colston Hall |
| | | | | 5924 | Dinton Hall |
| | | | | 5925 | Eastcote Hall |
| | | | | 5926 | Grotrian Hall |

## 0-6-0PT     5700 Class

| | | | | | |
|---|---|---|---|---|---|
| 5706 | 5758 | 5773 | 5783 | 5927 | Guild Hall |
| 5720 | 5761 | 5774 | 5787 | 5928 | Haddon Hall |
| 5728 | 5766 | 5775 | 5789 | 5929 | Hanham Hall |
| 5744 | 5768 | 5778 | 5791 | 5930 | Hannington Hall |
| 5746 | 5770 | 5779 | 5793 | 5931 | Hatherley Hall |
| 5749 | 5771 | 5780 | 5798 | 5932 | Haydon Hall |
| 5756 | | | | 5933 | Kingsway Hall |
| | | | | 5934 | Kneller Hall |
| | | | | 5935 | Norton Hall |
| | | | | 5936 | Oakley Hall |
| | | | | 5937 | Stanford Hall |

## 0-4-2T     5800 Class

| | | |
|---|---|---|
| 5815 | 5938 | Stanley Hall |
| | 5939 | Tangley Hall |
| | 5940 | Whitbourne Hall |
| | 5941 | Campion Hall |
| | 5942 | Doldowlod Hall |
| | 5943 | Elmdon Hall |
| | 5944 | Ickenham Hall |

## 4-6-0     4900 Class
### " Hall "

| | | |
|---|---|---|
| | 5945 | Leckhampton Hall |
| | 5946 | Marwell Hall |
| 5900 Hinderton Hall | 5947 | Saint Benet's Hall |
| 5901 Hazel Hall | 5948 | Siddington Hall |
| | 5949 | Trematon Hall |

| | |
|---|---|
| 5950 | Wardley Hall |
| 5951 | Clyffe Hall |
| 5952 | Cogan Hall |
| 5953 | Dunley Hall |
| 5954 | Faendre Hall |
| 5955 | Garth Hall |
| 5956 | Horsley Hall |
| 5957 | Hutton Hall |
| 5958 | Knolton Hall |
| 5959 | Mawley Hall |
| 5960 | Saint Edmund Hall |
| 5961 | Toynbee Hall |
| 5962 | Wantage Hall |
| 5963 | Wimpole Hall |
| 5964 | Wolseley Hall |
| 5965 | Woollas Hall |
| 5966 | Ashford Hall |
| 5967 | Bickmarsh Hall |
| 5968 | Cory Hall |
| 5969 | Honington Hall |
| 5970 | Hengrave Hall |
| 5971 | Merevale Hall |
| 5972 | Olton Hall |
| 5973 | Rolleston Hall |
| 5974 | Wallsworth Hall |
| 5975 | Winslow Hall |
| 5976 | Ashwicke Hall |
| 5977 | Beckford Hall |
| 5978 | Bodinnick Hall |
| 5979 | Cruckton Hall |
| 5980 | Dingley Hall |
| 5981 | Frensham Hall |
| 5982 | Harrington Hall |
| 5983 | Henley Hall |
| 5984 | Linden Hall |
| 5985 | Mostyn Hall |
| 5986 | Arbury Hall |
| 5987 | Brocket Hall |
| 5988 | Bostock Hall |
| 5989 | Cransley Hall |
| 5990 | Dorford Hall |
| 5991 | Gresham Hall |
| 5992 | Horton Hall |
| 5993 | Kirby Hall |
| 5994 | Roydon Hall |
| 5995 | Wick Hall |
| 5996 | Mytton Hall |

| | |
|---|---|
| 5997 | Sparkford Hall |
| 5998 | Trevor Hall |
| 5999 | Wollaton Hall |

## 4-6-0    6000 Class
### " King "

| | |
|---|---|
| 6000 | King George V |
| 6001 | King Edward VII |
| 6002 | King William IV |
| 6003 | King George IV |
| 6004 | King George III |
| 6005 | King George II |
| 6006 | King George I |
| 6007 | King William III |
| 6008 | King James II |
| 6009 | King Charles II |
| 6010 | King Charles I |
| 6011 | King James I |
| 6012 | King Edward VI |
| 6013 | King Henry VIII |
| 6014 | King Henry VII |
| 6015 | King Richard III |
| 6016 | King Edward V |
| 6017 | King Edward IV |
| 6018 | King Henry VI |
| 6019 | King Henry V |
| 6020 | King Henry IV |
| 6021 | King Richard II |
| 6022 | King Edward III |
| 6023 | King Edward II |
| 6024 | King Edward I |
| 6025 | King Henry III |
| 6026 | King John |
| 6027 | King Richard I |
| 6028 | King George VI |
| 6029 | King Edward VIII |

## 2-6-2T    6100 Class

| 6101 | 6106 | 6108 | 6110 |
|---|---|---|---|
| 6103 | 6107 | 6109 | 6111 |

22

| 6112 | 6128 | 6142 | 6156 |
|------|------|------|------|
| 6113 | 6129 | 6143 | 6157 |
| 6114 | 6130 | 6144 | 6158 |
| 6115 | 6131 | 6145 | 6159 |
| 6116 | 6132 | 6146 | 6160 |
| 6117 | 6133 | 6147 | 6161 |
| 6118 | 6134 | 6148 | 6162 |
| 6119 | 6135 | 6149 | 6163 |
| 6120 | 6136 | 6150 | 6164 |
| 6122 | 6137 | 6151 | 6165 |
| 6123 | 6138 | 6152 | 6166 |
| 6124 | 6139 | 6153 | 6167 |
| 6125 | 6140 | 6154 | 6168 |
| 6126 | 6141 | 6155 | 6169 |
| 6127 |      |      |      |

## 2-6-0          4300 Class

| 6301 | 6330 | 6353 | 6375 |
|------|------|------|------|
| 6302 | 6335 | 6356 | 6376 |
| 6304 | 6336 | 6357 | 6378 |
| 6306 | 6337 | 6361 | 6379 |
| 6309 | 6338 | 6362 | 6380 |
| 6310 | 6339 | 6363 | 6381 |
| 6312 | 6340 | 6364 | 6384 |
| 6313 | 6341 | 6365 | 6385 |
| 6314 | 6342 | 6366 | 6386 |
| 6316 | 6344 | 6367 | 6387 |
| 6317 | 6345 | 6368 | 6388 |
| 6319 | 6346 | 6369 | 6390 |
| 6320 | 6347 | 6370 | 6391 |
| 6324 | 6348 | 6372 | 6392 |
| 6326 | 6349 | 6373 | 6394 |
| 6327 | 6350 | 6374 | 6395 |
| 6329 |      |      |      |

## 0-6-0PT          6400 Class

| 6400 | 6413 | 6422 | 6433 |
|------|------|------|------|
| 6403 | 6415 | 6424 | 6434 |
| 6408 | 6416 | 6426 | 6435 |
| 6410 | 6418 | 6429 | 6436 |
| 6411 | 6419 | 6430 | 6437 |
| 6412 | 6421 | 6431 | 6438 |

## 0-6-2T          5600 Class

| 6600 | 6625 | 6650 | 6675 |
|------|------|------|------|
| 6601 | 6626 | 6651 | 6676 |
| 6602 | 6627 | 6652 | 6677 |
| 6603 | 6628 | 6653 | 6678 |
| 6604 | 6629 | 6654 | 6679 |
| 6605 | 6630 | 6655 | 6680 |
| 6606 | 6631 | 6656 | 6681 |
| 6607 | 6632 | 6657 | 6682 |
| 6608 | 6633 | 6658 | 6683 |
| 6609 | 6634 | 6659 | 6684 |
| 6610 | 6635 | 6660 | 6685 |
| 6611 | 6636 | 6661 | 6686 |
| 6612 | 6637 | 6662 | 6687 |
| 6613 | 6638 | 6663 | 6688 |
| 6614 | 6639 | 6664 | 6689 |
| 6615 | 6640 | 6665 | 6690 |
| 6616 | 6641 | 6666 | 6691 |
| 6617 | 6642 | 6667 | 6692 |
| 6618 | 6643 | 6668 | 6693 |
| 6619 | 6644 | 6669 | 6694 |
| 6620 | 6645 | 6670 | 6695 |
| 6621 | 6646 | 6671 | 6696 |
| 6622 | 6647 | 6672 | 6697 |
| 6623 | 6648 | 6673 | 6698 |
| 6624 | 6649 | 6674 | 6699 |

## 0-6-0PT          5700 Class

| 6700 | 6742 | 6760 | 6768 |
|------|------|------|------|
| 6714 | 6749 | 6762 | 6769 |
| 6720 | 6754 | 6763 | 6770 |
| 6724 | 6755 | 6764 | 6772 |
| 6738 | 6757 | 6765 | 6777 |
| 6739 | 6758 | 6767 | 6778 |
| 6741 |      |      |      |

## 4-6-0          6800 Class
## " Grange "

| 6800 | Arlington Grange |
|------|------------------|
| 6802 | Bampton Grange |
| 6803 | Bucklebury Grange |
| 6804 | Brockington Grange |

| | | | |
|---|---|---|---|
| 6805 | Broughton Grange | 6852 | Headbourne Grange |
| 6806 | Blackwell Grange | 6853 | Morehampton Grange |
| 6807 | Birchwood Grange | 6854 | Roundhill Grange |
| 6808 | Beenham Grange | 6855 | Saighton Grange |
| 6809 | Burghclere Grange | 6856 | Stowe Grange |
| 6810 | Blakemere Grange | 6857 | Tudor Grange |
| 6811 | Cranbourne Grange | 6858 | Woolston Grange |
| 6812 | Chesford Grange | 6859 | Yiewsley Grange |
| 6813 | Eastbury Grange | 6860 | Aberporth Grange |
| 6814 | Enborne Grange | 6861 | Crynant Grange |
| 6815 | Frilford Grange | 6862 | Derwent Grange |
| 6816 | Frankton Grange | 6863 | Dolhywel Grange |
| 6817 | Gwenddwr Grange | 6864 | Dymock Grange |
| 6818 | Hardwick Grange | 6865 | Hopton Grange |
| 6819 | Highnam Grange | 6866 | Morfa Grange |
| 6820 | Kingstone Grange | 6867 | Peterston Grange |
| 6821 | Leaton Grange | 6868 | Penrhos Grange |
| 6822 | Manton Grange | 6869 | Resolven Grange |
| 6823 | Oakley Grange | 6870 | Bodicote Grange |
| 6824 | Ashley Grange | 6871 | Bourton Grange |
| 6825 | Llanvair Grange | 6872 | Crawley Grange |
| 6826 | Nannerth Grange | 6873 | Caradoc Grange |
| 6827 | Llanfrechfa Grange | 6874 | Haughton Grange |
| 6828 | Trellech Grange | 6875 | Hindford Grange |
| 6829 | Burmington Grange | 6876 | Kingsland Grange |
| 6830 | Buckenhill Grange | 6877 | Llanfair Grange |
| 6831 | Bearley Grange | 6878 | Longford Grange |
| 6832 | Brockton Grange | 6879 | Overton Grange |
| 6833 | Calcot Grange | | |
| 6834 | Dummer Grange | | |
| 6835 | Eastham Grange | | |
| 6836 | Estevarney Grange | | |
| 6837 | Forthampton Grange | | |
| 6838 | Goodmoor Grange | **4-6-0** | **4900 Class** |
| 6839 | Hewell Grange | | **" Hall "** |
| 6840 | Hazeley Grange | | |
| 6841 | Marlas Grange | 6900 | Abney Hall |
| 6842 | Nunhold Grange | 6901 | Arley Hall |
| 6843 | Poulton Grange | 6902 | Butlers Hall |
| 6844 | Penhydd Grange | 6903 | Belmont Hall |
| 6845 | Paviland Grange | 6904 | Charfield Hall |
| 6846 | Ruckley Grange | 6905 | Claughton Hall |
| 6847 | Tidmarsh Grange | 6906 | Chicheley Hall |
| 6848 | Toddington Grange | 6907 | Davenham Hall |
| 6849 | Walton Grange | 6908 | Downham Hall |
| 6850 | Cleeve Grange | 6909 | Frewin Hall |
| 6851 | Hurst Grange | 6910 | Gossington Hall |
| | | 6911 | Holker Hall |

| | | 4-6-0 | 6959 Class |
| | | | "Modified Hall" |

| | | | |
|---|---|---|---|
| 6912 | Helmster Hall | | |
| 6913 | Levens Hall | | |
| 6914 | Langton Hall | | |
| 6915 | Mursley Hall | 6959 | Peatling Hall |
| 6916 | Misterton Hall | 6960 | Raveningham Hall |
| 6917 | Oldlands Hall | 6961 | Stedham Hall |
| 6918 | Sandon Hall | 6962 | Soughton Hall |
| 6919 | Tylney Hall | 6963 | Throwley Hall |
| 6920 | Barningham Hall | 6964 | Thornbridge Hall |
| 6921 | Borwick Hall | 6965 | Thirlestaine Hall |
| 6922 | Burton Hall | 6966 | Witchingham Hall |
| 6923 | Croxteth Hall | 6967 | Willesley Hall |
| 6924 | Grantley Hall | 6968 | Woodcock Hall |
| 6925 | Hackness Hall | 6969 | Wraysbury Hall |
| 6926 | Holkham Hall | 6970 | Whaddon Hall |
| 6927 | Lilford Hall | 6971 | Athelhampton Hall |
| 6928 | Underley Hall | 6972 | Beningbrough Hall |
| 6929 | Whorlton Hall | 6973 | Bricklehampton Hall |
| 6930 | Aldersey Hall | 6974 | Bryngwyn Hall |
| 6931 | Aldborough Hall | 6975 | Capesthorne Hall |
| 6932 | Burwarton Hall | 6976 | Graythwaite Hall |
| 6933 | Birtles Hall | 6977 | Grundisburgh Hall |
| 6934 | Beachamwell Hall | 6978 | Haroldstone Hall |
| 6935 | Browsholme Hall | 6979 | Helperly Hall |
| 6936 | Breccles Hall | 6980 | Llanrumney Hall |
| 6937 | Conyngham Hall | 6981 | Marbury Hall |
| 6938 | Corndean Hall | 6982 | Melmerby Hall |
| 6939 | Calveley Hall | 6983 | Otterington Hall |
| 6940 | Didlington Hall | 6984 | Owsden Hall |
| 6941 | Fillongley Hall | 6985 | Parwick Hall |
| 6942 | Eshton Hall | 6986 | Rydal Hall |
| 6943 | Farnley Hall | 6987 | Shervington Hall |
| 6944 | Fledborough Hall | 6988 | Swithland Hall |
| 6945 | Glasfryn Hall | 6989 | Wightwick Hall |
| 6946 | Heatherden Hall | 6990 | Witherslack Hall |
| 6947 | Helmingham Hall | 6991 | Acton Burnell Hall |
| 6948 | Holbrooke Hall | 6992 | Arborfield Hall |
| 6949 | Haberfield Hall | 6993 | Arthog Hall |
| 6950 | Kingsthorpe Hall | 6994 | Baggrave Hall |
| 6951 | Impney Hall | 6995 | Benthall Hall |
| 6952 | Kimberley Hall | 6996 | Blackwell Hall |
| 6953 | Leighton Hall | 6997 | Bryn-Ivor Hall |
| 6954 | Lotherton Hall | 6998 | Burton Agnes Hall |
| 6955 | Lydcott Hall | 6999 | Capel Dewi Hall |
| 6956 | Mottram Hall | | |
| 6957 | Norcliffe Hall | | |
| 6958 | Oxburgh Hall | | |

## 4-6-0       4073 Class
### "Castle"

| 7000 | Viscount Portal |
| 7001 | Sir James Milne |
| 7002 | Devizes Castle |
| 7003 | Elmley Castle |
| 7004 | Eastnor Castle |
| 7005 | Sir Edward Elgar |
| 7006 | Lydford Castle |
| 7007 | Great Western |
| 7008 | Swansea Castle |
| 7009 | Athelney Castle |
| 7010 | Avondale Castle |
| 7011 | Banbury Castle |
| 7012 | Barry Castle |
| 7013 | Bristol Castle |
| 7014 | Caerhays Castle |
| 7015 | Carn Brea Castle |
| 7016 | Chester Castle |
| 7017 | G. J. Churchward |
| 7018 | Drysllwyn Castle |
| 7019 | Fowey Castle |
| 7020 | Gloucester Castle |
| 7021 | Haverfordwest Castle |
| 7022 | Hereford Castle |
| 7023 | Penrice Castle |
| 7024 | Powis Castle |
| 7025 | Sudeley Castle |
| 7026 | Tenby Castle |
| 7027 | Thornbury Castle |
| 7028 | Cadbury Castle |
| 7029 | Clun Castle |
| 7030 | Cranbrook Castle |
| 7031 | Cromwell's Castle |
| 7032 | Denbigh Castle |
| 7033 | Hartlebury Castle |
| 7034 | Ince Castle |
| 7035 | Ogmore Castle |
| 7036 | Taunton Castle |
| 7037 | Swindon |

| 7212 | 7223 | 7234 | 7244 |
|------|------|------|------|
| 7213 | 7224 | 7235 | 7245 |
| 7214 | 7225 | 7236 | 7246 |
| 7215 | 7226 | 7237 | 7247 |
| 7216 | 7227 | 7238 | 7248 |
| 7217 | 7228 | 7239 | 7249 |
| 7218 | 7229 | 7240 | 7250 |
| 7219 | 7230 | 7241 | 7251 |
| 7220 | 7231 | 7242 | 7252 |
| 7221 | 7232 | 7243 | 7253 |
| 7222 | 7233 |      |      |

## 2-6-0       4300 Class

| 7300 | 7311 | 7322 | 7333 |
|------|------|------|------|
| 7301 | 7312 | 7323 | 7334 |
| 7302 | 7313 | 7324 | 7335 |
| 7303 | 7314 | 7325 | 7336 |
| 7304 | 7315 | 7326 | 7337 |
| 7305 | 7316 | 7327 | 7338 |
| 7306 | 7317 | 7328 | 7339 |
| 7307 | 7318 | 7329 | 7340 |
| 7308 | 7319 | 7330 | 7341 |
| 7309 | 7320 | 7331 |      |
| 7310 | 7321 | 7332 |      |

## 0-6-0PT       7400 Class

| 7402 | 7414 | 7428 | 7439 |
|------|------|------|------|
| 7403 | 7417 | 7429 | 7440 |
| 7404 | 7418 | 7430 | 7441 |
| 7405 | 7421 | 7431 | 7442 |
| 7406 | 7422 | 7432 | 7443 |
| 7407 | 7423 | 7433 | 7444 |
| 7408 | 7424 | 7434 | 7445 |
| 7409 | 7425 | 7435 | 7446 |
| 7412 | 7426 | 7436 | 7448 |
| 7413 | 7427 | 7437 | 7449 |

## 2-8-2T       7200 Class

| 7200 | 7203 | 7206 | 7209 |
|------|------|------|------|
| 7201 | 7204 | 7207 | 7210 |
| 7202 | 7205 | 7208 | 7211 |

## 0-6-0PT       5700 Class

| 7700 | 7718 | 7724 | 7736 |
|------|------|------|------|
| 7713 | 7720 | 7729 | 7739 |
| 7715 | 7721 | 7732 | 7741 |

| 7744 | 7756 | 7780 | 7787 |
|------|------|------|------|
| 7745 | 7760 | 7782 | 7788 |
| 7747 | 7762 | 7783 | 7790 |
| 7748 | 7764 | 7784 | 7796 |
| 7749 | 7765 | 7785 | 7798 |
| 7753 | 7771 | 7786 | 7799 |
| 7755 | 7772 |      |      |

## 4-6-0　　　　7800 Class
### " Manor "

| 7800 | Torquay Manor |
|------|---------------|
| 7801 | Anthony Manor |
| 7802 | Bradley Manor |
| 7803 | Barcote Manor |
| 7804 | Baydon Manor |
| 7805 | Broome Manor |
| 7806 | Cockington Manor |
| 7807 | Compton Manor |
| 7808 | Cookham Manor |
| 7809 | Childrey Manor |
| 7810 | Draycott Manor |
| 7811 | Dunley Manor |
| 7812 | Erlestoke Manor |
| 7813 | Freshford Manor |
| 7814 | Fringford Manor |
| 7815 | Fritwell Manor |
| 7816 | Frilsham Manor |
| 7817 | Garsington Manor |
| 7818 | Granville Manor |
| 7819 | Hinton Manor |
| 7820 | Dinmore Manor |
| 7821 | Ditcheat Manor |
| 7822 | Foxcote Manor |
| 7823 | Hook Norton Manor |
| 7824 | Iford Manor |
| 7825 | Lechlade Manor |
| 7826 | Longworth Manor |
| 7827 | Lydham Manor |
| 7828 | Odney Manor |
| 7829 | Ramsbury Manor |

## 4-6-0　　　　6959 Class
### " Modified Hall "

| 7900 | Saint Peter's Hall |
|------|--------------------|
| 7901 | Dodington Hall |
| 7902 | Eaton Mascot Hall |
| 7903 | Foremarke Hall |
| 7904 | Fountains Hall |
| 7905 | Fowey Hall |
| 7906 | Fron Hall |
| 7907 | Hart Hall |
| 7908 | Henshall Hall |
| 7909 | Heveningham Hall |
| 7910 | Hown Hall |
| 7911 | Lady Margaret Hall |
| 7912 | Little Linford Hall |
| 7913 | Little Wyrley Hall |
| 7914 | Lleweni Hall |
| 7915 | Mere Hall |
| 7916 | Mobberley Hall |
| 7917 | North Aston Hall |
| 7918 | Rhose Wood Hall |
| 7919 | Runter Hall |
| 7920 | Coney Hall |
| 7921 | Edstone Hall |
| 7922 | Salford Hall |
| 7923 | Speke Hall |
| 7924 | Thornycroft Hall |
| 7925 | Westol Hall |
| 7926 | Willey Hall |
| 7927 | Willington Hall |
| 7928 | Wolf Hall |
| 7929 | Wyke Hall |

## 2-6-2T　　　　8100 Class

| 8100 | 8102 | 8104 | 8107 |
|------|------|------|------|
| 8101 | 8103 | 8106 | 8109 |

## 0-6-0PT　　　　9400 Class

| 8400 | 8404 | 8414 | 8420 |
|------|------|------|------|
| 8401 | 8405 | 8415 | 8422 |
| 8402 | 8407 | 8416 | 8425 |
| 8403 | 8409 | 8418 | 8426 |

27

| 8428 | 8449 | 8470 | 8486 |
|------|------|------|------|
| 8430 | 8451 | 8471 | 8487 |
| 8431 | 8452 | 8472 | 8488 |
| 8433 | 8453 | 8474 | 8489 |
| 8435 | 8456 | 8475 | 8490 |
| 8436 | 8458 | 8477 | 8491 |
| 8437 | 8459 | 8478 | 8493 |
| 8438 | 8461 | 8479 | 8494 |
| 8439 | 8464 | 8480 | 8495 |
| 8440 | 8465 | 8481 | 8496 |
| 8441 | 8466 | 8482 | 8497 |
| 8444 | 8467 | 8483 | 8498 |
| 8445 | 8469 | 8484 | 8499 |
| 8446 |      |      |      |

## 0-6-0PT　　　　9400 Class

| 9401 | 9424 | 9454 | 9477 |
|------|------|------|------|
| 9404 | 9425 | 9455 | 9478 |
| 9405 | 9426 | 9456 | 9479 |
| 9406 | 9429 | 9457 | 9480 |
| 9407 | 9430 | 9460 | 9482 |
| 9408 | 9431 | 9461 | 9483 |
| 9409 | 9433 | 9463 | 9484 |
| 9410 | 9435 | 9464 | 9485 |
| 9411 | 9437 | 9465 | 9486 |
| 9412 | 9440 | 9466 | 9487 |
| 9413 | 9441 | 9467 | 9488 |
| 9415 | 9442 | 9469 | 9489 |
| 9416 | 9444 | 9470 | 9490 |
| 9418 | 9446 | 9471 | 9493 |
| 9419 | 9448 | 9472 | 9494 |
| 9420 | 9450 | 9473 | 9495 |
| 9421 | 9451 | 9474 | 9497 |
| 9422 | 9452 | 9475 | 9498 |
| 9423 | 9453 | 9476 |      |

## 0-6-0PT　　　　5700 Class

| 8700 | 8727 | 8751 | 8777 |
|------|------|------|------|
| 8701 | 8728 | 8752 | 8779 |
| 8702 | 8729 | 8753 | 8780 |
| 8705 | 8730 | 8756 | 8781 |
| 8706 | 8731 | 8757 | 8782 |
| 8707 | 8732 | 8759 | 8783 |
| 8709 | 8733 | 8760 | 8784 |
| 8710 | 8734 | 8761 | 8785 |
| 8711 | 8735 | 8762 | 8786 |
| 8712 | 8736 | 8763 | 8787 |
| 8713 | 8737 | 8764 | 8788 |
| 8714 | 8738 | 8765 | 8789 |
| 8715 | 8739 | 8766 | 8790 |
| 8716 | 8740 | 8767 | 8791 |
| 8717 | 8741 | 8768 | 8792 |
| 8718 | 8742 | 8769 | 8793 |
| 8719 | 8743 | 8770 | 8794 |
| 8720 | 8744 | 8771 | 8795 |
| 8721 | 8745 | 8772 | 8796 |
| 8722 | 8746 | 8773 | 8797 |
| 8723 | 8747 | 8774 | 8798 |
| 8724 | 8748 | 8775 | 8799 |
| 8725 | 8749 | 8776 |      |
| 8726 | 8750 |      |      |

## 0-6-0PT　　　　5700 Class

| 9600 | 9616 | 9632 | 9648 |
|------|------|------|------|
| 9601 | 9617 | 9633 | 9649 |
| 9602 | 9618 | 9634 | 9650 |
| 9603 | 9619 | 9635 | 9651 |
| 9604 | 9620 | 9636 | 9652 |
| 9605 | 9621 | 9637 | 9653 |
| 9606 | 9622 | 9638 | 9654 |
| 9607 | 9623 | 9639 | 9655 |
| 9608 | 9624 | 9640 | 9656 |
| 9609 | 9625 | 9641 | 9657 |
| 9610 | 9626 | 9642 | 9658 |
| 9611 | 9627 | 9643 | 9659 |
| 9612 | 9628 | 9644 | 9660 |
| 9613 | 9629 | 9645 | 9661 |
| 9614 | 9630 | 9646 | 9662 |
| 9615 | 9631 | 9647 | 9663 |

| | | | | | | | |
|---|---|---|---|---|---|---|---|
| 9664 | 9705 | 9728 | 9752 | 9775 | 9781 | 9787 | 9793 |
| 9665 | 9706 | 9729 | 9753 | 9776 | 9782 | 9788 | 9794 |
| 9666 | 9707 | 9730 | 9754 | 9777 | 9783 | 9789 | 9796 |
| 9667 | 9709 | 9731 | 9755 | 9778 | 9784 | 9790 | 9797 |
| 9668 | 9710 | 9732 | 9756 | 9779 | 9785 | 9791 | 9798 |
| 9669 | 9711 | 9733 | 9757 | 9780 | 9786 | 9792 | 9799 |
| 9670 | 9712 | 9734 | 9758 | | | | |
| 9671 | 9713 | 9735 | 9759 | | | | |
| 9672 | 9714 | 9736 | 9760 | | | | |
| 9674 | 9715 | 9738 | 9761 | | | | |
| 9675 | 9716 | 9739 | 9762 | | | | |
| 9676 | 9717 | 9740 | 9763 | | | | |
| 9677 | 9718 | 9741 | 9764 | | | | |
| 9678 | 9719 | 9742 | 9765 | | | | |
| 9679 | 9720 | 9743 | 9766 | | | | |
| 9680 | 9721 | 9744 | 9767 | | | | |
| 9681 | 9722 | 9745 | 9768 | | | | |
| 9682 | 9723 | 9746 | 9769 | | | | |
| 9700 | 9724 | 9747 | 9770 | | | | |
| 9702 | 9725 | 9748 | 9771 | | | | |
| 9703 | 9726 | 9750 | 9773 | | | | |
| 9704 | 9727 | 9751 | 9774 | | | | |

## SERVICE LOCOMOTIVES

### Diesel Mechanical

| | | |
|---|---|---|
| 20 | PWM 651 | PWM 653 |
| PWM 650 | PWM 652 | PWM 654 |

**Total 6**

### Petrol

24   27

**Total 2**

## LOCOMOTIVE SUPERINTENDENTS AND CHIEF MECHANICAL ENGINEERS OF THE G.W.R. & W.R.

| | |
|---|---|
| Sir Daniel Gooch ... ... ... ... ... | 1837–1864 |
| Joseph Armstrong ... ... ... ... ... | { 1854–1864* <br> 1864–1877 |
| George Armstrong ... ... ... ... ... <br> (*Bro. of J. Armstrong*) | 1864–1896* |
| William Dean ... ... ... ... ... ... | 1877–1902 |
| G. J. Churchward ... ... ... ... ... | 1902–1921 |
| Charles B. Collett ... ... ... ... ... | 1922–1941 |
| F. W. Hawksworth ... ... ... ... ... | 1941–1949 |

\* In charge of standard gauge locomotives at Stafford Road Works, Wolverhampton, with wide powers in design and construction.

# SUMMARY OF SOUTHERN REGION STEAM LOCOMOTIVE CLASSES

## IN ALPHABETICAL ORDER
## WITH HISTORICAL NOTES AND DIMENSIONS

The Code given in smaller bold type at the head of each Class,
e.g. " 2F " denotes its British Railways power classification.

The number of locomotives in service has been checked in S.R. to February 10th,
1961, and W.R. to January 28th, 1961.

---

### Classes
### 0-6-0T  0P  A1 & A1X

*A1. Introduced 1872. Stroudley L.B.S.C. "Terrier," later fitted with Marsh boiler, retaining original type smokebox.

†A1X. Introduced 1911. Rebuild of A1 with Marsh boiler and extended smokebox.

‡A1X. Loco. with increased cylinder diameter.

Weight: {27 tons 10 cwt.*
{28 tons 5 cwt.†‡

Pressure: 150 lb.

Cyls.: {12″ × 20″.*†
{14⅛″ × 20″.‡

Driving Wheels: 4′ 0″.

T.E.: {7,650 lb.*†
{10,695 lb.‡

*DS680
†DS681,    32635/40/6/50/61/2/70/8
‡32636          **Total  A1  1**
                      **A1X 10**

---

### 0-4-0T  1F  Class B4

Introduced 1891. Adams L.S.W. design for dock shunting.

Weight: 33 tons 9 cwt.
Pressure: 140 lb. Cyls. (O): 16″ × 22″.
Driving Wheels: 3′ 9¾″.
T.E.: 14,650 lb.

30089/96, 30102          **Total 3**

---

### 0-6-0  2F  Class C

Introduced 1900. Wainwright S.E.C. design.

Weight: Loco. 43 tons 16 cwt.
Pressure: 160 lb.
Cyls.: 18½″ × 26″.
Driving Wheels: 5′ 2″.
T.E.: 19,520 lb.

31004/37/61/8,    31112/3/50, 31218/29/42/4/55/6/67/8/71/ 80/93,   31317,   31480/1/95/8/ 31510/73/5/8/9/83/4/8/9/92, 31682/4/6/9-91/3-5,  31714-7/ 9-24          **Total 5.**

---

### 0-6-0  2F  Class C2X

Introduced 1908. Marsh rebuild o R. J. Billinton L.B.S.C. C2 with large C3-type boiler, extended smokebox etc.

Weight: Loco. 45 tons 5 cwt.
Pressure: 170 lb.
Cyls.: 17½″ × 26″.
Driving Wheels: 5′ 0″.
T.E.: 19,175 lb.

32438/41/5/8-51, 32521-3/5/8/ 34-6/8/9/44-50/2/3          **Total 2**

---

### 4-4-0  3P  Class D

Introduced 1921. Maunsell rebuild o Wainwright S.E.C. D, with large superheated boiler, Belpaire firebox and long-travel piston valves.

Weight: Loco. 52 tons 4 cwt.
Pressure: 180 lb. Su.
Cyls.: 19″ × 26″.
Driving Wheels: 6′ 8″.
T.E.: 17,950 lb.

31145, 31246/7, 31487/9, 31505/
45, 31727/35/9/49

**Total 11**

### 4-4-0    3P    Class E1

Introduced 1919. Maunsell rebuild of
Wainwright S.E.C. E, with larger
superheated boiler, Belpaire firebox
and long-travel piston valves.
Weight: Loco. 53 tons 9 cwt.
Pressure: 180 lb.
Cyls.: 19″ × 26″.
Driving Wheels: 6′ 6″.
T.E.: 18,410 lb.

31019/67, 31507

**Total 3**

### 0-6-0T    2F    Class E1

Introduced 1874. Stroudley L.B.S.C.
design, reboilered by Marsh.
Weight: 44 tons 3 cwt.
Pressure: 170 lb.
Cyls.: 17″ × 24″.
Driving Wheels: 4′ 6″.
T.E.: 18,560 lb.

32694

**Total 1**

### 0-6-0T    3F    Class E2

*Introduced 1913. L. B. Billinton
L.B.S.C. design.
†Introduced 1915. Later locos. with
tanks extended further forward.
Weight: { 52 tons 15 cwt.*
{ 53 tons 10 cwt.†
Pressure: 170 lb.
Cyls.: 17½″ × 26″.
Driving Wheels: 4′ 6″.
T.E.: 21,305 lb.

*32100–4
†32105–9

**Total 10**

### 0-6-2T    2P2F    Class E4

Introduced 1897. R. J. Billinton
L.B.S.C. design, development of E3
with larger wheels, reboilered with
Marsh boiler and extended smokebox,
cylinder diameter reduced from 18″
by S.R.
Weight: 57 tons 10 cwt.
Pressure: 170 lb.
Cyls.: 17½″ × 26″.
Driving Wheels: 5′ 0″.
T.E.: 19,175 lb.

32468/70–2/5/9/87/98, 32500/3–
6/9/10/2/5/56/7/63–5/78/80/1

**Total 27**

### 0-6-2T    3F    Class E6

Introduced 1904. R. J. Billinton
L.B.S.C. design, development of E5
with smaller wheels, some with
higher pressure.
Weight: 61 tons.
Pressure: 160 lb. or 175 lb.
Cyls.: 18″ × 26″.
Driving Wheels: 4′ 6″.
T.E.: 21,215 lb. or 23,205 lb.

32408/10/5–8

**Total 6**

### 0-6-0T    2F    Class G6

Introduced 1894. Adams L.S.W.
design, later additions by Drummond,
but with Adams type boiler.
Weight: 47 tons 13 cwt.
Pressure: 160 lb.
Cyls.: 17½″ × 24″.
Driving Wheels: 4′ 10″.
T.E.: 17,235 lb.

30258/77, 30349, DS682,
DS3152

**Total 5**

**4-8-0T**    8F    **Class G16**

Introduced 1921.   Urie L.S.W.
" Hump " loco.
Weight: 95 tons 2 cwt.
Pressure: 180 lb. Su.
Cyls.: (O) 22" × 28".
Driving Wheels: 5' 1".
T.E.: 33,990 lb.
Walschaerts valve gear. P.V.

30494/5          **Total 2**

---

Weight: Loco. $\begin{cases} 79 \text{ tons } 19 \text{ cwt.} \\ 80 \text{ tons } 11 \text{ cwt.*} \end{cases}$
Pressure: $\begin{cases} 180 \text{ lb. Su.} \\ 175 \text{ lb. Su.*} \end{cases}$
Cyls.: (O) 21" × 28".
Driving Wheels: 6' 0".
T.E. $\begin{cases} 26,240 \text{ lb.} \\ 25,510 \text{ lb.*} \end{cases}$
Walschaerts valve gear.   P.V.

30475/6, 30521–4
*30331

         **Total 7**

---

**0-4-4T**    IP    **Class H**

Introduced 1904. Wainwright S.E.C.
design.

*Introduced 1949. Fitted for push-and-
pull working.

Weight: 54 tons 8 cwt.
Pressure: 160 lb.
Cyls.: 18" × 26".
Driving Wheels: 5' 6".
T.E.: 17,360 lb.

31261,   31305/7/26/8,   31542/
50/2
*31005, 31161/2/77/93, 31263/
76/8, 31306/8/22/4, 31500/12/
7–9/21/2/30/3/43/4/51/3
         **Total 33**

---

**4-6-2T**    6F    **Class H16**

Introduced 1921. Urie L.S.W. design
for heavy freight traffic.
Weight: 96 tons 8 cwt.
Pressure: 180 lb. Su.
Cyls.: (O) 21" × 28".
Driving Wheels: 5' 7".
T.E.: 28,200 lb.
Walschaerts valve gear.   P.V.

30516–20          **Total 5**

---

**2-6-0**    4P5F    **Class K**

Introduced 1913.   L. B. Billinton
L.B.S.C. design.
Weight: Loco. 63 tons 15 cwt.
Pressure: 180 lb. Su.
Cyls.: (O) 21" × 26".
Driving Wheels: 5'6".
T.E.: 26,580 lb.
P.V.

32337–53          **Total 17**

---

**4-6-0**    4P5F    **Class H15**

Introduced 1924. Maunsell development
of Urie locos. with N15-type boiler
and smaller tender.

*Introduced 1924. Maunsell rebuild of
Drummond F13 4-cyl. 4-6-0 introduced 1905, with detail differences
from rebuild of E14.

---

**4-4-0**    3P    **Class L**

Introduced 1914. Wainwright S.E.C.
design, with detail alterations by
Maunsell.

Class 1500 0-6-0PT No. 1501

[Brian E. Morrison

Class 9400 0-6-0PT No. 8430

[B. J. R. Yates

Class 5600 0-6-2T No. 6640

[J. C. Haydon

Top: Class 5700 0-6-0PT
No. 5787
[A. A. Delicat

Centre: Class 7400
0-6-0PT No. 7417
[J. C. Haydo

Left: Class 5700 0-6-0P
No. 9703 (with
condensing apparatus
[J. Davenpo

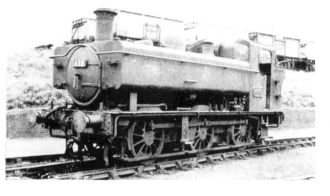

Top :
Class 1366 0-6-0PT
No. 1371
[P. J. Sharpe

Centre :
Class 1600 0-6-0PT
No. 1638
[Andrew F. Smith

Right :
Class 5400 0-6-0PT
No. 5412
[K. L. Cook

Class 6000 4-6-0 No. 6026 *King John*                    [*G. Wheeler*

Class 4073 4-6-0 No. 7017 *G. J. Churchward*            [*R. A. Panting*

Class 4073 4-6-0 No. 7008 *Swansea Castle* (fitted with double chimney)
                                                        [*P. Ransome-Wallis*

Class 1000 4-6-0 No. 1003 *County of Wilts*                    [L. King

Class 4900 4-6-0 No. 4979 *Wootton Hall*                    [B. J. R. Yates

Class 6800 4-6-0 No. 6853 *Morehampton Grange*                    [G. Wheele

Class 7800 4-6-0 No. 7818 *Granville Manor*

[*J. B. Bucknall*

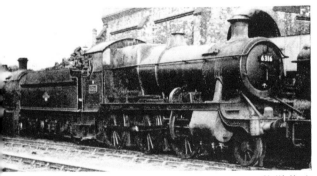

Class 4300 2-6-0 No. 6316

[*A. W. Martin*

G.W.R. City Class 4-4-0 No. 3440 *City of Truro*

[*A. A. Cameron*

Class 2800 2-8-0 No. 2861

[G. W. Morrison

Class 3800 2-8-0 No. 3808 (with side-window cab)

[P. H. Wells

Class 4700 2-8-0 No. 4702

[G. Wheeler

Weight: Loco. 57 tons 9 cwt.
Pressure: 160 lb. Su.
Cyls.: 20½" × 26".
Driving Wheels: 6' 8".
T.E.: 18,575 lb.
P.V.

31760/4–6/8/71/6/80

Total 8

## 4-4-0    3P    Class L1

Introduced 1926. Maunsell post-grouping development of L, with long-travel valves, side window cab and detail alterations.
Weight: Loco. 57 tons 16 cwt.
Pressure: 180 lb. Su.
Cyls.: 19½" × 26".
Driving Wheels: 6' 8".
T.E.: 18,910 lb.
P.V.

31753/4/6/7/9/82/3/6/9

Total 9

## 4-6-0    7P    Class LN

*Introduced 1926. Maunsell design, cylinders and tender modified by Bulleid from 1938, and fitted with multiple-jet blastpipe and large-diameter chimney.
†Introduced 1929. Loco. fitted experimentally with smaller driving wheels.
‡Introduced 1929. Loco. fitted experimentally with longer boiler..
Weight: Loco. $\begin{cases} 83 \text{ tons } 10 \text{ cwt.*†} \\ 84 \text{ tons } 16 \text{ cwt.‡} \end{cases}$
Pressure: 220 lb. Su.
Cyls.: (4) 16½" × 26".
Driving Wheels: $\begin{cases} 6'7''.*‡ \\ 6'3''.† \end{cases}$
T.E.: $\begin{cases} 33,510 \text{ lb.*‡} \\ 35,300 \text{ lb.†} \end{cases}$
Walschaerts valve gear. P.V.

*30850–8/61–5      ‡30860

†30859

Total 16

## 0-4-4T    2P    Class M7

*Introduced 1897. Drummond L.S.W. M7 design.

†Introduced 1903. Drummond X14 design, with increased front overhang, steam reverser and detail alterations, now classified M7 (30254 originally M7).

‡Introduced 1925. Fitted for push-and-pull working.

Weight: $\begin{cases} 60 \text{ tons } 4 \text{ cwt.*} \\ 60 \text{ tons } 3 \text{ cwt.†} \\ 62 \text{ tons } 0 \text{ cwt.‡} \end{cases}$

Pressure: 175 lb.

Cyls.: 18½" × 26".

Driving Wheels: 5' 7".

T.E.: 19,755 lb.

*30023–5/32–6/9/40/3/4, 30112, 30241/5–9/51/3, 30320/1/57, 30667–70/4/6

†30124/7/32, 30254, 30375/7/8, 30479

‡30021/8/9/31/45/8–53/5–7/9/60, 30104/5/7–11/25/9/31/3, 30328/79, 30480

Total 68

## 4-6-2    8P    Class MN

Introduced 1941. Bulleid design originally with 280 lb. pressure, multiple-jet blastpipe and Bulleid valve gear. Rebuilt since 1956 with Walschaerts valve gear and modified details ; air-smoothed casing removed.

Weight: Loco. 97 tons 18 cwt.

Pressure: 250 lb.

Cyls: (3) 18" × 24".

Driving Wheels: 6' 2".

T.E.: 33,495 lb.

P.V.

35001–30

Total 30

## Classes N & N1

**2-6-0**  4P5F

*N. Introduced 1917. Maunsell S.E.C. mixed traffic design.

†N1. Introduced 1922. 3-cylinder development of N.

Weight: Loco. $\begin{cases} 61 \text{ tons } 4 \text{ cwt.}^* \\ 64 \text{ tons } 5 \text{ cwt.†} \end{cases}$

Pressure: 200 lb. Su.

Cyls.: $\begin{cases} (O) \ 19'' \times 28''.^* \\ (3) \ 16'' \times 28''.† \end{cases}$

Driving Wheels: 5′ 6″.

T.E.: $\begin{cases} 26,035 \text{ lb.}^* \\ 27,695 \text{ lb.†} \end{cases}$

Walschaerts valve gear.  P.V.

*31400–14, 31810–21/3–75
†31822/76–80

**Total    N 80**
**N1 6**

---

**4-6-0**  5P  **Class N15**

*Introduced 1925. Maunsell development of Urie locos. with long-travel valves, increased boiler pressure, smaller fireboxes, and tenders from Drummond G14 4-6-0s.

†Introduced 1925. Later locos, with detail alterations and increased weight.

‡Introduced 1925. Locos. with modified cabs to suit Eastern Section, and new bogie tenders.

§Introduced 1926. Locos. with detail alterations and most with six-wheeled tenders for Central Section.

Weight: Loco. $\begin{cases} 79 \text{ tons } 18 \text{ cwt.}^* \\ 80 \text{ tons } 19 \text{ cwt.†‡} \\ 81 \text{ tons } 17 \text{ cwt. §} \end{cases}$

Pressure: 200 lb. Su.
Cyls.: (O) 20½″ × 28″.
Driving Wheels: 6′ 7″.
T.E.: 25,320 lb.
Walschaerts valve gear.  P.V.

*30453/7        †30451
‡30764/5/8/70–3/7/81–3/8/90
§30793/5/6/8–30800/2–4/6

**Total 26**

---

**0-6-0**  2F  **Class O1**

Introduced 1903. Wainwright rebuild with domed boiler and new cab of Stirling S.E. Class O 0-6-0 (introduced 1878).

Weight: Loco. 41 tons 1 cwt.
Pressure: 150 lb.
Cyls.: 18″ × 26″.
Driving Wheels: 5′ 2″.
T.E.: 17,325 lb.

31065

**Total i**

---

**0-4-4T**  0P  **Class O2**

*Introduced 1889. Adams L.S.W. design.

†Introduced 1923. Fitted with Westinghouse brake for I.O.W. Bunkers enlarged from 1932.

‡Fitted with Drummond-type boiler.

§Fitted for push-and-pull working.

Weight: $\begin{cases} 46 \text{ tons } 18 \text{ cwt.}^*‡ \\ 48 \text{ tons } 8 \text{ cwt.†} \end{cases}$

Pressure: 160 lb.
Cyls.: 17½″ × 24″.
Driving Wheels: 4′ 10″.
T.E.: 17,235 lb.

*30192/3/9,  30200/25/9
†14/6–3/20–2/4–6/8–33
†§35/6
‡2730223        ‡§30183

**Total 27**

---

**0-6-0T**  Unclass.  **Class P**

Introduced 1909. Wainwright S.E.C. design for push-and-pull work, now used for shunting.
Weight: 28 tons 10 cwt.
Pressure: 160 lb.
Cyls.: 12″ × 18″.
Driving Wheels: 3′ 9⅛″.
T.E.: 7,810 lb.

31027, 31556

**Total 2**

---

**0-6-0**  4F  **Class Q**

Introduced 1938. Maunsell design, later fitted with multiple-jet blastpipe and large-diameter chimney. (30545 since fitted with B.R. Chimney, and 30549 with Stovepipe Chimney.)
Weight: Loco. 49 tons 10 cwt.
Pressure: 200 lb. Su.
Cyls.: 19″ × 25″.

Driving Wheels: 5' 1".
T.E.: 26,160 lb.
P.V.

30530–49             **Total 20**

## 0-6-0    5F    Class Q1

Introduced 1942. Bulleid "Austerity"
  design.
Weight: Loco. 51 tons 5 cwt.
Pressure: 230 lb. Su.
Cyls.: 19" × 26".
Driving Wheels: 5' 1".
T.E.: 30,080 lb.
P.V.

33001–40             **Total 40**

## 4-6-0    6F    Class S15

*Introduced 1920. Urie L.S.W. design,
  development of N15 for mixed traffic
  work.
†Introduced 1927. Maunsell design,
  with higher pressure, smaller grate,
  modified footplating and other detail
  differences. 30833–7 with 6-wheel
  tenders for Central Section.
‡Introduced 1936. Later locos. with
  detail differences and reduced weight.
Weight: Loco. $\begin{cases} 79 \text{ tons } 16 \text{ cwt.*} \\ 80 \text{ tons } 14 \text{ cwt.†} \\ 79 \text{ tons } 5 \text{ cwt.‡} \end{cases}$
Pressure: $\begin{cases} 180 \text{ lb. Su.*} \\ 200 \text{ lb. Su.†‡} \end{cases}$
Cyls.: $\begin{cases} (O) 21" \times 28".* \\ (O) 20\frac{1}{2}" \times 28".†‡ \end{cases}$
Driving Wheels: 5' 7".
T.E. $\begin{cases} 28,200 \text{ lb.*} \\ 29,855 \text{ lb.†‡} \end{cases}$
Walschaerts valve gear.   P.V.

*30496–30515      †30823–37
‡30838–47

                     **Total 45**

## 4-4-0    3P    Class T9

*Introduced 1899. Drummond L.S.W.
  design, fitted with superheater and
  larger cylinders by Urie from 1922.
†Introduced 1899. Locos. with detail
  differences (originally fitted with
  firebox watertubes).
‡Introduced 1900. Locos. with wider
  cab and splashers, without coupling
  rod splashers and originally fitted
  with firebox watertubes.

Weight: Loco. $\begin{cases} 51 \text{ tons } 18 \text{ cwt.*} \\ 51 \text{ tons } 16 \text{ cwt.†} \\ 51 \text{ tons } 7 \text{ cwt.‡} \end{cases}$
Pressure: 175 lb. Su.
Cyls.: 19" × 26".
Driving Wheels: 6' 7".
T.E.: 17,675 lb.

*30117/20, 30287
†30707/9/15/7–9/29
‡30300/13/38

                     **Total 13**

## Classes
## 2-6-0    4P3F    U & U1

*U. Introduced 1928. Rebuild of
  Maunsell S.E.C. Class K ("River")
  2-6-4T (introduced 1917).
†U. Introduced 1928. Locos. built as
  Class U, with smaller splashers and
  detail alterations.
‡U1. Introduced 1928. 3-cylinder
  development of Class U (prototype
  31890, rebuilt from 2-6-4T, originally
  built 1925).
Weight: Loco. $\begin{cases} 63 \text{ tons.*} \\ 62 \text{ tons } 6 \text{ cwt.†} \\ 65 \text{ tons } 6 \text{ cwt.‡} \end{cases}$
Pressure: 200 lb. Su.
Cyls.: $\begin{cases} (O) 19" \times 28".*† \\ (3) 16" \times 28".‡ \end{cases}$
Driving Wheels: 6' 0".
T.E.: $\begin{cases} 23,865 \text{ lb.*†} \\ 25,385 \text{ lb.‡} \end{cases}$
Walschaerts valve gear.   P.V.

*31790–31809      †31610–39
‡31890–31910

        **Total Class U 50**
                **Class U1 21**

## 0-6-0T    3F    Class USA

Introduced 1942. U.S. Army Trans-
portation Corps design, purchased by
S.R. 1946, and fitted with modified cab
and bunker and other detail altera-
tions.
Weight: 46 tons 10 cwt.
Pressure: 210 lb.
Cyls.: (O) 16½" × 24".
Driving Wheels: 4' 6".
T.E.: 21,600 lb.
Walschaerts valve gear.   P.V.

30061–74           **Total 14**

## 4-4-0  5P  Class V

*Introduced 1930. Maunsell design.
†Introduced 1938. Fitted with multiple-jet blastpipe and large-diameter chimney by Bulleid.
Weight: Loco. 67 tons 2 cwt.
Pressure: 220 lb. Su.
Cyls.: (3) $16\frac{1}{4}'' \times 26''$.
Driving Wheels: 6' 7".
T.E.: 25,135 lb.
Walschaerts valve gear.  P.V.

*30902–6/8/10–2/6/22/3/5–8/
35/6

†30900/1/7/9/13–5/7/8/20/1/4/
29–31/3/4/7–9  **Total 38**

## 2-6-4T  6F  Class W

Introduced 1931. Maunsell design, developed from Class N: 2-6-0.
Weight: 90 tons 14 cwt.
Pressure: 200 lb. Su.
Cyls.: (3) $16\frac{1}{2}'' \times 28'$.
Driving Wheels: 5' 6".
T.E.: 29,450 lb.
Walschaerts valve gear.  P.V.

31911–25  **Total 15**

## Classes
## 4-6-2  7P5F  WC & BB

*Introduced 1945. Bulleid " West Country " Class, with Bulleid valve gear.
†Introduced 1946. Bulleid " Battle of Britain " Class, with Bulleid valve gear.
‡Introduced 1957. Rebuilt with Walschaerts valve gear, modified details and air-smoothed casing removed.
Weight: Loco. $\begin{cases} 86 \text{ tons } 0 \text{ cwt.}^{*†} \\ 90 \text{ tons } 1 \text{ cwt.}^{‡} \end{cases}$
Pressure: 250 lb. Su.
Cyls.: (3) $16\frac{3}{8}'' \times 24''$.
Driving Wheels: 6' 2".
T.E.: 27,715 lb.
Bulleid valve gear.  P.V.

*34002/6/7/11/5/9/20/3/30/3/5/8/
41/3/91/2/4/6/9,  34102–8

†34049/51/4/5/7/61/3–70/2–6/8–
81/3/4/6, 341/10

*‡34001/3–5/8–10/2–4/6–8/21/2/
4–9/31/2/4/6/7/9/40/2/4–8/93/
5/7/8, 34100/1

††34050/2/3/6/8/9/60/2/71/7/82/
5/7–9/90, 34109  **Total 110**

## 0-8-0T  6F  Class Z

Introduced 1929. Maunsell design for heavy shunting.
Weight: 71 tons 12 cwt.
Pressure: 180 lb.
Cyls.: (3) $16'' \times 28''$.
Driving Wheels: 4' 8".
T.E.: 29,375 lb.
Walschaerts valve gear.  P.V.

30950–7  **Total 8**

## 0-6-0  3F  Class 700

Introduced 1897. Drummond L.S.W. design, superheated from 1921.
Weight: Loco. 46 tons 14 cwt.
Pressure: 180 lb. Su.
Cyls.: $19'' \times 26'$.
Driving Wheels: 5' 1".
T.E.: 23,540 lb.

30306/8/9/15–7/25–7/39/46/50/
68, 30689–30701

**Total 26**

## 2-4-0WT  0P  Class 0298

Introduced 1874. Beattie L.S.W. design, rebuilt by Adams (1884–92). Urie (1921–2) and Maunsell (1931–5).
Weight: 37 tons 16 cwt.
Pressure: 160 lb.
Cyls.: (O) $16\frac{1}{2}'' \times 20''$.
Driving Wheels: 5' 7".
T.E.: 11,050 lb.

30585–7  **Total 3**

## 4-4-2T  1P  Class 0415

Introduced 1882. Adams L.S.W. design, later reboilered.
Weight: 55 tons 2 cwt.
Pressure: 160 lb.
Cyls.: (O) $17\frac{1}{2}'' \times 24''$.
Driving Wheels: 5' 7".
T.E.: 14,920 lb.

30582/3  **Total 2**

# BRITISH RAILWAYS LOCOMOTIVES
## Nos. 30021-35030
### and Isle of Wight Locos.

| No. | Class | No. | Class | No. | Class | No. | Class |
|---|---|---|---|---|---|---|---|
| 30021 | M7 | 30069 | U.S.A. | 30246 | M7 | 30357 | M7 |
| 30023 | M7 | 30070 | U.S.A. | 30247 | M7 | 30368 | 700 |
| 30024 | M7 | 30071 | U.S.A. | 30248 | M7 | 30375 | M7 |
| 30025 | M7 | 30072 | U.S.A. | 30249 | M7 | 30377 | M7 |
| 30028 | M7 | 30073 | U.S.A. | 30251 | M7 | 30378 | M7 |
| 30029 | M7 | 30074 | U.S.A. | 30253 | M7 | 30379 | M7 |
| 30031 | M7 | 30089 | B4 | | | | |
| 30032 | M7 | 30096 | B4 | 30451 Sir Lamorak | N15 | | |
| 30033 | M7 | 30102 | B4 | 30453 King Arthur | N15 | | |
| 30034 | M7 | 30104 | M7 | 30457 Sir Bedivere | N15 | | |
| 30035 | M7 | 30105 | M7 | | | 30475 | H15 |
| 30036 | M7 | 30107 | M7 | 30254 | M7 | 30476 | H15 |
| 30039 | M7 | 30108 | M7 | 30258 | G6 | 30479 | M7 |
| 30040 | M7 | 30109 | M7 | 30277 | G6 | 30480 | M7 |
| 30043 | M7 | 30110 | M7 | 30287 | T9 | 30494 | G16 |
| 30044 | M7 | 30111 | M7 | 30300 | T9 | 30495 | G16 |
| 30045 | M7 | 30112 | M7 | 30306 | 700 | 30496 | S15 |
| 30048 | M7 | 30117 | T9 | 30308 | 700 | 30497 | S15 |
| 30049 | M7 | 30120 | T9 | 30309 | 700 | 30498 | S15 |
| 30050 | M7 | 30124 | M7 | 30313 | T9 | 30499 | S15 |
| 30051 | M7 | 30125 | M7 | 30315 | 700 | 30500 | S15 |
| 30052 | M7 | 30127 | M7 | 30316 | 700 | 30501 | S15 |
| 30053 | M7 | 30129 | M7 | 30317 | 700 | 30502 | S15 |
| 30055 | M7 | 30131 | M7 | 30320 | M7 | 30503 | S15 |
| 30056 | M7 | 30132 | M7 | 30321 | M7 | 30504 | S15 |
| 30057 | M7 | 30133 | M7 | 30325 | 700 | 30505 | S15 |
| 30059 | M7 | 30183 | O2 | 30326 | 700 | 30506 | S15 |
| 30060 | M7 | 30192 | O2 | 30327 | 700 | 30507 | S15 |
| 30061 | U.S.A. | 30193 | O2 | 30328 | M7 | 30508 | S15 |
| 30062 | U.S.A. | 30199 | O2 | 30331 | H15 | 30509 | S15 |
| 30063 | U.S.A. | 30200 | O2 | 30338 | T9 | 30510 | S15 |
| 30064 | U.S.A. | 30223 | O2 | 30339 | 700 | 30511 | S15 |
| 30065 | U.S.A. | 30225 | O2 | 30346 | 700 | 30512 | S15 |
| 30066 | U.S.A. | 30229 | O2 | 30349 | G6 | 30513 | S15 |
| 30067 | U.S.A. | 30241 | M7 | 30350 | 700 | | |
| 30068 | U.S.A. | 30245 | M7 | | | | |

| No. | Class | No. | Class | No. | Class | No. | Class |
|---|---|---|---|---|---|---|---|
| 30514 | S15 | 30582 | 0415 | 30790 | Sir Villiars | | N15 |
| 30515 | S15 | 30583 | 0415 | 30793 | Sir Ontzlake | | N15 |
| 30516 | H16 | 30585 | 0298 | 30795 | Sir Dinadan | | N15 |
| 30517 | H16 | 30586 | 0298 | 30796 | Sir Dodinas le Savage | | |
| 30518 | H16 | 30587 | 0298 | | | | N15 |
| 30519 | H16 | 30667 | M7 | 30798 | Sir Hectimere | | N15 |
| 30520 | H16 | 30668 | M7 | 30799 | Sir Ironside | | N15 |
| 30521 | H15 | 30669 | M7 | 30800 | Sir Meleaus de Lile | | N15 |
| 30522 | H15 | 30670 | M7 | 30802 | Sir Durnore | | N15 |
| 30523 | H15 | 30674 | M7 | 30803 | Sir Harry le Fise Lake | | |
| 30524 | H15 | 30676 | M7 | | | | N15 |
| 30530 | Q | 30689 | 700 | 30804 | Sir Cador of Cornwall | | |
| 30531 | Q | 30690 | 700 | | | | N15 |
| 30532 | Q | 30691 | 700 | 30806 | Sir Galleron | | N15 |
| 30533 | Q | 30692 | 700 | 30823 | S15 | | |
| 30534 | Q | 30693 | 700 | 30824 | S15 | 30836 | S15 |
| 30535 | Q | 30694 | 700 | 30825 | S15 | 30837 | S15 |
| 30536 | Q | 30695 | 700 | 30826 | S15 | 30838 | S15 |
| 30537 | Q | 30696 | 700 | 30827 | S15 | 30839 | S15 |
| 30538 | Q | 30697 | 700 | 30828 | S15 | 30840 | S15 |
| 30539 | Q | 30698 | 700 | 30829 | S15 | 30841 | S15 |
| 30540 | Q | 30699 | 700 | 30830 | S15 | 30842 | S15 |
| 30541 | Q | 30700 | 700 | 30831 | S15 | 30843 | S15 |
| 30542 | Q | 30701 | 700 | 30832 | S15 | 30844 | S15 |
| 30543 | Q | 30707 | T9 | 30833 | S15 | 30845 | S15 |
| 30544 | Q | 30709 | T9 | 30834 | S15 | 30846 | S15 |
| 30545 | Q | 30715 | T9 | 30835 | S15 | 30847 | S15 |
| 30546 | Q | 30717 | T9 | | | | |
| 30547 | Q | 30718 | T9 | 30850 | Lord Nelson | | LN |
| 30548 | Q | 30719 | T9 | 30851 | Sir Francis Drake | | LN |
| 30549 | Q | 30729 | T9 | 30852 | Sir Walter Raleigh | | LN |
| | | | | 30853 | Sir Richard Grenville | | LN |
| 30764 | Sir Gawain | | N15 | 30854 | Howard of Effingham | | LN |
| 30765 | Sir Gareth | | N15 | 30855 | Robert Blake | | LN |
| 30768 | Sir Balin | | N15 | 30856 | Lord St. Vincent | | LN |
| 30770 | Sir Prianius | | N15 | 30857 | Lord Howe | | LN |
| 30771 | Sir Sagramore | | N15 | 30858 | Lord Duncan | | LN |
| 30772 | Sir Percivale | | N15 | 30859 | Lord Hood | | LN |
| 30773 | Sir Lavaine | | N15 | 30860 | Lord Hawke | | LN |
| 30777 | Sir Lamiel | | N15 | 30861 | Lord Anson | | LN |
| 30781 | Sir Aglovale | | N15 | 30862 | Lord Collingwood | | LN |
| 30782 | Sir Brian | | N15 | 30863 | Lord Rodney | | LN |
| 30783 | Sir Gillemere | | N15 | 30864 | Sir Martin Frobisher | | LN |
| 30788 | Sir Urre of the Mount | | | 30865 | Sir John Hawkins | | LN |
| | | | N15 | | | | |

| No. | Class | No. | Class | No. | Class | No. | Class |
|---|---|---|---|---|---|---|---|
| 30900 | Eton | V | | 31005 | H | 31402 | N |
| 30901 | Winchester | V | | 31019 | E1 | 31403 | N |
| 30902 | Wellington | V | | 31027 | P | 31404 | N |
| 30903 | Charterhouse | V | | 31037 | C | 31405 | N |
| 30904 | Lancing | V | | 31061 | C | 31406 | N |
| 30905 | Tonbridge | V | | 31065 | O1 | 31407 | N |
| 30906 | Sherborne | V | | 31067 | E1 | 31408 | N |
| 30907 | Dulwich | V | | 31068 | C | 31409 | N |
| 30908 | Westminster | V | | 31112 | C | 31410 | N |
| 30909 | St. Paul's | V | | 31113 | C | 31411 | N |
| 30910 | Merchant Taylors | V | | 31145 | D1 | 31412 | N |
| 30911 | Dover | V | | 31150 | C | 31413 | N |
| 30912 | Downside | V | | 31161 | H | 31414 | N |
| 30913 | Christ's Hospital | V | | 31162 | H | 31480 | C |
| 30914 | Eastbourne | V | | 31177 | H | 31481 | C |
| 30915 | Brighton | V | | 31193 | H | 31487 | D1 |
| 30916 | Whitgift | V | | 31218 | C | 31489 | D1 |
| 30917 | Ardingly | V | | 31229 | C | 31495 | C |
| 30918 | Hurstpierpoint | V | | 31242 | C | 31498 | C |
| 30920 | Rugby | V | | 31244 | C | 31500 | H |
| 30921 | Shrewsbury | V | | 31246 | D1 | 31505 | D1 |
| 30922 | Marlborough | V | | 31247 | D1 | 31507 | E1 |
| 30923 | Bradfield | V | | 31255 | C | 31510 | C |
| 30924 | Haileybury | V | | 31256 | C | 31512 | H |
| 30925 | Cheltenham | V | | 31261 | H | 31517 | H |
| 30926 | Repton | V | | 31263 | H | 31518 | H |
| 30927 | Clifton | V | | 31267 | C | 31519 | H |
| 30928 | Stowe | V | | 31268 | C | 31521 | H |
| 30929 | Malvern | V | | 31271 | C | 31522 | H |
| 30930 | Radley | V | | 31276 | H | 31530 | H |
| 30931 | King's Wimbledon | V | | 31278 | H | 31533 | H |
| 30933 | King's Canterbury | V | | 31280 | C | 31542 | H |
| 30934 | St. Lawrence | V | | 31293 | C | 31543 | H |
| 30935 | Sevenoaks | V | | 31305 | H | 31544 | H |
| 30936 | Cranleigh | V | | 31306 | H | 31545 | D1 |
| 30937 | Epsom | V | | 31307 | H | 31550 | H |
| 30938 | St. Olave's | V | | 31308 | H | 31551 | H |
| 30939 | Leatherhead | V | | 31317 | C | 31552 | H |
| 30950 | Z | | | 31322 | H | 31553 | H |
| 30951 | Z | 30955 | Z | 31324 | H | 31556 | P |
| 30952 | Z | 30956 | Z | 31326 | H | 31573 | C |
| 30953 | Z | 30957 | Z | 31328 | H | 31575 | C |
| 30954 | Z | 31004 | C | 31400 | N | 31578 | C |
| | | | | 31401 | N | 31579 | C |
| | | | | | | 31583 | C |

**31584-31902**

| No. | Class | No. | Class | No. | Class | No. | Class | No. | Class |
|---|---|---|---|---|---|---|---|---|---|
| 31584 | C | 31715 | C | 31804 | U | 31849 | N | | |
| 31588 | C | 31716 | C | 31805 | U | 31850 | N | | |
| 31589 | C | 31717 | C | 31806 | U | 31851 | N | | |
| 31592 | C | 31719 | C | 31807 | U | 31852 | N | | |
| 31610 | U | 31720 | C | 31808 | U | 31853 | N | | |
| 31611 | U | 31721 | C | 31809 | U | 31854 | N | | |
| 31612 | U | 31722 | C | 31810 | N | 31855 | N | | |
| 31613 | U | 31723 | C | 31811 | N | 31856 | N | | |
| 31614 | U | 31724 | C | 31812 | N | 31857 | N | | |
| 31615 | U | 31727 | DI | 31813 | N | 31858 | N | | |
| 31616 | U | 31735 | DI | 31814 | N | 31859 | N | | |
| 31617 | U | 31739 | DI | 31815 | N | 31860 | N | | |
| 31618 | U | 31749 | DI | 31816 | N | 31861 | N | | |
| 31619 | U | 31753 | LI | 31817 | N | 31862 | N | | |
| 31620 | U | 31754 | LI | 31818 | N | 31863 | N | | |
| 31621 | U | 31756 | LI | 31819 | N | 31864 | N | | |
| 31622 | U | 31757 | LI | 31820 | N | 31865 | N | | |
| 31623 | U | 31759 | LI | 31821 | N | 31866 | N | | |
| 31624 | U | 31760 | L | 31822 | NI | 31867 | N | | |
| 31625 | U | 31764 | L | 31823 | N | 31868 | N | | |
| 31626 | U | 31765 | L | 31824 | N | 31869 | N | | |
| 31627 | U | 31766 | L | 31825 | N | 31870 | N | | |
| 31628 | U | 31768 | L | 31826 | N | 31871 | N | | |
| 31629 | U | 31771 | L | 31827 | N | 31872 | N | | |
| 31630 | U | 31776 | L | 31828 | N | 31873 | N | | |
| 31631 | U | 31780 | L | 31829 | N | 31874 | N | | |
| 31632 | U | 31782 | LI | 31830 | N | 31875 | N | | |
| 31633 | U | 31783 | LI | 31831 | N | 31876 | NI | | |
| 31634 | U | 31786 | LI | 31832 | N | 31877 | NI | | |
| 31635 | U | 31789 | LI | 31833 | N | 31878 | NI | | |
| 31636 | U | 31790 | U | 31834 | N | 31879 | NI | | |
| 31637 | U | 31791 | U | 31835 | N | 31880 | NI | | |
| 31638 | U | 31792 | U | 31836 | N | 31890 | UI | | |
| 31639 | U | 31793 | U | 31837 | N | 31891 | UI | | |
| 31682 | C | 31794 | U | 31838 | N | 31892 | UI | | |
| 31684 | C | 31795 | U | 31839 | N | 31893 | UI | | |
| 31686 | C | 31796 | U | 31840 | N | 31894 | UI | | |
| 31689 | C | 31797 | U | 31841 | N | 31895 | UI | | |
| 31690 | C | 31798 | U | 31842 | N | 31896 | UI | | |
| 31691 | C | 31799 | U | 31843 | N | 31897 | UI | | |
| 31693 | C | 31800 | U | 31844 | N | 31898 | UI | | |
| 31694 | C | 31801 | U | 31845 | N | 31899 | UI | | |
| 31695 | C | 31802 | U | 31846 | N | 31900 | UI | | |
| 31714 | C | 31803 | U | 31847 | N | 31901 | UI | | |
| | | | | 31848 | N | 31902 | UI | | |

# 31903-34009

| No. | Class | No. | Class | No. | Class | No. | Class |
|---|---|---|---|---|---|---|---|
| 31903 | UI | 32349 | K | 32538 | C2X | 33006 | QI |
| 31904 | UI | 32350 | K | 32539 | C2X | 33007 | QI |
| 31905 | UI | 32351 | K | 32544 | C2X | 33008 | QI |
| 31906 | UI | 32352 | K | 32545 | C2X | 33009 | QI |
| 31907 | UI | 32353 | K | 32546 | C2X | 33010 | QI |
| 31908 | UI | 32408 | E6 | 32547 | C2X | 33011 | QI |
| 31909 | UI | 32410 | E6 | 32548 | C2X | 33012 | QI |
| 31910 | UI | 32415 | E6 | 32549 | C2X | 33013 | QI |
| 31911 | W | 32416 | E6 | 32550 | C2X | 33014 | QI |
| 31912 | W | 32417 | E6 | 32552 | C2X | 33015 | QI |
| 31913 | W | 32418 | E6 | 32553 | C2X | 33016 | QI |
| 31914 | W | 32438 | C2X | 32556 | E4 | 33017 | QI |
| 31915 | W | 32441 | C2X | 32557 | E4 | 33018 | QI |
| 31916 | W | 32445 | C2X | 32563 | E4 | 33019 | QI |
| 31917 | W | 32448 | C2X | 32564 | E4 | 33020 | QI |
| 31918 | W | 32449 | C2X | 32565 | E4 | 33021 | QI |
| 31919 | W | 32450 | C2X | 32578 | E4 | 33022 | QI |
| 31920 | W | 32451 | C2X | 32580 | E4 | 33023 | QI |
| 31921 | W | 32468 | E4 | 32581 | E4 | 33024 | QI |
| 31922 | W | 32469 | E4 | 32635 | AIX | 33025 | QI |
| 31923 | W | 32470 | E4 | 32636 | AIX | 33026 | QI |
| 31924 | W | 32472 | E4 | 32640 | AIX | 33027 | QI |
| 31925 | W | 32473 | E4 | 32646 | AIX | 33028 | QI |
| 32100 | E2 | 32474 | E4 | 32650 | AIX | 33029 | QI |
| 32101 | E2 | 32475 | E4 | 32661 | AIX | 33030 | QI |
| 32102 | E2 | 32479 | E4 | 32662 | AIX | 33031 | QI |
| 32103 | E2 | 32487 | E4 | 32670 | AIX | 33032 | QI |
| 32104 | E2 | 32498 | E4 | 32678 | AIX | 33033 | QI |
| 32105 | E2 | 32500 | E4 | 32694 | EI | 33034 | QI |
| 32106 | E2 | 32503 | E4 | 33001 | QI | 33035 | QI |
| 32107 | E2 | 32504 | E4 | 33002 | QI | 33036 | QI |
| 32108 | E2 | 32505 | E4 | 33003 | QI | 33037 | QI |
| 32109 | E2 | 32506 | E4 | 33004 | QI | 33038 | QI |
| 32337 | K | 32509 | E4 | 33005 | QI | 33039 | QI |
| 32338 | K | 32510 | E4 | | | 33040 | QI |
| 32339 | K | 32512 | E4 | | | | |
| 32340 | K | 32515 | E4 | 34001 | Exeter | | WC |
| 32341 | K | 32521 | C2X | 34002 | Salisbury | | WC |
| 32342 | K | 32522 | C2X | 34003 | Plymouth | | WC |
| 32343 | K | 32523 | C2X | 34004 | Yeovil | | WC |
| 32344 | K | 32525 | C2X | 34005 | Barnstaple | | WC |
| 32345 | K | 32528 | C2X | 34006 | Bude | | WC |
| 32346 | K | 32534 | C2X | 34007 | Wadebridge | | WC |
| 32347 | K | 32535 | C2X | 34008 | Padstow | | WC |
| 32348 | K | 32536 | C2X | 34009 | Lyme Regis | | WC |

49

| No. | | Class | No. | | Class |
|---|---|---|---|---|---|
| 34010 | Sidmouth | WC | 34053 | Sir Keith Park | BB |
| 34011 | Tavistock | WC | 34054 | Lord Beaverbrook | BB |
| 34012 | Launceston | WC | 34055 | Fighter Pilot | BB |
| 34013 | Okehampton | WC | 34056 | Croydon | BB |
| 34014 | Budleigh Salterton | WC | 34057 | Biggin Hill | BB |
| 34015 | Exmouth | WC | 34058 | Sir Frederick Pile | BB |
| 34016 | Bodmin | WC | 34059 | Sir Archibald Sinclair | BB |
| 34017 | Ilfracombe | WC | 34060 | 25 Squadron | BB |
| 34018 | Axminster | WC | 34061 | 73 Squadron | BB |
| 34019 | Bideford | WC | 34062 | 17 Squadron | BB |
| 34020 | Seaton | WC | 34063 | 229 Squadron | BB |
| 34021 | Dartmoor | WC | 34064 | Fighter Command | BB |
| 34022 | Exmoor | WC | 34065 | Hurricane | BB |
| 34023 | Blackmore Vale | WC | 34066 | Spitfire | BB |
| 34024 | Tamar Valley | WC | 34067 | Tangmere | BB |
| 34025 | Whimple | WC | 34068 | Kenley | BB |
| 34026 | Yes Tor | WC | 34069 | Hawkinge | BB |
| 34027 | Taw Valley | WC | 34070 | Manston | BB |
| 34028 | Eddystone | WC | 34071 | 601 Squadron | BB |
| 34029 | Lundy | WC | 34072 | 257 Squadron | BB |
| 34030 | Watersmeet | WC | 34073 | 249 Squadron | BB |
| 34031 | Torrington | WC | 34074 | 46 Squadron | BB |
| 34032 | Camelford | WC | 34075 | 264 Squadron | BB |
| 34033 | Chard | WC | 34076 | 41 Squadron | BB |
| 34034 | Honiton | WC | 34077 | 603 Squadron | BB |
| 34035 | Shaftesbury | WC | 34078 | 222 Squadron | BB |
| 34036 | Westward Ho | WC | 34079 | 141 Squadron | BB |
| 34037 | Clovelly | WC | 34080 | 74 Squadron | BB |
| 34038 | Lynton | WC | 34081 | 92 Squadron | BB |
| 34039 | Boscastle | WC | 34082 | 615 Squadron | BB |
| 34040 | Crewkerne | WC | 34083 | 605 Squadron | BB |
| 34041 | Wilton | WC | 34084 | 253 Squadron | BB |
| 34042 | Dorchester | WC | 34085 | 501 Squadron | BB |
| 34043 | Combe Martin | WC | 34086 | 219 Squadron | BB |
| 34044 | Woolacombe | WC | 34087 | 145 Squadron | BB |
| 34045 | Ottery St. Mary | WC | 34088 | 213 Squadron | BB |
| 34046 | Braunton | WC | 34089 | 602 Squadron | BB |
| 34047 | Callington | WC | 34090 | Sir Eustace Missenden, | |
| 34048 | Crediton | WC | | Southern Railway | BB |
| 34049 | Anti-Aircraft Command | BB | 34091 | Weymouth | WC |
| 34050 | Royal Observer Corps | BB | 34092 | City of Wells | WC |
| | | | 34093 | Saunton | WC |
| | | | 34094 | Mortehoe | WC |
| 34051 | Winston Churchill | BB | 34095 | Brentor | WC |
| 34052 | Lord Dowding | BB | 34096 | Trevone | WC |

| No. | | Class | No. | | Class |
|---|---|---|---|---|---|
| 34097 | Holsworthy | WC | 35026 | Lamport & Holt Line | |
| 34098 | Templecombe | WC | | | MN |
| 34099 | Lynmouth | WC | 35027 | Port Line | MN |
| 34100 | Appledore | WC | 35028 | Clan Line | MN |
| 34101 | Hartland | WC | 35029 | Ellerman Lines | MN |
| 34102 | Lapford | WC | 35030 | Elder Dempster Lines | |
| 34103 | Calstock | WC | | | MN |
| 34104 | Bere Alston | WC | | | |
| 34105 | Swanage | WC | | | |
| 34106 | Lydford | WC | | | |
| 34107 | Blandford Forum | WC | | | |
| 34108 | Wincanton | WC | | | |
| 34109 | Sir Trafford | | | | |
| | Leigh-Mallory | BB | | | |

## ISLE OF WIGHT LOCOMOTIVES

| No. | | Class | No. | | Class |
|---|---|---|---|---|---|
| 34110 | 66 Squadron | BB | 14 | Fishbourne | O2 |
| 35001 | Channel Packet | MN | 16 | Ventnor | O2 |
| 35002 | Union Castle | MN | 17 | Seaview | O2 |
| 35003 | Royal Mail | MN | 18 | Ningwood | O2 |
| 35004 | Cunard White Star | MN | 20 | Shanklin | O2 |
| 35005 | Canadian Pacific | MN | 21 | Sandown | O2 |
| 35006 | Peninsular & Oriental | | 22 | Brading | O2 |
| | S.N. Co. | MN | 24 | Calbourne | O2 |
| 35007 | Aberdeen | | 25 | Godshill | O2 |
| | Commonwealth | MN | 26 | Whitwell | O2 |
| 35008 | Orient Line | MN | 27 | Merstone | O2 |
| 35009 | Shaw Savill | MN | 28 | Ashey | O2 |
| 35010 | Blue Star | MN | 29 | Alverstone | O2 |
| 35011 | General Steam | | 30 | Shorwell | O2 |
| | Navigation | MN | 31 | Chale | O2 |
| 35012 | United States Lines | MN | 32 | Bonchurch | O2 |
| 35013 | Blue Funnel | MN | 33 | Bembridge | O2 |
| 35014 | Nederland Line | MN | 35 | Freshwater | O2 |
| 35015 | Rotterdam Lloyd | MN | 36 | Carisbrooke | O2 |
| 35016 | Elders Fyffes | MN | | | |
| 35017 | Belgian Marine | MN | | | |
| 35018 | British India Line | MN | | | |
| 35019 | French Line CGT | MN | | | |
| 35020 | Bibby Line | MN | | | |
| 35021 | New Zealand Line | MN | | | |
| 35022 | Holland-America Line | | | | |
| | | MN | | | |
| 35023 | Holland-Afrika Line | MN | | | |
| 35024 | East Asiatic Company | | | | |
| | | MN | | | |
| 35025 | Brocklebank Line | MN | | | |

DO NOT

TRESPASS

ON THE

RAILWAY

# SOUTHERN RAILWAY LOCOMOTIVE SUPERINTENDENTS AND CHIEF MECHANICAL ENGINEERS OF CONSTITUENT COMPANIES

## LONDON & SOUTH WESTERN RAILWAY

| | | | |
|---|---|---|---|
| J. Woods ... | ... | ... | 1835–1841 |
| J. V. Gooch | ... | ... | 1841–1850 |
| J. Beattie ... | ... | ... | 1850–1871 |
| W. G. Beattie | ... | ... | 1871–1878 |
| W. Adams ... | ... | ... | 1878–1895 |
| D. Drummond | ... | ... | 1895–1912 |
| R. W. Urie... | ... | ... | 1912–1922 |

## LONDON, BRIGHTON AND SOUTH COAST RAILWAY

| | | | |
|---|---|---|---|
| —. Statham | ... | ... | ? –1845 |
| J. Gray ... | ... | ... | 1845–1847 |
| S. Kirtley ... | ... | ... | 1847 |
| J. C. Craven | ... | ... | 1847–1869 |
| W. Stroudley | ... | ... | 1870–1889 |
| R. J. Billinton | ... | ... | 1890–1904 |
| D. Earle Marsh | ... | ... | 1905–1911 |
| L. B. Billinton | ... | ... | 1911–1922 |

## SOUTH EASTERN RAILWAY

| | | | |
|---|---|---|---|
| B. Cubitt ... | ... | ... | 1842–1845 |
| J. Cudworth | ... | ... | 1845–1876 |
| A. M. Watkin | ... | ... | 1876 |
| R. Mansell ... | ... | ... | 1877–1878 |
| J. Stirling ... | ... | ... | 1878–1898 |

## LONDON, CHATHAM AND DOVER RAILWAY

| | | | |
|---|---|---|---|
| W. Cubitt ... | ... | ... | 1853–1860 |
| W. Martley | ... | ... | 1860–1874 |
| W. Kirtley... | ... | ... | 1874–1898 |

## SOUTH EASTERN AND CHATHAM RAILWAY

| | | | |
|---|---|---|---|
| H. S. Wainwright... | ... | 1899–1913 |
| R. E. L. Maunsell ... | ... | 1913–1922 |

## SOUTHERN RAILWAY

| | | | |
|---|---|---|---|
| R. E. L. Maunsell ... | ... | 1923–1937 |
| O. V. Bulleid | ... | ... | 1937–1949 |

## SOUTHERN REGION SERVICE LOCOMOTIVES

| No. | Old No. | Class | Station |
|---|---|---|---|
| *DS   74 | — | Bo-Bo Electric | Durnsford Road |
| *DS   75 | — | Bo Electric | Waterloo & City |
| DS   680 | { L.B.S.C. 654 }{ S.E.C. 751 } | A1 | { Lancing { Carriage Works |
| DS   681 | L.B.S.C. 659 | A1X | { Lancing { Carriage Works |
| DS   682 | 30238 | G6 | Meldon Quarry |
| DS 1169 | — | 0-4-0 Diesel | Broad Clyst |
| DS 1173 | 2217 | 0-6-0 Diesel | Engineer's Department |
| DS 3152 | 30272 | G6 | Meldon Quarry |

## HISTORIC LOCOMOTIVES PRESERVED IN STORE

| Type | Originating Company | Pre-Grouping No. | S.R. No. | Name | Place of Preservation |
|---|---|---|---|---|---|
| 4-4-0 | L. & S.W | 563 | 563 | — | Clapham |
| 0-6-0T | L.B. & S.C. | 82 | (380S) | Boxhill | Clapham |
| 4-4-0 | S.E & C. | 737 | (1737) | — | Clapham |

# BRITISH RAILWAYS LOCOMOTIVES

## Nos. 40000-59999

The code given in bold type to the right of each Class heading,
e.g. "2P" denotes its British Railways power classification.

The numbers of locomotives in service have been checked for L.M.R. to January
28th, 1961, E. & N.E.R. to February 4th, 1961, Sc.R. to January 14th, 1961, S.R.
to February 10th, 1961, and W.R. to December 31st, 1960.

---

### 2-6-2T        3

Introduced 1930. Fowler L.M.S. design
with parallel boiler.
*Introduced 1930. Condensing locos.
for working to Moorgate, London.
Weight: { 70 tons 10 cwt.
{ 71 tons 16 cwt.*
Pressure: 200 lb. Su.
Cyls.: (O) 17½" × 26".
Driving Wheels: 5' 3".
T.E.: 21,485 lb.
Walschaerts valve gear. P.V.

| | | | |
|---|---|---|---|
| 40003 | 40018 | 40032* | 40049 |
| 40006S | 40020 | 40033* | 40050 |
| 40007 | 40022* | 40034* | 40051 |
| 40009 | 40024* | 40035* | 40053 |
| 40010 | 40026* | 40037* | 40054 |
| 40015 | 40029* | 40038* | 40063 |
| 40016 | 40031* | 40042 | 40064 |

**Total 28**

### 2-6-2T        3

Introduced 1935. Stanier L.M.S. taper
boiler development of Fowler design
(above).
*Introduced 1941. Rebuilt with larger
boiler.
Weight: { 71 tons 5 cwt.
{ 72 tons 10 cwt.*
Pressure: 200 lb. Su.
Cyls.: (O) 17½" × 26".
Driving Wheels: 5' 3".
T.E.: 21,485 lb.
Walschaerts valve gear. P.V.

| | | | |
|---|---|---|---|
| 40071 | 40105 | 40140 | 40177 |
| 40072 | 40106 | 40141 | 40178 |
| 40073 | 40107 | 40142 | 40179 |
| 40074 | 40108 | 40143 | 40180 |
| 40075 | 40109 | 40144 | 40181 |
| 40076 | 40110 | 40145 | 40182 |
| 40077 | 40111 | 40146 | 40183 |
| 40078 | 40112 | 40147 | 40184 |
| 40079 | 40113 | 40148* | 40185 |
| 40080 | 40114 | 40149 | 40186 |
| 40081 | 40115 | 40150 | 40187 |
| 40082 | 40116 | 40151 | 40188 |
| 40083 | 40117 | 40152 | 40189 |
| 40085 | 40118 | 40153 | 40190 |
| 40086 | 40119 | 40154 | 40191 |
| 40087 | 40120 | 40155 | 40192 |
| 40088 | 40121 | 40156 | 40193 |
| 40089 | 40122 | 40157 | 40194 |
| 40090 | 40123 | 40158 | 40195 |
| 40091 | 40124 | 40159 | 40196 |
| 40092 | 40126 | 40162 | 40197 |
| 40093 | 40128 | 40164 | 40198 |
| 40094 | 40129 | 40165 | 40199 |
| 40095 | 40130 | 40166 | 40200 |
| 40097 | 40131 | 40167* | 40201 |
| 40098 | 40132 | 40168 | 40202 |
| 40099 | 40133 | 40170 | 40203* |
| 40100 | 40134 | 40171 | 40205 |
| 40101 | 40135 | 40173 | 40206 |
| 40102 | 40136 | 40174 | 40207 |
| 40103 | 40137 | 40175 | 40208 |
| 40104 | 40138 | 40176 | 40209 |

**Total 128**

## 4-4-0       2P

Introduced 1912. Fowler rebuild of Johnson locos. with superheater and piston valves.

Weight: Loco. 53 tons 7 cwt.
Pressure: 160 lb. Su.
Cyls.: $20\frac{1}{2}'' \times 26''$.
Driving Wheels: $7'\ 0\frac{1}{2}''$.
T.E.: 17,585 lb.
P.V.

| | | | |
|---|---|---|---|
| 40396 | 40453 | 40537 | 40557 |
| 40411 | 40502 | 40540 | |

**Total 7**

## 4-4-0       2P

Introduced 1928. Post-grouping development of Midland design, with modified dimensions and reduced boiler mountings.
*Introduced 1928. Locos. built for S. & D.J.R. (taken into L.M.S. stock, 1930).

Weight: Loco. 54 tons 1 cwt.
Pressure: 180 lb. Su.
Cyls.: $19'' \times 26''$.
Driving Wheels: $6'\ 9''$.
T.E.: 17,730 lb.
P.V.

| | | | |
|---|---|---|---|
| 40563 | 40585 | 40614 | 40632 |
| 40564 | 40586 | 40615 | 40634* |
| 40566 | 40592 | 40618 | 40635* |
| 40569 | 40593 | 40619 | 40637 |
| 40570 | 40595 | 40620 | 40638 |
| 40571 | 40596 | 40621 | 40640 |
| 40572 | 40597 | 40622 | 40641 |
| 40574 | 40602 | 40623 | 40642 |
| 40575 | 40603 | 40624 | 40643 |
| 40577 | 40604 | 40625 | 40645 |
| 40578 | 40609 | 40626 | 40646 |
| 40579 | 40612 | 40627 | 40647 |
| 40580 | 40613 | 40629 | 40648 |

| | | | |
|---|---|---|---|
| 40650 | 40665 | 40682 | 40691 |
| 40651 | 40668 | 40683 | 40692 |
| 40657 | 40669 | 40684 | 40694 |
| 40659 | 40670 | 40685 | 40695 |
| 40661 | 40672 | 40686 | 40696 |
| 40663 | 40678 | 40687 | 40697 |
| 40664 | 40681 | 40689 | 40700 |

**Total 80**

## 4-4-0 (3-Cyl. Compd.)       4P

Introduced 1924. Post-grouping development of Johnson Midland compound with modified dimensions and reduced boiler mountings.

Weight: Loco. 61 tons 14 cwt.
Pressure: 200 lb. Su.
Cyls.: $\begin{cases} \text{L.P. (2) } 21'' \times 26''. \\ \text{H.P. (1) } 19'' \times 26''. \end{cases}$
Driving Wheels: $6'\ 9''$.
T.E. (of L.P. cyls. at 80% boiler pressure): 22,650 lb.
P.V. (H.P. cyl. only).

41168

**Total 1**

## 2-6-2T       2

Introduced 1946. Ivatt L.M.S. taper boiler design.

Weight: 63 tons 5 cwt.
Pressure: 200 lb. Su.
Cyls.: $\begin{cases} \text{(O) } 16'' \times 24''. \\ \text{(O) } 16\frac{1}{2}'' \times 24''.* \end{cases}$
Driving Wheels: $5'\ 0''$.
T.E.: $\begin{cases} 17,410 \text{ lb.} \\ 18,510 \text{ lb.*} \end{cases}$
Walschaerts valve gear. P.V.

| | | | |
|---|---|---|---|
| 41200 | 41204 | 41208 | 41212 |
| 41201 | 41205 | 41209 | 41213 |
| 41202 | 41206 | 41210 | 41214 |
| 41203 | 41207 | 41211 | 41215 |

| | | | |
|---|---|---|---|
| 41216 | 41245 | 41274 | 41302* |
| 41217 | 41246 | 41275 | 41303* |
| 41218 | 41247 | 41276 | 41304* |
| 41219 | 41248 | 41277 | 41305* |
| 41220 | 41249 | 41278 | 41306* |
| 41221 | 41250 | 41279 | 41307* |
| 41222 | 41251 | 41280 | 41308* |
| 41223 | 41252 | 41281 | 41309* |
| 41224 | 41253 | 41282 | 41310* |
| 41225 | 41254 | 41283 | 41311* |
| 41226 | 41255 | 41284 | 41312* |
| 41227 | 41256 | 41285 | 41313* |
| 41228 | 41257 | 41286 | 41314* |
| 41229 | 41258 | 41287 | 41315* |
| 41230 | 41259 | 41288 | 41316* |
| 41231 | 41260 | 41289 | 41317* |
| 41232 | 41261 | 41290* | 41318* |
| 41233 | 41262 | 41291* | 41319* |
| 41234 | 41263 | 41292* | 41320* |
| 41235 | 41264 | 41293* | 41321* |
| 41236 | 41265 | 41294* | 41322* |
| 41237 | 41266 | 41295* | 41323* |
| 41238 | 41267 | 41296* | 41324* |
| 41239 | 41268 | 41297* | 41325* |
| 41240 | 41269 | 41298* | 41326* |
| 41241 | 41270 | 41299* | 41327* |
| 41242 | 41271 | 41300* | 41328* |
| 41243 | 41272 | 41301* | 41329* |
| 41244 | 41273 | | |

Total 130

## 0-6-0T 1F

Introduced 1878. Johnson Midland design.

*Rebuilt with Belpaire firebox.

Weight: 39 tons 11 cwt.

Pressure: { 150 lb.
{ 140 lb.*

Cyls.: 17" × 24".

Driving Wheels: 4' 7".

T.E.: { 16,080 lb.
{ 15,005 lb.*

| | | | |
|---|---|---|---|
| 41702* | 41734* | 41769* | 41844* |
| 41708* | 41739* | 41804* | 41875* |
| 41712* | 41763* | 41835 | |

Total 11

## 0-4-4T 2P

Introduced 1932. Stanier L.M.S. design. Push-and-pull fitted.

Weight: 58 tons 1 cwt.

Pressure: 160 lb.

Cyls.: 18" × 26".

Driving Wheels: 5' 7".

T.E.: 17,100 lb.

41900

Total 1

## 0-4-0T 0F

Introduced 1907. Deeley Midland design.

Weight: 32 tons 16 cwt.

Pressure: 160 lb.

Cyls.: (O) 15" × 22".

Driving Wheels: 3' 9½".

T.E.: 14,635 lb.

Walschaerts valve gear.

| | | | |
|---|---|---|---|
| 41528 | 41531 | 41533 | 41536 |
| 41529 | 41532 | 41535 | 41537 |

Total 8

## 0-6-2T 3F

Introduced 1903. Whitelegg L.T. & S. "69" Class.

Weight: 64 tons 13 cwt.

Pressure: 170 lb.

Cyls.: 18" × 26".

Driving Wheels: 5' 3"..

T.E.: 19,320 lb.

41981

Total 1

## 2-6-4T 4

*Introduced 1927. Fowler L.M.S. parallel boiler design.

†Introduced 1933. As earlier engines, but with side-window cab and doors.

‡Introduced 1934. Stanier taperboiler 3-cylinder design for L.T. & S.

§Introduced 1935. Stanier taperboiler 2-cylinder design.

¶Introduced 1945. Fairburn development of Stanier design with shorter wheelbase and detail alterations.

Weight:
$\begin{cases} 86 \text{ tons } 5 \text{ cwt.*†} \\ 92 \text{ tons } 5 \text{ cwt.‡} \\ 87 \text{ tons } 17 \text{ cwt.§} \\ 85 \text{ tons } 5 \text{ cwt.¶} \end{cases}$

Pressure (all types): 200 lb. Su.

Cyls.:
$\begin{cases} \text{(O) } 19'' \times 26''.*† \\ \text{(3) } 16'' \times 26''.‡ \\ \text{(O) } 19\tfrac{5}{8}'' \times 26''.§¶ \end{cases}$

Driving Wheels (all types): 5' 9".

T.E.:
$\begin{cases} 23,125 \text{ lb.*†} \\ 24,600 \text{ lb.‡} \\ 24,670 \text{ lb.§¶} \end{cases}$

Walschaerts valve gear. P.V.

### ¶FAIRBURN LOCOS.

| | | | |
|---|---|---|---|
| 42050 | 42071 | 42092 | 42113 |
| 42051 | 42072 | 42093 | 42114 |
| 42052 | 42073 | 42094 | 42115 |
| 42053 | 42074 | 42095 | 42116 |
| 42054 | 42075 | 42096 | 42117 |
| 42055 | 42076 | 42097 | 42118 |
| 42056 | 42077 | 42098 | 42119 |
| 42057 | 42078 | 42099 | 42120 |
| 42058 | 42079 | 42100 | 42121 |
| 42059 | 42080 | 42101 | 42122 |
| 42060 | 42081 | 42102 | 42123 |
| 42061 | 42082 | 42103 | 42124 |
| 42062 | 42083 | 42104 | 42125 |
| 42063 | 42084 | 42105 | 42126 |
| 42064 | 42085 | 42106 | 42127 |
| 42065 | 42086 | 42107 | 42128 |
| 42066 | 42087 | 42108 | 42129 |
| 42067 | 42088 | 42109 | 42130 |
| 42068 | 42089 | 42110 | 42131 |
| 42069 | 42090 | 42111 | 42132 |
| 42070 | 42091 | 42112 | 42133 |

| | | | |
|---|---|---|---|
| 42134 | 42176 | 42218 | 42259 |
| 42135 | 42177 | 42219 | 42260 |
| 42136 | 42178 | 42220 | 42261 |
| 42137 | 42179 | 42221 | 42262 |
| 42138 | 42180 | 42222 | 42263 |
| 42139 | 42181 | 42223 | 42264 |
| 42140 | 42182 | 42224 | 42265 |
| 42141 | 42183 | 42225 | 42266 |
| 42142 | 42184 | 42226 | 42267 |
| 42143 | 42185 | 42227 | 42268 |
| 42144 | 42186 | 42228 | 42269 |
| 42145 | 42187 | 42229 | 42270 |
| 42146 | 42188 | 42230 | 42271 |
| 42147 | 42189 | 42231 | 42272 |
| 42148 | 42190 | 42232 | 42273 |
| 42149 | 42191 | 42233 | 42274 |
| 42150 | 42192 | 42234 | 42275 |
| 42151 | 42193 | 42235 | 42276 |
| 42152 | 42194 | 42236 | 42277 |
| 42153 | 42195 | 42237 | 42278 |
| 42154 | 42196 | 42238 | 42279 |
| 42155 | 42197 | 42239 | 42280 |
| 42156 | 42198 | 42240 | 42281 |
| 42157 | 42199 | 42241 | 42282 |
| 42158 | 42200 | 42242 | 42283 |
| 42159 | 42201 | 42243 | 42284 |
| 42160 | 42202 | 42244 | 42285 |
| 42161 | 42203 | 42245 | 42286 |
| 42162 | 42204 | 42246 | 42287 |
| 42163 | 42205 | 42247 | 42288 |
| 42164 | 42206 | 42248 | 42289 |
| 42165 | 42207 | 42249 | 42290 |
| 42166 | 42208 | 42250 | 42291 |
| 42167 | 42209 | 42251 | 42292 |
| 42168 | 42210 | 42252 | 42293 |
| 42169 | 42211 | 42253 | 42294 |
| 42170 | 42212 | 42254 | 42295 |
| 42171 | 42213 | 42255 | 42296 |
| 42172 | 42214 | 42256 | 42297 |
| 42173 | 42215 | 42257 | 42298 |
| 42174 | 42216 | 42258 | 42299 |
| 42175 | 42217 | | |

### *FOWLER LOCOS.

| | | | |
|---|---|---|---|
| 42301 | 42303 | 42305 | 42307 |
| 42302 | 42304 | 42306 | 42309 |

| | | | | | | | |
|---|---|---|---|---|---|---|---|
| 42310 | 42332 | 42355 | 42375 | 42466 | 42473 | 42480 | 42487 |
| 42311 | 42333 | 42356 | 42376 | 42467 | 42474 | 42481 | 42488 |
| 42313 | 42334 | 42357 | 42377 | 42468 | 42475 | 42482 | 42489 |
| 42314 | 42335 | 42358 | 42378 | 42469 | 42476 | 42483 | 42491 |
| 42315 | 42336 | 42359 | 42379 | 42470 | 42477 | 42484 | 42492 |
| 42316 | 42337 | 42360 | 42381 | 42471 | 42478 | 42485 | 42493 |
| 42317 | 42338 | 42361 | 42382 | 42472 | 42479 | 42486 | 42494 |
| 42318 | 42339 | 42362 | 42383 | | | | |
| 42319 | 42340 | 42363 | 42384 | | | | |
| 42320 | 42342 | 42364 | 42385 | | | | |
| 42322 | 42343 | 42366 | 42386 | | | | |
| 42323 | 42344 | 42367 | 42387 | | | | |

### ‡STANIER 3-CYL. LOCOS.

| 42324 | 42347 | 42368 | 42388 | | | | |
|---|---|---|---|---|---|---|---|
| 42325 | 42348 | 42369 | 42389 | 42500 | 42509 | 42519 | 42528 |
| 42327 | 42349 | 42370 | 42391 | 42501 | 42510 | 42520 | 42529 |
| 42328 | 42350 | 42371 | 42392 | 42502 | 42511 | 42521 | 42530 |
| 42329 | 42351 | 42372 | 42393 | 42503 | 42513 | 42522 | 42531 |
| 42330 | 42352 | 42374 | 42394 | 42504 | 42514 | 42523 | 42532 |
| 42331 | 42353 | | | 42505 | 42515 | 42524 | 42533 |
| | | | | 42506 | 42516 | 42525 | 42534 |
| | | | | 42507 | 42517 | 42526 | 42535 |
| | | | | 42508 | 42518 | 42527 | 42536 |

### †FOWLER LOCOS. WITH SIDE-WINDOW CAB

| 42395 | 42405 | 42412 | 42419 | | | | |
|---|---|---|---|---|---|---|---|
| 42396 | 42406 | 42413 | 42420 | | | | |
| 42400 | 42407 | 42414 | 42421 | | | | |

### §STANIER 2-CYL. LOCOS.

| 42401 | 42408 | 42415 | 42422 | 42537 | 42557 | 42577 | 42597 |
|---|---|---|---|---|---|---|---|
| 42402 | 42409 | 42416 | 42423 | 42538 | 42558 | 42578 | 42598 |
| 42403 | 42410 | 42417 | 42424 | 42539 | 42559 | 42579 | 42599 |
| 42404 | 42411 | | | 42540 | 42560 | 42580 | 42600 |
| | | | | 42541 | 42561 | 42581 | 42601 |
| | | | | 42542 | 42562 | 42582 | 42602 |
| | | | | 42543 | 42563 | 42583 | 42603 |
| | | | | 42544 | 42564 | 42584 | 42604 |
| | | | | 42545 | 42565 | 42585 | 42605 |

### §STANIER 2-CYL. LOCOS.

| | | | | 42546 | 42566 | 42586 | 42606 |
|---|---|---|---|---|---|---|---|
| 42425 | 42435 | 42445 | 42456 | 42547 | 42567 | 42587 | 42607 |
| 42426 | 42436 | 42446 | 42457 | 42548 | 42568 | 42588 | 42608 |
| 42427 | 42437 | 42447 | 42458 | 42549 | 42569 | 42589 | 42609 |
| 42428 | 42438 | 42448 | 42459 | 42550 | 42570 | 42590 | 42610 |
| 42429 | 42439 | 42449 | 42460 | 42551 | 42571 | 42591 | 42611 |
| 42430 | 42440 | 42451 | 42461 | 42552 | 42572 | 42592 | 42612 |
| 42431 | 42441 | 42452 | 42462 | 42553 | 42573 | 42593 | 42613 |
| 42432 | 42442 | 42453 | 42463 | 42554 | 42574 | 42594 | 42614 |
| 42433 | 42443 | 42454 | 42464 | 42555 | 42575 | 42595 | 42615 |
| 42434 | 42444 | 42455 | 42465 | 42556 | 42576 | 42596 | 42616 |

| | | | |
|---|---|---|---|
| 42617 | 42631 | 42645 | 42659 |
| 42618 | 42632 | 42646 | 42660 |
| 42619 | 42633 | 42647 | 42661 |
| 42620 | 42634 | 42648 | 42662 |
| 42621 | 42635 | 42649 | 42663 |
| 42622 | 42636 | 42650 | 42664 |
| 42623 | 42637 | 42651 | 42665 |
| 42624 | 42638 | 42652 | 42666 |
| 42625 | 42639 | 42653 | 42667 |
| 42626 | 42640 | 42654 | 42668 |
| 42627 | 42641 | 42655 | 42669 |
| 42628 | 42642 | 42656 | 42670 |
| 42629 | 42643 | 42657 | 42671 |
| 42630 | 42644 | 42658 | 42672 |

## ¶FAIRBURN LOCOS.

| | | | |
|---|---|---|---|
| 42673 | 42680 | 42687 | 42694 |
| 42674 | 42681 | 42688 | 42695 |
| 42675 | 42682 | 42689 | 42696 |
| 42676 | 42683 | 42690 | 42697 |
| 42677 | 42684 | 42691 | 42698 |
| 42678 | 42685 | 42692 | 42699 |
| 42679 | 42686 | 42693 | |

Total 625

## 2-6-0      6P5F

Introduced 1926. Hughes L.M.S. design built under Fowler's direction. Walschaerts valve gear. P.V.
*Introduced 1953. Locos. rebuilt experimentally with Lentz R.C. poppet valves in 1931; rebuilt with Reidinger rotary poppet valve gear in 1953.
Weight: Loco. 66 tons 0 cwt.
Pressure: 180 lb. Su.
Cyls.: (O) 21″ × 26″.
Driving Wheels: 5′ 6″.
T.E.: 26,580 lb.

| | | | |
|---|---|---|---|
| 42700 | 42703 | 42706 | 42709 |
| 42701 | 42704 | 42707 | 42710 |
| 42702 | 42705 | 42708 | 42711 |

| | | | |
|---|---|---|---|
| 42712 | 42759 | 42806 | 42853 |
| 42713 | 42760 | 42807 | 42854 |
| 42714 | 42761 | 42808 | 42855 |
| 42715 | 42762 | 42809 | 42856 |
| 42716 | 42763 | 42810 | 42857 |
| 42717 | 42764 | 42811 | 42858 |
| 42718 | 42765 | 42812 | 42859 |
| 42719 | 42766 | 42813 | 42860 |
| 42720 | 42767 | 42814 | 42861 |
| 42721 | 42768 | 42815 | 42862 |
| 42722 | 42769 | 42816 | 42863 |
| 42723 | 42770 | 42817 | 42864 |
| 42724 | 42771 | 42818* | 42865 |
| 42725 | 42772 | 42819 | 42866 |
| 42726 | 42773 | 42820 | 42867 |
| 42727 | 42774 | 42821 | 42868 |
| 42728 | 42775 | 42822* | 42869 |
| 42729 | 42776 | 42823 | 42870 |
| 42730 | 42777 | 42824* | 42871 |
| 42731 | 42778 | 42825* | 42872 |
| 42732 | 42779 | 42826 | 42873 |
| 42733 | 42780 | 42827 | 42874 |
| 42734 | 42781 | 42828 | 42875 |
| 42735 | 42782 | 42829* | 42876 |
| 42736 | 42783 | 42830 | 42877 |
| 42737 | 42784 | 42831 | 42878 |
| 42738 | 42785 | 42832 | 42879 |
| 42739 | 42786 | 42833 | 42880 |
| 42740 | 42787 | 42834 | 42881 |
| 42741 | 42788 | 42835 | 42882 |
| 42742 | 42789 | 42836 | 42883 |
| 42743 | 42790 | 42837 | 42884 |
| 42744 | 42791 | 42838 | 42885 |
| 42745 | 42792 | 42839 | 42886 |
| 42746 | 42793 | 42840 | 42887 |
| 42747 | 42794 | 42841 | 42888 |
| 42748 | 42795 | 42842 | 42889 |
| 42749 | 42796 | 42843 | 42890 |
| 42750 | 42797 | 42844 | 42891 |
| 42751 | 42798 | 42845 | 42892 |
| 42752 | 42799 | 42846 | 42893 |
| 42753 | 42800 | 42847 | 42894 |
| 42754 | 42801 | 42848 | 42895 |
| 42755 | 42802 | 42849 | 42896 |
| 42756 | 42803 | 42850 | 42897 |
| 42757 | 42804 | 42851 | 42898 |
| 42758 | 42805 | 42852 | 42899 |

| | | | |
|---|---|---|---|
| 42900 | 42912 | 42923 | 42934 |
| 42901 | 42913 | 42924 | 42935 |
| 42902 | 42914 | 42925 | 42936 |
| 42903 | 42915 | 42926 | 42937 |
| 42904 | 42916 | 42927 | 42938 |
| 42905 | 42917 | 42928 | 42939 |
| 42906 | 42918 | 42929 | 42940 |
| 42907 | 42919 | 42930 | 42941 |
| 42908 | 42920 | 42931 | 42942 |
| 42909 | 42921 | 42932 | 42943 |
| 42910 | 42922 | 42933 | 42944 |
| 42911 | | | |

Total 245

## 2-6-0       6P5F

Introduced 1933. Stanier L.M.S. taper boiler design, some with safety valves mounted on the top feed.
Weight: Loco. 69 tons 2 cwt.
Pressure: 225 lb. Su.
Cyls.: (O) 18" × 28".
Driving Wheels: 5' 6".
T.E.: 26,290 lb.
Walschaerts valve gear. P.V.

| | | | |
|---|---|---|---|
| 42945 | 42955 | 42965 | 42975 |
| 42946 | 42956 | 42966 | 42976 |
| 42947 | 42957 | 42967 | 42977 |
| 42948 | 42958 | 42968 | 42978 |
| 42949 | 42959 | 42969 | 42979 |
| 42950 | 42960 | 42970 | 42980 |
| 42951 | 42961 | 42971 | 42981 |
| 42952 | 42962 | 42972 | 42982 |
| 42953 | 42963 | 42973 | 42983 |
| 42954 | 42964 | 42974 | 42984 |

Total 40

## 2-6-0       4

Introduced 1947. Ivatt L.M.S. taper boiler design with double chimney. Later engines introduced with single chimney, with which earlier engines are being rebuilt.
Weight: Loco. 59 tons 2 cwt.
Pressure: 225 lb. Su.
Cyls.: (O) 17½" × 26".
Driving Wheels: 5' 3".
T.E.: 24,170 lb.
Walschaerts valve gear. P.V.

| | | | |
|---|---|---|---|
| 43000 | 43002 | 43004 | 43006 |
| 43001 | 43003 | 43005 | 43007 |

| | | | |
|---|---|---|---|
| 43008 | 43047 | 43086 | 43124 |
| 43009 | 43048 | 43087 | 43125 |
| 43010 | 43049 | 43088 | 43126 |
| 43011 | 43050 | 43089 | 43127 |
| 43012 | 43051 | 43090 | 43128 |
| 43013 | 43052 | 43091 | 43129 |
| 43014 | 43053 | 43092 | 43130 |
| 43015 | 43054 | 43093 | 43131 |
| 43016 | 43055 | 43094 | 43132 |
| 43017 | 43056 | 43095 | 43133 |
| 43018 | 43057 | 43096 | 43134 |
| 43019 | 43058 | 43097 | 43135 |
| 43020 | 43059 | 43098 | 43136 |
| 43021 | 43060 | 43099 | 43137 |
| 43022 | 43061 | 43100 | 43138 |
| 43023 | 43062 | 43101 | 43139 |
| 43024 | 43063 | 43102 | 43140 |
| 43025 | 43064 | 43103 | 43141 |
| 43026 | 43065 | 43104 | 43142 |
| 43027 | 43066 | 43105 | 43143 |
| 43028 | 43067 | 43106 | 43144 |
| 43029 | 43068 | 43107 | 43145 |
| 43030 | 43069 | 43108 | 43146 |
| 43031 | 43070 | 43109 | 43147 |
| 43032 | 43071 | 43110 | 43148 |
| 43033 | 43072 | 43111 | 43149 |
| 43034 | 43073 | 43112 | 43150 |
| 43035 | 43074 | 43113 | 43151 |
| 43036 | 43075 | 43114 | 43152 |
| 43037 | 43076 | 43115 | 43153 |
| 43038 | 43077 | 43116 | 43154 |
| 43039 | 43078 | 43117 | 43155 |
| 43040 | 43079 | 43118 | 43156 |
| 43041 | 43080 | 43119 | 43157 |
| 43042 | 43081 | 43120 | 43158 |
| 43043 | 43082 | 43121 | 43159 |
| 43044 | 43083 | 43122 | 43160 |
| 43045 | 43084 | 43123 | 43161 |
| 43046 | 43085 | | |

Total 162

DO NOT TRESPASS
ON THE RAILWAY

## 43185-43929

### 0-6-0      3F

Introduced 1885. Johnson Midland locos., rebuilt from 1916 by Fowler with Belpaire firebox.

\*Introduced 1885. Johnson Midland locos., rebuilt from 1920 by Fowler with Belpaire firebox.

†Introduced 1896. Locos. built for S. & D.J. (taken into L.M.S. stock 1930).

Weight: Loco. 43 tons 17 cwt.

Pressure: 175 lb.

Cyls.: 18″ × 26″.

Driving Wheels: { 5′ 3″. / 5′ 3″.† / 4′ 11″.\* }

T.E.: { 19,890 lb. / 19,890 lb.† / 21,240 lb.\* }

| | | | |
|---|---|---|---|
| 43185\* | 43325 | 43496 | 43645 |
| 43200 | 43330 | 43499 | 43657 |
| 43211† | 43342 | 43507 | 43658 |
| 43213 | 43368 | 43510 | 43668 |
| 43214 | 43371 | 43514 | 43669 |
| 43216† | 43374 | 43515 | 43673 |
| 43225 | 43386 | 43521 | 43679 |
| 43240 | 43389 | 43529 | 43680 |
| 43242 | 43395 | 43548 | 43681 |
| 43245 | 43400 | 43562 | 43682 |
| 43250 | 43405 | 43565 | 43687 |
| 43254 | 43410 | 43580 | 43709 |
| 43257 | 43411 | 43583 | 43714 |
| 43261 | 43427 | 43585 | 43715 |
| 43263 | 43428 | 43586 | 43721 |
| 43266 | 43435 | 43593 | 43729 |
| 43267 | 43436 | 43599 | 43734 |
| 43268 | 43446 | 43605 | 43737 |
| 43277 | 43449 | 43608 | 43751 |
| 43282 | 43453 | 43615 | 43754 |
| 43284 | 43459 | 43618 | 43756 |
| 43295 | 43464 | 43620 | 43760 |
| 43306 | 43468 | 43621 | 43762 |
| 43309 | 43474 | 43624 | 43763 |
| 43321 | 43482 | 43637 | 43766 |

Total 100

### 0-6-0      3F

Introduced 1906. Deeley Midland design. Rebuilt by Fowler with Belpaire firebox.

Weight: Loco. 46 tons 3 cwt.

Pressure: 175 lb.

Cyls.: 18½″ × 26″.

Driving Wheels: 5′ 3″.

T.E.: 21,010 lb.

| | | | |
|---|---|---|---|
| 43778 | 43808 | 43822 | 43826 |
| 43789 | 43809 | 43825 | 43832 |
| 43793 | 43812 | | |

Total 10

### 0-6-0      4F

Introduced 1911. Fowler superheated Midland design.

Weight: Loco. 48 tons 15 cwt.

Pressure: 175 lb. Su.

Cyls.: 20″ × 26″.

Driving Wheels: 5′ 3″.

T.E.: 24,555 lb.

P.V.

| | | | |
|---|---|---|---|
| 43844 | 43863 | 43887 | 43914 |
| 43845 | 43865 | 43888 | 43915 |
| 43846 | 43869 | 43893 | 43917 |
| 43848 | 43870 | 43899 | 43918 |
| 43849 | 43871 | 43900 | 43920 |
| 43850 | 43872 | 43902 | 43921 |
| 43853 | 43876 | 43903 | 43922 |
| 43854 | 43880 | 43905 | 43923 |
| 43855 | 43882 | 43906 | 43924 |
| 43856 | 43883 | 43908 | 43925 |
| 43859 | 43884 | 43911 | 43928 |
| 43861 | 43885 | 43913 | 43929 |

60

| | | | |
|---|---|---|---|
| 43931 | 43953 | 43977 | 44003 |
| 43932 | 43954 | 43979 | 44004 |
| 43933 | 43955 | 43981 | 44007 |
| 43935 | 43957 | 43982 | 44008 |
| 43937 | 43958 | 43983 | 44009 |
| 43938 | 43960 | 43985 | 44010 |
| 43940 | 43962 | 43986 | 44011 |
| 43942 | 43963 | 43987 | 44012 |
| 43944 | 43964 | 43988 | 44013 |
| 43945 | 43967 | 43991 | 44015 |
| 43947 | 43968 | 43994 | 44016 |
| 43948 | 43969 | 43995 | 44020 |
| 43949 | 43971 | 43996 | 44022 |
| 43950 | 43972 | 43999 | 44023 |
| 43951 | 43975 | 44001 | 44025 |
| 43952 | 43976 | 44002 | 44026 |

Total 112

## 0-6-0      4F

Introduced 1924. Post-grouping development of Midland design with reduced boiler mountings.
*Introduced 1922. Locos. built for S. & D.J.R. to M.R. design (taken into L.M.S. stock 1930).
Weight: Loco. 48 tons 15 cwt.
Pressure: 175 lb. Su.
Cyls.: 20″ × 26″.
Driving Wheels: 5′ 3″
T.E.: 24,555 lb.
P.V.

| | | | |
|---|---|---|---|
| 44027 | 44041 | 44054 | 44067 |
| 44028 | 44042 | 44055 | 44068 |
| 44030 | 44043 | 44056 | 44069 |
| 44033 | 44044 | 44057 | 44070 |
| 44034 | 44045 | 44059 | 44071 |
| 44035 | 44046 | 44060 | 44074 |
| 44036 | 44047 | 44061 | 44075 |
| 44037 | 44048 | 44062 | 44076 |
| 44038 | 44049 | 44063 | 44078 |
| 44039 | 44051 | 44065 | 44079 |
| 44040 | 44053 | 44066 | 44080 |

| | | | |
|---|---|---|---|
| 44081 | 44135 | 44191 | 44244 |
| 44082 | 44137 | 44192 | 44245 |
| 44083 | 44138 | 44193 | 44246 |
| 44085 | 44139 | 44194 | 44247 |
| 44086 | 44141 | 44195 | 44248 |
| 44087 | 44143 | 44196 | 44249 |
| 44088 | 44146 | 44197 | 44250 |
| 44089 | 44147 | 44198 | 44251 |
| 44090 | 44148 | 44199 | 44252 |
| 44091 | 44149 | 44200 | 44253 |
| 44092 | 44150 | 44202 | 44254 |
| 44094 | 44151 | 44203 | 44255 |
| 44096 | 44152 | 44205 | 44256 |
| 44097 | 44153 | 44206 | 44257 |
| 44098 | 44154 | 44207 | 44258 |
| 44099 | 44155 | 44208 | 44259 |
| 44100 | 44156 | 44209 | 44260 |
| 44101 | 44157 | 44210 | 44261 |
| 44102 | 44158 | 44211 | 44262 |
| 44104 | 44160 | 44212 | 44263 |
| 44105 | 44162 | 44213 | 44264 |
| 44106 | 44164 | 44214 | 44265 |
| 44107 | 44165 | 44215 | 44266 |
| 44109 | 44166 | 44216 | 44267 |
| 44110 | 44166 | 44218 | 44268 |
| 44111 | 44167 | 44219 | 44269 |
| 44112 | 44168 | 44220 | 44270 |
| 44113 | 44169 | 44221 | 44271 |
| 44114 | 44170 | 44222 | 44272 |
| 44115 | 44171 | 44223 | 44273 |
| 44117 | 44172 | 44224 | 44274 |
| 44119 | 44174 | 44226 | 44275 |
| 44121 | 44176 | 44228 | 44276 |
| 44122 | 44177 | 44229 | 44277 |
| 44123 | 44178 | 44231 | 44278 |
| 44124 | 44179 | 44232 | 44279 |
| 44125 | 44180 | 44233 | 44280 |
| 44126 | 44181 | 44234 | 44281 |
| 44127 | 44182 | 44235 | 44282 |
| 44128 | 44183 | 44236 | 44283 |
| 44129 | 44184 | 44237 | 44284 |
| 44130 | 44185 | 44238 | 44286 |
| 44131 | 44186 | 44239 | 44287 |
| 44132 | 44187 | 44240 | 44288 |
| 44133 | 44188 | 44241 | 44289 |
| 44134 | 44189 | 44242 | 44290 |
| | 44190 | 44243 | 44292 |

| | | | | | | | |
|---|---|---|---|---|---|---|---|
| 44294 | 44348 | 44408 | 44464 | 44527 | 44547 | 44568 | 44588 |
| 44295 | 44349 | 44409 | 44465 | 44528 | 44548 | 44569 | 44589 |
| 44296 | 44350 | 44411 | 44466 | 44529 | 44549 | 44570 | 44590 |
| 44297 | 44351 | 44413 | 44467 | 44530 | 44550 | 44571 | 44591 |
| 44299 | 44352 | 44414 | 44468 | 44531 | 44551 | 44572 | 44592 |
| 44300 | 44353 | 44416 | 44469 | 44532 | 44552 | 44573 | 44593 |
| 44301 | 44354 | 44417 | 44470 | 44533 | 44553 | 44574 | 44594 |
| 44302 | 44355 | 44418 | 44472 | 44534 | 44554 | 44575 | 44595 |
| 44303 | 44356 | 44419 | 44474 | 44535 | 44556 | 44576 | 44596 |
| 44304 | 44358 | 44420 | 44475 | 44536 | 44557* | 44577 | 44597 |
| 44305 | 44359 | 44421 | 44476 | 44537 | 44558* | 44578 | 44598 |
| 44307 | 44362 | 44422 | 44477 | 44538 | 44559* | 44579 | 44599 |
| 44308 | 44363S | 44424 | 44478 | 44539 | 44560* | 44580 | 44601 |
| 44309 | 44364 | 44425 | 44479 | 44540 | 44561* | 44581 | 44602 |
| 44310 | 44367 | 44426 | 44481 | 44541 | 44562 | 44582 | 44603 |
| 44311 | 44368 | 44428 | 44482 | 44542 | 44564 | 44583 | 44604 |
| 44312 | 44370 | 44429 | 44484 | 44543 | 44565 | 44584 | 44605 |
| 44314 | 44371 | 44431 | 44485 | 44544 | 44566 | 44586 | 44606 |
| 44315 | 44373S | 44432 | 44486 | 44545 | 44567 | 44587 | |
| 44318 | 44374S | 44433 | 44487 | | | | |
| 44319 | 44376 | 44434 | 44489 | | | | |
| 44320 | 44377 | 44435 | 44490 | | | | |
| 44321 | 44378 | 44436 | 44491 | | | | |
| 44322 | 44379 | 44437 | 44492 | | | | |
| 44323 | 44380 | 44439 | 44493 | | | | |
| 44324 | 44381 | 44440 | 44494 | | | | |
| 44325 | 44384 | 44441 | 44497 | | | | |
| 44327 | 44386 | 44442 | 44499 | | | | |
| 44328 | 44387 | 44443 | 44500 | | | | |
| 44329 | 44388 | 44444 | 44501 | | | | |
| 44330 | 44389 | 44445 | 44504 | | | | |
| 44331 | 44390 | 44446 | 44505 | | | | |
| 44332 | 44392 | 44447 | 44508 | | | | |
| 44333 | 44393 | 44448 | 44509 | | | | |
| 44334 | 44394 | 44449 | 44512 | | | | |
| 44335 | 44395 | 44450 | 44514 | | | | |
| 44336 | 44396 | 44451 | 44516 | | | | |
| 44337 | 44397 | 44452 | 44517 | | | | |
| 44338 | 44398 | 44454 | 44518 | | | | |
| 44339 | 44399 | 44455 | 44519 | | | | |
| 44340 | 44400 | 44456 | 44520 | | | | |
| 44341 | 44401 | 44457 | 44521 | | | | |
| 44342 | 44402 | 44458 | 44522 | | | | |
| 44344 | 44403 | 44460 | 44523 | | | | |
| 44345 | 44404 | 44461 | 44524 | | | | |
| 44346 | 44405 | 44462 | 44525 | | | | |
| 44347 | 44407 | 44463 | 44526 | | | | |

**Total 495**

## 4-6-0                     5

Introduced 1934. Stanier L.M.S. taper boiler design.

**Experimental locomotives:—**
1. Introduced 1947. Stephenson link motion (outside), Timken roller bearings.
2. Introduced 1948. Caprotti valve gear.
3. Introduced 1948. Caprotti valve gear, Timken roller bearings.
4. Introduced 1948. Caprotti valve gear, Timken roller bearings, double chimney.
5. Introduced 1947. Timken roller bearings.
6. Introduced 1947. Timken roller bearings, double chimney.
7. Introduced 1949. Fitted with steel firebox.
8. Introduced 1950. Skefko roller bearings.
9. Introduced 1950. Timken roller bearings on driving coupled axle only.

10. Introduced 1950. Skefko roller bearings on driving coupled axle only.

11. Introduced 1951. Caprotti valve gear, Skefko roller bearings.

Weight: Loco. { 72 tons 2 cwt. / 75 tons 6 cwt. (1, 5, 6, 8, 9, 10). / 74 tons 0 cwt. (2, 3, 4, 11). / 72 tons 2 cwt. (7). }

Pressure: 225 lb. Su.
Cyls.: (O) 18¼" × 28".
Driving Wheels: 6' 0".
T.E.: 25,455 lb.
Walschaerts valve gear and P.V. except where otherwise shown.

| | | | |
|---|---|---|---|
| 44726[7] | 44756[4] | 44786 | 44816 |
| 44727[7] | 44757[4] | 44787 | 44817 |
| 44728 | 44758[5] | 44788 | 44818 |
| 44729 | 44759[6] | 44789 | 44819 |
| 44730 | 44760[5] | 44790 | 44820 |
| 44731 | 44761[5] | 44791 | 44821 |
| 44732 | 44762[6] | 44792 | 44822 |
| 44733 | 44763[6] | 44793 | 44823 |
| 44734 | 44764[5] | 44794 | 44824 |
| 44735 | 44765[6] | 44795 | 44825 |
| 44736 | 44766[6] | 44796 | 44826 |
| 44737 | 44767[1] | 44797 | 44827 |
| 44738[2] | 44768 | 44798 | 44828 |
| 44739[2] | 44769 | 44799 | 44829 |
| 44740[2] | 44770 | 44800 | 44830 |
| 44741[2] | 44771 | 44801 | 44831 |
| 44742[2] | 44772 | 44802 | 44832 |
| 44743[2] | 44773 | 44803 | 44833 |
| 44744[2] | 44774 | 44804 | 44834 |
| 44745[2] | 44775 | 44805 | 44835 |
| 44746[2] | 44776 | 44806 | 44836 |
| 44747[2] | 44777 | 44807 | 44837 |
| 44748[3] | 44778 | 44808 | 44838 |
| 44749[3] | 44779 | 44809 | 44839 |
| 44750[3] | 44780 | 44810 | 44840 |
| 44751[3] | 44781 | 44811 | 44841 |
| 44752[3] | 44782 | 44812 | 44842 |
| 44753[3] | 44783 | 44813 | 44843 |
| 44754[3] | 44784 | 44814 | 44844 |
| 44755[4] | 44785 | 44815 | 44845 |

| | | | |
|---|---|---|---|
| 44658 | 44675[10] | 44692[9] | 44709 |
| 44659 | 44676[10] | 44693[9] | 44710 |
| 44660 | 44677[10] | 44694[9] | 44711 |
| 44661 | 44678[8] | 44695[9] | 44712 |
| 44662 | 44679[8] | 44696[9] | 44713 |
| 44663 | 44680[8] | 44697[9] | 44714 |
| 44664 | 44681[8] | 44698 | 44715 |
| 44665 | 44682[8] | 44699 | 44716 |
| 44666 | 44683[8] | 44700 | 44717 |
| 44667 | 44684[8] | 44701 | 44718[7] |
| 44668[10] | 44685[8] | 44702 | 44719[7] |
| 44669[10] | 44686[11] | 44703 | 44720[7] |
| 44670[10] | 44687[11] | 44704 | 44721[7] |
| 44671[10] | 44688[9] | 44705 | 44722[7] |
| 44672[10] | 44689[9] | 44706 | 44723[7] |
| 44673[10] | 44690[9] | 44707 | 44724[7] |
| 44674[10] | 44691[9] | 44708 | 44725[7] |

| | | | | | | | |
|---|---|---|---|---|---|---|---|
| 44846 | 44893 | 44940 | 44987 | 45034 | 45074 | 45114 | 45154* |
| 44847 | 44894 | 44941 | 44988 | 45035 | 45075 | 45115 | 45155 |
| 44848 | 44895 | 44942 | 44989 | 45036 | 45076 | 45116 | 45156* |
| 44849 | 44896 | 44943 | 44990 | 45037 | 45077 | 45117 | 45157* |
| 44850 | 44897 | 44944 | 44991 | 45038 | 45078 | 45118 | 45158* |
| 44851 | 44898 | 44945 | 44992 | 45039 | 45079 | 45119 | 45159 |
| 44852 | 44899 | 44946 | 44993 | 45040 | 45080 | 45120 | 45160 |
| 44853 | 44900 | 44947 | 44994 | 45041 | 45081 | 45121 | 45161 |
| 44854 | 44901 | 44948 | 44995 | 45042 | 45082 | 45122 | 45162 |
| 44855 | 44902 | 44949 | 44996 | 45043 | 45083 | 45123 | 45163 |
| 44856 | 44903 | 44950 | 44997 | 45044 | 45084 | 45124 | 45164 |
| 44857 | 44904 | 44951 | 44998 | 45045 | 45085 | 45125 | 45165 |
| 44858 | 44905 | 44952 | 44999 | 45046 | 45086 | 45126 | 45166 |
| 44859 | 44906 | 44953 | 45000 | 45047 | 45087 | 45127 | 45167 |
| 44860 | 44907 | 44954 | 45001 | 45048 | 45088 | 45128 | 45168 |
| 44861 | 44908 | 44955 | 45002 | 45049 | 45089 | 45129 | 45169 |
| 44862 | 44909 | 44956 | 45003 | 45050 | 45090 | 45130 | 45170 |
| 44863 | 44910 | 44957 | 45004 | 45051 | 45091 | 45131 | 45171 |
| 44864 | 44911 | 44958 | 45005 | 45052 | 45092 | 45132 | 45172 |
| 44865 | 44912 | 44959 | 45006 | 45053 | 45093 | 45133 | 45173 |
| 44866 | 44913 | 44960 | 45007 | 45054 | 45094 | 45134 | 45174 |
| 44867 | 44914 | 44961 | 45008 | 45055 | 45095 | 45135 | 45175 |
| 44868 | 44915 | 44962 | 45009 | 45056 | 45096 | 45136 | 45176 |
| 44869 | 44916 | 44963 | 45010 | 45057 | 45097 | 45137 | 45177 |
| 44870 | 44917 | 44964 | 45011 | 45058 | 45098 | 45138 | 45178 |
| 44871 | 44918 | 44965 | 45012 | 45059 | 45099 | 45139 | 45179 |
| 44872 | 44919 | 44966 | 45013 | 45060 | 45100 | 45140 | 45180 |
| 44873 | 44920 | 44967 | 45014 | 45061 | 45101 | 45141 | 45181 |
| 44874 | 44921 | 44968 | 45015 | 45062 | 45102 | 45142 | 45182 |
| 44875 | 44922 | 44969 | 45016 | 45063 | 45103 | 45143 | 45183 |
| 44876 | 44923 | 44970 | 45017 | 45064 | 45104 | 45144 | 45184 |
| 44877 | 44924 | 44971 | 45018 | 45065 | 45105 | 45145 | 45185 |
| 44878 | 44925 | 44972 | 45019 | 45066 | 45106 | 45146 | 45186 |
| 44879 | 44926 | 44973 | 45020 | 45067 | 45107 | 45147 | 45187 |
| 44880 | 44927 | 44974 | 45021 | 45068 | 45108 | 45148 | 45188 |
| 44881 | 44928 | 44975 | 45022 | 45069 | 45109 | 45149 | 45189 |
| 44882 | 44929 | 44976 | 45023 | 45070 | 45110 | 45150 | 45190 |
| 44883 | 44930 | 44977 | 45024 | 45071 | 45111 | 45151 | 45191 |
| 44884 | 44931 | 44978 | 45025 | 45072 | 45112 | 45152 | 45192 |
| 44885 | 44932 | 44979 | 45026 | 45073 | 45113 | 45153 | 45193 |
| 44886 | 44933 | 44980 | 45027 | | | | |
| 44887 | 44934 | 44981 | 45028 | | | | |
| 44888 | 44935 | 44982 | 45029 | * NAMES : | | | |
| 44889 | 44936 | 44983 | 45030 | 45154 | Lanarkshire Yeomanry | | |
| 44890 | 44937 | 44984 | 45031 | 45156 | Ayrshire Yeomanry | | |
| 44891 | 44938 | 44985 | 45032 | 45157 | The Glasgow Highlander | | |
| 44892 | 44939 | 44986 | 45033 | 45158 | Glasgow Yeomanry | | |

| | | | | | | | |
|---|---|---|---|---|---|---|---|
| 45194 | 45241 | 45288 | 45335 | 45382 | 45412 | 45442 | 45472 |
| 45195 | 45242 | 45289 | 45336 | 45383 | 45413 | 45443 | 45473 |
| 45196 | 45243 | 45290 | 45337 | 45384 | 45414 | 45444 | 45474 |
| 45197 | 45244 | 45291 | 45338 | 45385 | 45415 | 45445 | 45475 |
| 45198 | 45245 | 45292 | 45339 | 45386 | 45416 | 45446 | 45476 |
| 45199 | 45246 | 45293 | 45340 | 45387 | 45417 | 45447 | 45477 |
| 45200 | 45247 | 45294 | 45341 | 45388 | 45418 | 45448 | 45478 |
| 45201 | 45248 | 45295 | 45342 | 45389 | 45419 | 45449 | 45479 |
| 45202 | 45249 | 45296 | 45343 | 45390 | 45420 | 45450 | 45480 |
| 45203 | 45250 | 45297 | 45344 | 45391 | 45421 | 45451 | 45481 |
| 45204 | 45251 | 45298 | 45345 | 45392 | 45422 | 45452 | 45482 |
| 45205 | 45252 | 45299 | 45346 | 45393 | 45423 | 45453 | 45483 |
| 45206 | 45253 | 45300 | 45347 | 45394 | 45424 | 45454 | 45484 |
| 45207 | 45254 | 45301 | 45348 | 45395 | 45425 | 45455 | 45485 |
| 45208 | 45255 | 45302 | 45349 | 45396 | 45426 | 45456 | 45486 |
| 45209 | 45256 | 45303 | 45350 | 45397 | 45427 | 45457 | 45487 |
| 45210 | 45257 | 45304 | 45351 | 45398 | 45428 | 45458 | 45488 |
| 45211 | 45258 | 45305 | 45352 | 45399 | 45429 | 45459 | 45489 |
| 45212 | 45259 | 45306 | 45353 | 45400 | 45430 | 45460 | 45490 |
| 45213 | 45260 | 45307 | 45354 | 45401 | 45431 | 45461 | 45491 |
| 45214 | 45261 | 45308 | 45355 | 45402 | 45432 | 45462 | 45492 |
| 45215 | 45262 | 45309 | 45356 | 45403 | 45433 | 45463 | 45493 |
| 45216 | 45263 | 45310 | 45357 | 45404 | 45434 | 45464 | 45494 |
| 45217 | 45264 | 45311 | 45358 | 45405 | 45435 | 45465 | 45495 |
| 45218 | 45265 | 45312 | 45359 | 45406 | 45436 | 45466 | 45496 |
| 45219 | 45266 | 45313 | 45360 | 45407 | 45437 | 45467 | 45497 |
| 45220 | 45267 | 45314 | 45361 | 45408 | 45438 | 45468 | 45498 |
| 45221 | 45268 | 45315 | 45362 | 45409 | 45439 | 45469 | 45499 |
| 45222 | 45269 | 45316 | 45363 | 45410 | 45440 | 45470 | |
| 45223 | 45270 | 45317 | 45364 | 45411 | 45441 | 45471 | |
| 45224 | 45271 | 45318 | 45365 | | | | |
| 45225 | 45272 | 45319 | 45366 | | | | |
| 45226 | 45273 | 45320 | 45367 | | | | |
| 45227 | 45274 | 45321 | 45368 | | | | |
| 45228 | 45275 | 45322 | 45369 | | | | |
| 45229 | 45276 | 45323 | 45370 | | | | |
| 45230 | 45277 | 45324 | 45371 | | | | |
| 45231 | 45278 | 45325 | 45372 | | | | |
| 45232 | 45279 | 45326 | 45373 | | | | |
| 45233 | 45280 | 45327 | 45374 | | | | |
| 45234 | 45281 | 45328 | 45375 | | | | |
| 45235 | 45282 | 45329 | 45376 | | | | |
| 45236 | 45283 | 45330 | 45377 | | | | |
| 45237 | 45284 | 45331 | 45378 | | | | |
| 45238 | 45285 | 45332 | 45379 | | | | |
| 45239 | 45286 | 45333 | 45380 | | | | |
| 45240 | 45287 | 45334 | 45381 | | | | |

Total 842

## " Patriot " Class

### 4-6-0                6P5F & 7P

*6P5F. Introduced 1930. Fowler 3-cyl. rebuild of L.N.W. " Claughton " Class (introduced 1912), retaining original wheels and other details.

Remainder. Introduced 1933. New locos. to Fowler design (45502–41 were officially considered as rebuilds).

†7P. Introduced 1946. Ivatt rebuild of Fowler locos. with larger taper boiler, new cylinders and double chimney.

65

Weight: Loco. $\begin{cases} 80 \text{ tons } 15 \text{ cwt.} \\ 80 \text{ tons } 15 \text{ cwt.*} \\ 82 \text{ tons } 0 \text{ cwt.†} \end{cases}$

Pressure: $\begin{cases} 200 \text{ lb. Su.} \\ 200 \text{ lb. Su.*} \\ 250 \text{ lb. Su.†} \end{cases}$

Cyls : $\begin{cases} (3) \ 18'' \times 26''. \\ (3) \ 18'' \times 26''.* \\ (3) \ 17'' \times 26''.† \end{cases}$

Driving Wheels: 6' 9".

T.E.: $\begin{cases} 26,520 \text{ lb.} \\ 26,520 \text{ lb.*} \\ 29,570 \text{ lb.†} \end{cases}$

Walschaerts valve gear. P.V.

| 45500* | Patriot |
| 45501* | St. Dunstan's |
| 45503 | The Royal Leicestershire Regiment |
| 45504 | Royal Signals |
| 45505 | The Royal Army Ordnance Corps |
| 45506 | The Royal Pioneer Corps |
| 45507 | Royal Tank Corps |
| 45509 | The Derbyshire Yeomanry |
| 45510 | |
| 45511 | Isle of Man |
| 45512† | Bunsen |
| 45513 | |
| 45514† | Holyhead |
| 45515 | Caernarvon |
| 45516 | The Bedfordshire and Hertfordshire Regiment |
| 45517 | |
| 45518 | Bradshaw |
| 45519 | Lady Godiva |
| 45520 | Llandudno |
| 45521† | Rhyl |
| 45522† | Prestatyn |
| 45523† | Bangor |
| 45524 | Blackpool |
| 45525† | Colwyn Bay |
| 45526† | Morecambe and Heysham |
| 45527† | Southport |
| 45528† | R.E.M.E. |
| 45529† | Stephenson |
| 45530† | Sir Frank Ree |
| 45531† | Sir Frederick Harrison |

| 45532† | Illustrious |
| 45533 | Lord Rathmore |
| 45534† | E. Tootal Broadhurst |
| 45535† | Sir Herbert Walker K.C.B. |
| 45536† | Private W. Wood, V.C. |
| 45537 | Private E. Sykes, V.C. |
| 45538 | Giggleswick |
| 45539 | E. C. Trench |
| 45540† | Sir Robert Turnbull |
| 45541 | Duke of Sutherland |
| 45542 | |
| 45543 | Home Guard |
| 45544 | |
| 45545† | Planet |
| 45546 | Fleetwood |
| 45547 | |
| 45548 | Lytham St. Annes |
| 45549 | |
| 45550 | |
| 45551 | |

**Total 50**

## "Jubilee" Class

### 4-6-0     6P5F & 7P

**6P5F.** Introduced 1934. Stanier L.M.S. taper boiler development of the "Patriot" class.

**\*7P.** Introduced 1942. Rebuilt with larger boiler and double chimney.

Weight: Loco. $\begin{cases} 79 \text{ tons } 11 \text{ cwt.} \\ 82 \text{ tons } 0 \text{ cwt.*} \end{cases}$

Pressure: $\begin{cases} 225 \text{ lb. Su.} \\ 250 \text{ lb. Su.*} \end{cases}$

Cyls.: (3) 17" × 26".

Driving Wheels: 6' 9".

T.E.: $\begin{cases} 26,610 \text{ lb.} \\ 29,570 \text{ lb.*} \end{cases}$

Walschaerts valve gear. P.V.

| 45552 | Silver Jubilee |
| 45553 | Canada |
| 45554 | Ontario |
| 45555 | Quebec |

| | | | |
|---|---|---|---|
| 45556 | Nova Scotia | 45603 | Solomon Islands |
| 45557 | New Brunswick | 45604 | Ceylon |
| 45558 | Manitoba | 45605 | Cyprus |
| 45559 | British Columbia | 45606 | Falkland Islands |
| 45560 | Prince Edward Island | 45607 | Fiji |
| 45561 | Saskatchewan | 45608 | Gibraltar |
| 45562 | Alberta | 45610 | Ghana |
| 45563 | Australia | 45611 | Hong Kong |
| 45564 | New South Wales | 45612 | Jamaica |
| 45565 | Victoria | 45613 | Kenya |
| 45566 | Queensland | 45614 | Leeward Islands |
| 45567 | South Australia | 45615 | Malay States |
| 45568 | Western Australia | 45617 | Mauritius |
| 45569 | Tasmania | 45618 | New Hebrides |
| 45570 | New Zealand | 45619 | Nigeria |
| 45571 | South Africa | 45620 | North Borneo |
| 45572 | Eire | 45621 | Northern Rhodesia |
| 45573 | Newfoundland | 45622 | Nyasaland |
| 45574 | India | 45623 | Palestine |
| 45575 | Madras | 45624 | St. Helena |
| 45576 | Bombay | 45625 | Sarawak |
| 45577 | Bengal | 45626 | Seychelles |
| 45578 | United Provinces | 45627 | Sierra Leone |
| 45579 | Punjab | 45628 | Somaliland |
| 45580 | Burma | 45629 | Straits Settlements |
| 45581 | Bihar and Orissa | 45630 | Swaziland |
| 45582 | Central Provinces | 45631 | Tanganyika |
| 45583 | Assam | 45632 | Tonga |
| 45584 | North West Frontier | 45633 | Aden |
| 45585 | Hyderabad | 45634 | Trinidad |
| 45586 | Mysore | 45635 | Tobago |
| 45587 | Baroda | 45636 | Uganda |
| 45588 | Kashmir | 45638 | Zanzibar |
| 45589 | Gwalior | 45639 | Raleigh |
| 45590 | Travancore | 45640 | Frobisher |
| 45591 | Udaipur | 45641 | Sandwich |
| 45592 | Indore | 45642 | Boscawen |
| 45593 | Kolhapur | 45643 | Rodney |
| 45594 | Bhopal | 45644 | Howe |
| 45595 | Southern Rhodesia | 45645 | Collingwood |
| 45596 | Bahamas | 45646 | Napier |
| 45597 | Barbados | 45647 | Sturdee |
| 45598 | Basutoland | 45648 | Wemyss |
| 45599 | Bechuanaland | 45649 | Hawkins |
| 45600 | Bermuda | 45650 | Blake |
| 45601 | British Guiana | 45651 | Shovell |
| 45602 | British Honduras | 45652 | Hawke |

| | | | |
|---|---|---|---|
| 45653 | Barham | 45699 | Galatea |
| 45654 | Hood | 45700 | Amethyst |
| 45655 | Keith | 45701 | Conqueror |
| 45656 | Cochrane | 45702 | Colossus |
| 45657 | Tyrwhitt | 45703 | Thunderer |
| 45658 | Keyes | 45704 | Leviathan |
| 45659 | Drake | 45705 | Seahorse |
| 45660 | Rooke | 45706 | Express |
| 45661 | Vernon | 45707 | Valiant |
| 45662 | Kempenfelt | 45708 | Resolution |
| 45663 | Jervis | 45709 | Implacable |
| 45664 | Nelson | 45710 | Irresistible |
| 45665 | Lord Rutherford of | 45711 | Courageous |
| | Nelson | 45712 | Victory |
| 45666 | Cornwallis | 45713 | Renown |
| 45667 | Jellicoe | 45714 | Revenge |
| 45668 | Madden | 45715 | Invincible |
| 45669 | Fisher | 45716 | Swiftsure |
| 45670 | Howard of Effingham | 45717 | Dauntless |
| 45671 | Prince Rupert | 45718 | Dreadnought |
| 45672 | Anson | 45719 | Glorious |
| 45673 | Keppel | 45720 | Indomitable |
| 45674 | Duncan | 45721 | Impregnable |
| 45675 | Hardy | 45722 | Defence |
| 45676 | Codrington | 45723 | Fearless |
| 45677 | Beatty | 45724 | Warspite |
| 45678 | De Robeck | 45725 | Repulse |
| 45679 | Armada | 45726 | Vindictive |
| 45680 | Camperdown | 45727 | Inflexible |
| 45681 | Aboukir | 45728 | Defiance |
| 45682 | Trafalgar | 45729 | Furious |
| 45683 | Hogue | 45730 | Ocean |
| 45684 | Jutland | 45731 | Perseverance |
| 45685 | Barfleur | 45732 | Sanspareil |
| 45686 | St. Vincent | 45733 | Novelty |
| 45687 | Neptune | 45734 | Meteor |
| 45688 | Polyphemus | 45735* | Comet |
| 45689 | Ajax | 45736* | Phoenix |
| 45690 | Leander | 45737 | Atlas |
| 45691 | Orion | 45738 | Samson |
| 45692 | Cyclops | 45739 | Ulster |
| 45693 | Agamemnon | 45740 | Munster |
| 45694 | Bellerophon | 45741 | Leinster |
| 45695 | Minotaur | 45742 | Connaught |
| 45696 | Arethusa | | |
| 45697 | Achilles | | |
| 45698 | Mars | | |

Total 188

# "Royal Scot" Class

## 4-6-0          7P

Introduced 1943. Stanier rebuild of Fowler L.M.S. locos. (introduced 1927) with taper boiler, new cylinders and double chimney.

*Introduced 1935. Stanier taper boiler rebuild with simple cylinders of experimental high pressure compound loco. No. 6399 Fury. (Introduced 1929.)

Weight: Loco. $\begin{cases} 83 \text{ tons.} \\ 84 \text{ tons 1 cwt.}^* \end{cases}$

Pressure: 250 lb. Su.

Cyls.: (3) 18" × 26".

Driving Wheels: 6' 9".

T.E.: 33,150 lb.

Walschaerts valve gear. P.V.

| | |
|---|---|
| 46100 | Royal Scot |
| 46101 | Royal Scots Grey |
| 46102 | Black Watch |
| 46103 | Royal Scots Fusilier |
| 46104 | Scottish Borderer |
| 46105 | Cameron Highlander |
| 46106 | Gordon Highlander |
| 46107 | Argyll and Sutherland Highlander |
| 46108 | Seaforth Highlander |
| 46109 | Royal Engineer |
| 46110 | Grenadier Guardsman |
| 46111 | Royal Fusilier |
| 46112 | Sherwood Forester |
| 46113 | Cameronian |
| 46114 | Coldstream Guardsman |
| 46115 | Scots Guardsman |
| 46116 | Irish Guardsman |
| 46117 | Welsh Guardsman |
| 46118 | Royal Welch Fusilier |
| 46119 | Lancashire Fusilier |
| 46120 | Royal Inniskilling Fusilier |
| 46121 | Highland Light Infantry, City of Glasgow Regiment |
| 46122 | Royal Ulster Rifleman |
| 46123 | Royal Irish Fusilier |
| 46124 | London Scottish |
| 46125 | 3rd Carabinier |
| 46126 | Royal Army Service Corps |
| 46127 | Old Contemptibles |
| 46128 | The Lovat Scouts |
| 46129 | The Scottish Horse |
| 46130 | The West Yorkshire Regiment |
| 46131 | The Royal Warwickshire Regiment |
| 46132 | The King's Regiment Liverpool |
| 46133 | The Green Howards |
| 46134 | The Cheshire Regiment |
| 46135 | The East Lancashire Regiment |
| 46136 | The Border Regiment |
| 46137 | The Prince of Wales's Volunteers (South Lancashire) |
| 46138 | The London Irish Rifleman |
| 46139 | The Welch Regiment |
| 46140 | The King's Royal Rifle Corps |
| 46141 | The North Staffordshire Regiment |
| 46142 | The York & Lancaster Regiment |
| 46143 | The South Staffordshire Regiment |
| 46144 | Honourable Artillery Company |
| 46145 | The Duke of Wellington's Regt. (West Riding) |
| 46146 | The Rifle Brigade |
| 46147 | The Northamptonshire Regiment |
| 46148 | The Manchester Regiment |
| 46149 | The Middlesex Regiment |
| 46150 | The Life Guardsman |
| 46151 | The Royal Horse Guardsman |
| 46152 | The King's Dragoon Guardsman |
| 46153 | The Royal Dragoon |
| 46154 | The Hussar |

| 46155 | The Lancer |
|---|---|
| 46156 | The South Wales Borderer |
| 46157 | The Royal Artilleryman |
| 46158 | The Loyal Regiment |
| 46159 | The Royal Air Force |
| 46160 | Queen Victoria's Rifleman |
| 46161 | King's Own |
| 46162 | Queen's Westminster Rifleman |
| 46163 | Civil Service Rifleman |
| 46164 | The Artists' Rifleman |
| 46165 | The Ranger (12th London Regt.) |
| 46166 | London Rifle Brigade |
| 46167 | The Hertfordshire Regiment |
| 46168 | The Girl Guide |
| 46169 | The Boy Scout |
| 46170* | British Legion |

**Total 71**

## " Princess " Class
### 4-6-2        8P

*Introduced 1933. Stanier L.M.S. taper boiler design.

*Remainder.* Introduced 1935. Development of original design with alterations to valve gear, boiler and other details.

Weight: Loco. 104 tons 10 cwt.

Pressure: 250 lb. Su.

Cyls.: (4) $16\frac{1}{4}'' \times 28''$.

Driving Wheels: 6' 6".

T.E.: 40,285 lb.

Walschaerts valve gear (inside valves operated by rocking shafts on No. 46205; remainder have four sets of valve gear). P.V.

| 46200* | The Princess Royal |
|---|---|
| 46201* | Princess Elizabeth |
| 46203 | Princess Margaret Rose |
| 46204 | Princess Louise |
| 46205 | Princess Victoria |

| 46206 | Princess Marie Louise |
|---|---|
| 46207 | Princess Arthur of Connaught |
| 46208 | Princess Helena Victoria |
| 46209 | Princess Beatrice |
| 46210 | Lady Patricia |
| 46211 | Queen Maud |
| 46212 | Duchess of Kent |

**Total 12**

## " Coronation " Class
### 4-6-2        8P

Introduced 1937. Stanier L.M.S. enlargement of " Princess Royal " class. All except Nos. 46230-4/49-55 originally streamlined. (Streamlining removed from 1946.)

*Introduced 1947. Ivatt development with roller bearings and detail alterations.

Weight: Loco. $\begin{cases} 105 \text{ tons } 5 \text{ cwt.} \\ 106 \text{ tons } 8 \text{ cwt.}^* \end{cases}$

Pressure: 250 lb. Su.

Cyls.: (4) $16\frac{1}{4}'' \times 28''$.

Driving Wheels: 6' 9".

T.E.: 40,000 lb.

Walschaerts valve gear and rocking shafts. P.V.

| 46220 | Coronation |
|---|---|
| 46221 | Queen Elizabeth |
| 46222 | Queen Mary |
| 46223 | Princess Alice |
| 46224 | Princess Alexandra |
| 46225 | Duchess of Gloucester |
| 46226 | Duchess of Norfolk |
| 46227 | Duchess of Devonshire |
| 46228 | Duchess of Rutland |
| 46229 | Duchess of Hamilton |
| 46230 | Duchess of Buccleuch |
| 46231 | Duchess of Atholl |
| 46232 | Duchess of Montrose |
| 46233 | Duchess of Sutherland |
| 46234 | Duchess of Abercorn |
| 46235 | City of Birmingham |
| 46236 | City of Bradford |
| 46237 | City of Bristol |

| | | | |
|---|---|---|---|
| 46238 | City of Carlisle | | |
| 46239 | City of Chester | | |
| 46240 | City of Coventry | | |
| 46241 | City of Edinburgh | | |
| 46242 | City of Glasgow | | |
| 46243 | City of Lancaster | | |
| 46244 | King George VI | | |
| 46245 | City of London | | |
| 46246 | City of Manchester | | |
| 46247 | City of Liverpool | | |
| 46248 | City of Leeds | | |
| 46249 | City of Sheffield | | |
| 46250 | City of Lichfield | | |
| 46251 | City of Nottingham | | |
| 46252 | City of Leicester | | |
| 46253 | City of St. Albans | | |
| 46254 | City of Stoke-on-Trent | | |
| 46255 | City of Hereford | | |
| 46256* | Sir William A. Stanier, F.R.S. | | |
| 46257* | City of Salford | | |

**Total 38**

| | | | |
|---|---|---|---|
| 46440 | 46462 | 46484* | 46506* |
| 46441 | 46463 | 46485* | 46507* |
| 46442 | 46464 | 46486* | 46508* |
| 46443 | 46465* | 46487* | 46509* |
| 46444 | 46466* | 46488* | 46510* |
| 46445 | 46467* | 46489* | 46511* |
| 46446 | 46468* | 46490* | 46512* |
| 46447 | 46469* | 46491* | 46513* |
| 46448 | 46470* | 46492* | 46514* |
| 46449 | 46471* | 46493* | 46515* |
| 46450 | 46472* | 46494* | 46516* |
| 46451 | 46473* | 46495* | 46517* |
| 46452 | 46474* | 46496* | 46518* |
| 46453 | 46475* | 46497* | 46519* |
| 46454 | 46476* | 46498* | 46520* |
| 46455 | 46477* | 46499* | 46521* |
| 46456 | 46478* | 46500* | 46522* |
| 46457 | 46479* | 46501* | 46523* |
| 46458 | 46480*. | 46502* | 46524* |
| 46459 | 46481* | 46503* | 46525* |
| 46460 | 46482* | 46504* | 46526* |
| 46461 | 46483* | 46505* | 46527* |

**Total 128**

## 2-6-0　　　　　　　　　　2

Introduced 1946. Ivatt L.M.S. taper boiler design.
Weight: Loco. 47 tons 2 cwt.
Pressure: 200 lb. Su.
Cyls.: $\begin{cases} \text{(O) } 16'' \times 24''. \\ \text{(O) } 16\frac{1}{2}'' \times 24''.* \end{cases}$
Driving Wheels: 5' 0".
T.E.: $\begin{cases} 17,410 \text{ lb.} \\ 18,510 \text{ lb.*} \end{cases}$
Walschaerts valve gear.　P.V.

| | | | |
|---|---|---|---|
| 46400 | 46410 | 46420 | 46430 |
| 46401 | 46411 | 46421 | 46431 |
| 46402 | 46412 | 46422 | 46432 |
| 46403 | 46413 | 46423 | 46433 |
| 46404 | 46414 | 46424 | 46434 |
| 46405 | 46415 | 46425 | 46435 |
| 46406 | 46416 | 46426 | 46436 |
| 46407 | 46417 | 46427 | 46437 |
| 46408 | 46418 | 46428 | 46438 |
| 46409 | 46419 | 46429 | 46439 |

## 0-4-0ST　　　　　　　0F

Introduced 1932. Kitson design prepared to Stanier's requirements for L.M.S.

*Introduced 1953. Extended side tanks and coal space.

Weight: $\begin{cases} 33 \text{ tons 0 cwt.} \\ 34 \text{ tons 0 cwt.*} \end{cases}$
Pressure: 160 lb.
Cyls.: (O) $15\frac{1}{2}'' \times 20''$.
Driving Wheels: 3' 10".
T.E.: 14,205 lb.

| | | | |
|---|---|---|---|
| 47000 | 47003 | 47006* | 47008* |
| 47001 | 47004 | 47007* | 47009* |
| 47002 | 47005* | | |

**Total 10**

## 0-6-0T        2F

Introduced 1928. Fowler L.M.S. short-wheelbase dock tanks.
Weight: 43 tons 12 cwt.
Pressure: 160 lb.
Cyls.: (O) 17″ × 22″.
Driving Wheels: 3′ 11″.
T.E.: 18,400 lb.
Walschaerts valve gear.

| | | | |
|---|---|---|---|
| 47160 | 47163 | 47165 | 47168 |
| 47161 | 47164 | 47166 | |

**Total 7**

## 0-4-0T        Sentinel

**Geared Sentinel locos.**

Introduced 1929. Single-speed locos. for S. & D.J. (taken into L.M.S. stock 1930).

Weight: 27 tons 15 cwt.
Pressure: 275 lb. Su.
Cyls.: (4) 6¾″ × 9″.
Driving Wheels: 3′ 1½″.
T.E.: 15,500 lb.
Poppet valves.

47190

**Total 1**

## 0-6-0T        3F

Introduced 1899. Johnson large Midland design, rebuilt with Belpaire firebox from 1919; fitted with condensing apparatus for London area.
*Introduced 1899. Non-condensing locos.
Weight: 48 tons 15 cwt.
Pressure: 160 lb.
Cyls.: 18″ × 26″.
Driving Wheels: 4′ 7″.
T.E.: 20,835 lb.

| | | | |
|---|---|---|---|
| 47200 | 47213 | 47225 | 47239* |
| 47201* | 47217 | 47228 | 47248* |
| 47202 | 47218 | 47230* | 47250* |
| 47204 | 47221 | 47231* | 47255* |
| 47207 | 47223 | 47235* | 47257* |
| 47209 | 47224 | 47236* | 47259* |
| 47211 | | | |

**Total 25**

## 0-6-0T        3F

Introduced 1924. Post-grouping development of Midland design with detail alterations.
*Introduced 1929. Locos. built for S. & D.J. (taken into L.M.S. stock 1930).
†Push-and-pull fitted.
Weight: 49 tons 10 cwt.
Pressure: 160 lb.
Cyls.: 18″ × 26″.
Driving Wheels: 4′ 7″.
T.E.: 20,835 lb.

| | | | |
|---|---|---|---|
| 47261 | 47304 | 47348S | 47388 |
| 47263 | 47305 | 47349 | 47389 |
| 47264 | 47306 | 47350 | 47390 |
| 47266 | 47307 | 47351 | 47391 |
| 47267 | 47308 | 47353 | 47392 |
| 47268 | 47310* | 47354 | 47393 |
| 47269 | 47312* | 47355 | 47395 |
| 47270 | 47313* | 47356 | 47396 |
| 47272 | 47314* | 47357 | 47397 |
| 47273 | 47316* | 47358 | 47398 |
| 47275 | 47317 | 47359 | 47399 |
| 47276 | 47318 | 47360 | 47400 |
| 47277 | 47319 | 47361 | 47402S |
| 47278 | 47320 | 47362 | 47403 |
| 47279 | 47321 | 47365 | 47404 |
| 47280 | 47322 | 47366 | 47405 |
| 47281 | 47324 | 47367 | 47406 |
| 47283 | 47325 | 47368 | 47408 |
| 47284 | 47326 | 47369 | 47410 |
| 47285 | 47327 | 47371 | 47412 |
| 47286S | 47328 | 47372 | 47413 |
| 47287 | 47330 | 47373 | 47414 |
| 47288 | 47332 | 47375 | 47415 |
| 47289 | 47333 | 47376 | 47416 |
| 47290 | 47334 | 47377 | 47417 |
| 47292 | 47336 | 47378 | 47418 |
| 47293 | 47338 | 47379 | 47419 |
| 47294 | 47340 | 47380 | 47420 |
| 47295 | 47341 | 47381 | 47421 |
| 47297 | 47342 | 47383 | 47422 |
| 47298 | 47343 | 47384 | 47423 |
| 47300 | 47344 | 47385 | 47424 |
| 47302 | 47345 | 47386 | 47425 |

Above:
Class 4500 2-6-2T
No. 4569
[K. R. Pirt

Right: Class 5101 2-6-2T
No. 5198
[M. Pope

Below: Class 6100
2-6-2T No. 6151
[P. H. Groom

Class 7200 2-8-2T No. 7202          [*J. Davenport*

Class 7200 2-8-2T No. 7220 (with straight footplate)      [*A. R. Carpenter*

Class 4200 2-8-0T No. 5236          [*J. Davenport*

Standard Class 7P6F 4-6-2 No. 70016 *Ariel*          [J. Davenport]

Standard Class 9F 2-10-0 No. 92250 (with Giesl exhaust ejector)          [G. Wheeler]

Standard Class 9F 2-10-0 No. 92220 *Evening Star* (with double chimney)          [W. L. Underhay]

Standard Class 5 4-6-0 No. 73086 *The Green Knight*

[P. H. Groom

Standard Class 4 4-6-0 No. 75072 (with double blast pipe and chimney and BR1B tender)

[Ivo Peters

Standard Class 4 4-6-0 No. 75003 (with double blast pipe and chimney and BR2 tender)

[L. Elsey

Standard Class 2 2-6-0 No. 78005

[*P. J. Sharpe*

Standard Class 4 2-6-0 No. 76063

[*J. Davenport*

Standard Class 3 2-6-2T No. 82030 (in green livery)

[*K. L. Cook*

Class MN 4-6-2 No. 35019 *French Line CGT*    [P. H. Groom

Rebuilt class WC 4-6-2 No. 34101 *Hartland*    [G. Wheeler

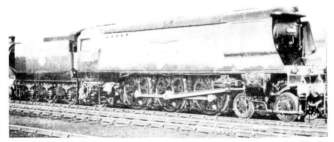

Class BB 4-6-2 No. 34054 *Lord Beaverbrook*    [G. Wheeler

Class LN 4-6-0 No. 30858 *Lord Duncan*                    [*P. H. Groom*

Class V 4-4-0 No. 30904 *Lancing*                         [*K. R. Pirt*

Class N15 4-6-0 No. 30773 *Sir Lavaine*                   [*R. A. Panting*

Class S15 4-6-0 No. 30499 (original Urie design)         [M. R. Galley

Class S15 4-6-0 No. 30836 (Maunsell development with six-wheel tender)    [K. R. Pirt

Class S15 4-6-0 No. 30840 (later Maunsell design with reduced weight)    [K. R. Pirt

Class DI 4-4-0 No. 31735

[L. Elsey

Class EI 4-4-0 No. 31507

[L. Elsey

Class LI 4-4-0 No. 31789

[K. L. Cook

Class U 2-6-0 No. 31798                         *[B. A. Haresnape*

Class U1 2-6-0 No. 31898                        *[J. H. Aston*

Class K 2-6-0 No. 32348                         *[R. K. Evans*

Class L 4-4-0 No. 31764       [*A. Trickett*

Class T9 4-4-0 No. 30120       [*J. B. Bucknall*

Class T9 4-4-0 No. 30313 (with wider cab and splashers)       [*P. H. Groom*

Class Q1 0-6-0 No. 33012                                    [J. B. Bucknall

Class Q 0-6-0 No. 30543                                     [P. H. Groom

Class Q 0-6-0 No. 30549 (with stovepipe chimney)

Class 700 0-6-0 No. 30306
[K. R. Pirt

Class C 0-6-0 No. 31004
[R. C. Riley

Class O1 0-6-0 No. 31065
[E. A. Woodland

Class W 2-6-4T No. 31913       [*C. P. Boocock*

Class G16 4-8-0T No. 30495       [*R. A. Panting*

Class H16 4-6-2T No. 30520       [*J. C. Haydon*

Class Z 0-8-0T No. 30955                                    [C. P. Boocock

Class 0415 4-4-2T No. 30582                                 [R. C. Riley

Class 0298 2-4-0WT No. 30587                               [R. C. Riley

Class M7 0-4-4T No. 30249                              [J. B. Bucknall

Class M7 0-4-4T No. 30060 (fitted for push-and pull working)        [L. Elsey

Class O2 0-4-4Ts Nos. 36 *Carisbrooke* and 16 *Ventnor*        [K. L. Cook

| | | | |
|---|---|---|---|
| 47426 | 47480† | 47536 | 47601 |
| 47427 | 47481† | 47539 | 47602 |
| 47428 | 47482 | 47540 | 47603 |
| 47429 | 47483 | 47542 | 47604 |
| 47430 | 47484 | 47543 | 47605 |
| 47431 | 47485 | 47544 | 47606 |
| 47432 | 47487 | 47545 | 47608 |
| 47433 | 47488 | 47546 | 47609 |
| 47434 | 47490 | 47547 | 47610 |
| 47435 | 47491 | 47548 | 47611 |
| 47437 | 47492 | 47549 | 47612 |
| 47438 | 47493 | 47550 | 47614 |
| 47439 | 47494 | 47551 | 47615 |
| 47441 | 47495 | 47552 | 47616 |
| 47442 | 47496 | 47554 | 47618S |
| 47444 | 47497 | 47555 | 47619 |
| 47445 | 47499 | 47556 | 47620 |
| 47447 | 47500 | 47557 | 47621 |
| 47448 | 47501 | 47558 | 47622 |
| 47449 | 47502 | 47559 | 47623 |
| 47450 | 47503 | 47562 | 47624 |
| 47451 | 47504 | 47564 | 47625 |
| 47452 | 47505 | 47565 | 47626 |
| 47453 | 47506 | 47566 | 47627 |
| 47454 | 47507 | 47570 | 47628 |
| 47455 | 47508 | 47571 | 47629 |
| 47457 | 47511 | 47572 | 47630 |
| 47458 | 47512 | 47574 | 47631 |
| 47459 | 47513 | 47577 | 47632 |
| 47460 | 47514 | 47578 | 47633 |
| 47461 | 47515 | 47579 | 47634 |
| 47462 | 47516 | 47580 | 47637 |
| 47464 | 47517 | 47581 | 47638 |
| 47465 | 47518 | 47582 | 47640 |
| 47466 | 47519 | 47583 | 47641 |
| 47467 | 47520 | 47584 | 47642 |
| 47468 | 47521 | 47587 | 47643 |
| 47469 | 47522 | 47588 | 47644 |
| 47470 | 47524 | 47589 | 47645 |
| 47471 | 47526 | 47590 | 47646 |
| 47472 | 47529 | 47592S | 47647 |
| 47473 | 47530 | 47593 | 47648 |
| 47474 | 47531 | 47594 | 47649 |
| 47475 | 47532 | 47596 | 47651 |
| 47476 | 47533 | 47597 | 47653 |
| 47478†S | 47534 | 47598 | 47654 |
| 47479†S | 47535 | 47599 | 47655† |

| | | | |
|---|---|---|---|
| 47656 | 47662 | 47669 | 47677 |
| 47657 | 47664 | 47671 | 47678 |
| 47658 | 47665 | 47673 | 47679 |
| 47659 | 47666 | 47674 | 47680 |
| 47660 | 47667 | 47675 | 47681† |
| 47661 | 47668 | 47676 | |

**Total 343**

## 2-8-0     8F

Introduced 1935. Stanier L.M.S. taper boiler design.

Weight: Loco. 72 tons 2 cwt.

Pressure: 225 lb. Su.

Cyls.: (O) $18\frac{1}{2}'' \times 28''$.

Driving Wheels: $4' 8\frac{1}{4}''$.

T.E.: 32,440 lb.

Walschaerts valve gear.  P.V.

| | | | |
|---|---|---|---|
| 48000 | 48020 | 48056 | 48078 |
| 48001 | 48024 | 48057 | 48079 |
| 48002 | 48026 | 48060 | 48080 |
| 48003 | 48027 | 48061 | 48081 |
| 48004 | 48029 | 48062 | 48082 |
| 48005 | 48033 | 48063 | 48083 |
| 48006 | 48035 | 48064 | 48084 |
| 48007 | 48036 | 48065 | 48085 |
| 48008 | 48037 | 48067 | 48088 |
| 48009 | 48039 | 48069 | 48089 |
| 48010 | 48045 | 48070 | 48090 |
| 48011 | 48046 | 48073 | 48092 |
| 48012 | 48050 | 48074 | 48093 |
| 48016 | 48053 | 48075 | 48094 |
| 48017 | 48054 | 48076 | 48095 |
| 48018 | 48055 | 48077 | 48096 |

| | | | | | | | |
|---|---|---|---|---|---|---|---|
| 48097 | 48144 | 48191 | 48258 | 48308 | 48355 | 48402 | 48449 |
| 48098 | 48145 | 48192 | 48259 | 48309 | 48356 | 48403 | 48450 |
| 48099 | 48146 | 48193 | 48260 | 48310 | 48357 | 48404 | 48451 |
| 48100 | 48147 | 48194 | 48261 | 48311 | 48358 | 48405 | 48452 |
| 48101 | 48148 | 48195 | 48262 | 48312 | 48359 | 48406 | 48453 |
| 48102 | 48149 | 48196 | 48263 | 48313 | 48360 | 48407 | 48454 |
| 48103 | 48150 | 48197 | 48264 | 48314 | 48361 | 48408 | 48455 |
| 48104 | 48151 | 48198 | 48265 | 48315 | 48362 | 48409 | 48456 |
| 48105 | 48152 | 48199 | 48266 | 48316 | 48363 | 48410 | 48457 |
| 48106 | 48153 | 48200 | 48267 | 48317 | 48364 | 48411 | 48458 |
| 48107 | 48154 | 48201 | 48268 | 48318 | 48365 | 48412 | 48459 |
| 48108 | 48155 | 48202 | 48269 | 48319 | 48366 | 48413 | 48460 |
| 48109 | 48156 | 48203 | 48270 | 48320 | 48367 | 48414 | 48461 |
| 48110 | 48157 | 48204 | 48271 | 48321 | 48368 | 48415 | 48462 |
| 48111 | 48158 | 48205 | 48272 | 48322 | 48369 | 48416 | 48463 |
| 48112 | 48159 | 48206 | 48273 | 48323 | 48370 | 48417 | 48464 |
| 48113 | 48160 | 48207 | 48274 | 48324 | 48371 | 48418 | 48465 |
| 48114 | 48161 | 48208 | 48275 | 48325 | 48372 | 48419 | 48466 |
| 48115 | 48162 | 48209 | 48276 | 48326 | 48373 | 48420 | 48467 |
| 48116 | 48163 | 48210 | 48277 | 48327 | 48374 | 48421 | 48468 |
| 48117 | 48164 | 48211 | 48278 | 48328 | 48375 | 48422 | 48469 |
| 48118 | 48165 | 48212 | 48279 | 48329 | 48376 | 48423 | 48470 |
| 48119 | 48166 | 48213 | 48280 | 48330 | 48377 | 48424 | 48471 |
| 48120 | 48167 | 48214 | 48281 | 48331 | 48378 | 48425 | 48472 |
| 48121 | 48168 | 48215 | 48282 | 48332 | 48379 | 48426 | 48473 |
| 48122 | 48169 | 48216 | 48283 | 48333 | 48380 | 48427 | 48474 |
| 48123 | 48170 | 48217 | 48284 | 48334 | 48381 | 48428 | 48475 |
| 48124 | 48171 | 48218 | 48285 | 48335 | 48382 | 48429 | 48476 |
| 48125 | 48172 | 48219 | 48286 | 48336 | 48383 | 48430 | 48477 |
| 48126 | 48173 | 48220 | 48287 | 48337 | 48384 | 48431 | 48478 |
| 48127 | 48174 | 48221 | 48288 | 48338 | 48385 | 48432 | 48479 |
| 48128 | 48175 | 48222 | 48289 | 48339 | 48396 | 48433 | 48490 |
| 48129 | 48176 | 48223 | 48290 | 48340 | 48387 | 48434 | 48491 |
| 48130 | 48177 | 48224 | 48291 | 48341 | 48388 | 48435 | 48492 |
| 48131 | 48178 | 48225 | 48292 | 48342 | 48389 | 48436 | 48493 |
| 48132 | 48179 | 48246 | 48293 | 48343 | 48390 | 48437 | 48494 |
| 48133 | 48180 | 48247 | 48294 | 48344 | 48391 | 48438 | 48495 |
| 48134 | 48181 | 48248 | 48295 | 48345 | 48392 | 48439 | 48500 |
| 48135 | 48182 | 48249 | 48296 | 48346 | 48393 | 48440 | 48501 |
| 48136 | 48183 | 48250 | 48297 | 48347 | 48394 | 48441 | 48502 |
| 48137 | 48184 | 48251 | 48301 | 48348 | 48395 | 48442 | 48503 |
| 48138 | 48185 | 48252 | 48302 | 48349 | 48396 | 48443 | 48504 |
| 48139 | 48186 | 48253 | 48303 | 48350 | 48397 | 48444 | 48505 |
| 48140 | 48187 | 48254 | 48304 | 48351 | 48398 | 48445 | 48506 |
| 48141 | 48188 | 48255 | 48305 | 48352 | 48399 | 48446 | 48507 |
| 48142 | 48189 | 48256 | 48306 | 48353 | 48400 | 48447 | 48508 |
| 48143 | 48190 | 48257 | 48307 | 48354 | 48401 | 48448 | 48509 |

| | | | | | | | |
|---|---|---|---|---|---|---|---|
| 48510 | 48557 | 48645 | 48692 | 48739 | 48749 | 48758 | 48767 |
| 48511 | 48558 | 48646 | 48693 | 48740 | 48750 | 48759 | 48768 |
| 48512 | 48559 | 48647 | 48694 | 48741 | 48751 | 48760 | 48769 |
| 48513 | 48600 | 48648 | 48695 | 48742 | 48752 | 48761 | 48770 |
| 48514 | 48601 | 48649 | 48696 | 48743 | 48753 | 48762 | 48771 |
| 48515 | 48602 | 48650 | 48697 | 48744 | 48754 | 48763 | 48772 |
| 48516 | 48603 | 48651 | 48698 | 48745 | 48755 | 48764 | 48773 |
| 48517 | 48604 | 48652 | 48699 | 48746 | 48756 | 48765 | 48774 |
| 48518 | 48605 | 48653 | 48700 | 48747 | 48757 | 48766 | 48775 |
| 48519 | 48606 | 48654 | 48701 | 48748 | | | |
| 48520 | 48607 | 48655 | 48702 | | | | |
| 48521 | 48608 | 48656 | 48703 | | | | |
| 48522 | 48609 | 48657 | 48704 | | | | |
| 48523 | 48610 | 48658 | 48705 | | | | |
| 48524 | 48611 | 48659 | 48706 | | | | |
| 48525 | 48612 | 48660 | 48707 | | | | |
| 48526 | 48613 | 48661 | 48708 | | | | |
| 48527 | 48614 | 48662 | 48709 | | | | |
| 48528 | 48615 | 48663 | 48710 | | | | |
| 48529 | 48617 | 48664 | 48711 | | | | |
| 48530 | 48618 | 48665 | 48712 | | | | |
| 48531 | 48619 | 48666 | 48713 | | | | |
| 48532 | 48620 | 48667 | 48714 | | | | |
| 48533 | 48621 | 48668 | 48715 | | | | |
| 48534 | 48622 | 48669 | 48716 | | | | |
| 48535 | 48623 | 48670 | 48717 | | | | |
| 48536 | 48624 | 48671 | 48718 | | | | |
| 48537 | 48625 | 48672 | 48719 | | | | |
| 48538 | 48626 | 48673 | 48720 | | | | |
| 48539 | 48627 | 48674 | 48721 | | | | |
| 48540 | 48628 | 48675 | 48722 | | | | |
| 48541 | 48629 | 48676 | 48723 | | | | |
| 48542 | 48630 | 48677 | 48724 | | | | |
| 48543 | 48631 | 48678 | 48725 | | | | |
| 48544 | 48632 | 48679 | 48726 | | | | |
| 48545 | 48633 | 48680 | 48727 | | | | |
| 48546 | 48634 | 48681 | 48728 | | | | |
| 48547 | 48635 | 48682 | 48729 | | | | |
| 48548 | 48636 | 48683 | 48730 | | | | |
| 48549 | 48637 | 48684 | 48731 | | | | |
| 48550 | 48638 | 48685 | 48732 | | | | |
| 48551 | 48639 | 48686 | 48733 | | | | |
| 48552 | 48640 | 48687 | 48734 | | | | |
| 48553 | 48641 | 48688 | 48735 | | | | |
| 48554 | 48642 | 48689 | 48736 | | | | |
| 48555 | 48643 | 48690 | 48737 | | | | |
| 48556 | 48644 | 48691 | 48738 | | | | |

**Total 665**

## 0-8-0          7F

Introduced 1936. L.N.W. G2a Class.
Bowen-Cooke G1 superheated design
of 1912, rebuilt with G2 boiler and
Belpaire firebox.

Weight: Loco. 62 tons 0 cwt.

Pressure: 175 lb. Su.

Cyls.: 20½″ × 24″.

Driving Wheels: 4′ 5½″.

T.E.: 28,045 lb.

Joy valve gear. P.V.

| | | | |
|---|---|---|---|
| 48895 | 49034 | 49122 | 49196 |
| 48898 | 49037 | 49125 | 49199 |
| 48915 | 49045 | 49126 | 49209 |
| 48927 | 49049 | 49129 | 49210 |
| 48930 | 49061 | 49130 | 49216 |
| 48932 | 49070 | 49134 | 49224 |
| 48942 | 49077 | 49137 | 49240 |
| 48950 | 49078 | 49139 | 49243 |
| 48951 | 49079 | 49141 | 49246 |
| 48953 | 49081 | 49142 | 49262 |
| 48964 | 49087 | 49144 | 49267 |
| 49002 | 49093 | 49147 | 49275 |
| 49007 | 49094 | 49154 | 49277 |
| 49008 | 49099 | 49155 | 49281 |
| 49020 | 49104 | 49158 | 49287 |
| 49021 | 49106 | 49164 | 49288 |
| 49023 | 49114 | 49173 | 49293 |
| 49025 | 49119 | 49191 | 49310 |

| 49313 | 49342 | 49357 | 49381 | 49508 | 49627 | 49637 | 49668 |
|-------|-------|-------|-------|-------|-------|-------|-------|
| 49314 | 49343 | 49361 | 49382 | 49618 | | | |
| 49323 | 49344 | 49373 | 49391 | | | | Total 5 |
| 49328 | 49350 | 49375 | 49392 | | | | |
| 49335 | 49352 | 49377 | 49394 | | | | |

Total 92

## 0-8-0      7F

Introduced 1921. Development of
L.N.W. G2 Class. Bowen-Cooke G1
superheated design of 1912 with
higher pressure boiler. Many later
rebuilt with Belpaire firebox.
Weight: Loco. 62 tons 0 cwt.
Pressure: 175 lb. Su.
Cyls.: $20\frac{1}{2}'' \times 24''$.
Driving Wheels: $4'\ 5\frac{1}{2}''$.
T.E.: 28,045 lb.
Joy valve gear.   P.V.

| 49399 | 49413 | 49430 | 49443 |
|-------|-------|-------|-------|
| 49401 | 49414 | 49431 | 49444 |
| 49402 | 49415 | 49432 | 49446 |
| 49403 | 49416 | 49433 | 49447 |
| 49404 | 49421 | 49434 | 49448 |
| 49405 | 49422 | 49437 | 49449 |
| 49406 | 49423 | 49438 | 49451 |
| 49407 | 49425 | 49439 | 49452 |
| 49408 | 49426 | 49440 | 49453 |
| 49411 | 49428 | 49441 | 49454 |
| 49412 | | | |

Total 41

## 0-8-0      7F

Introduced 1929. Fowler L.M.S. design,
developed from L.N.W. G2.
Weight: Loco. 60 tons 15 cwt.
Pressure: 200 lb. Su.
Cyls.: $19\frac{1}{2}'' \times 26''$.
Driving Wheels: $4'\ 8\frac{1}{2}''$.
T.E.: 29,745 lb.
Walschaerts valve gear.   P.V

## 2-4-2T      2P

Introduced 1889. Aspinall L. & Y.
Class 5 with 2 tons coal capacity.
*Introduced 1898. Locos. with longer
tanks and 4 tons coal capacity. Rebuilt
1910 with Belpaire firebox and exten-
ded smokebox.
Weight: $\begin{cases} 55 \text{ tons } 19 \text{ cwt.} \\ 59 \text{ tons } 3 \text{ cwt.*} \end{cases}$
Pressure: 180 lb.
Cyls.: $18'' \times 26''$.
Driving Wheels: $5'\ 8''$.
T.E.: 18,955 lb.
Joy valve gear.

50746    50850*

Total 2

## 0-4-0ST      0F

Introduced 1891. Aspinall L. & Y.
Class 21.
Weight: 21 tons 5 cwt.
Pressure: 160 lb.
Cyls.: $13'' \times 18''$.
Driving Wheels: $3'\ 0\frac{8}{8}''$.
T.E.: 11,335 lb.

| 51204 | 51217 | 51232 | 51244 |
|-------|-------|-------|-------|
| 51206 | 51218 | 51237 | 51246 |
| 51207 | 51222 | 51241 | 51253 |

Total 12

## 0-6-0ST                                    2F

Introduced 1891. Aspinall rebuild of
  L. & Y. Barton Wright Class 23 0-6-0.
  Originally introduced 1877.
Weight: 43 tons 17 cwt.
Pressure: 140 lb.
Cyls.: 17½" × 26".
Driving Wheels: 4' 6".
T.E.: 17,545 lb.

See also Service locomotives.

| | | | |
|---|---|---|---|
| 51371 | 51413 | 51441 | 51446S |
| 51408 | 51419 | 51444S | 51496 |
| 51412S | 51429S | | |

Total 14

| | | | |
|---|---|---|---|
| 52093S | 52218S | 52312*S | 52456 |
| 52119 | 52230 | 52345 | 52459S |
| 52121 | 52240 | 52393 | 52461 |
| 52129 | 52248 | 52413* | 52464S |
| 52171 | 52260 | 52415 | 52515 |
| 52182 | 52271 | 52438* | 52523 |
| 52201* | 52275 | 52441S | 52526 |
| 52207 | 52311 | | |

Total 30

## 0-6-0T                                     1F

Introduced 1897. Aspinail L. & Y.
  Class 24 dock tanks.
Weight: 50 tons 0 cwt.
Pressure: 140 lb.
Cyls.: (O) 17" × 24".
Driving Wheels: 4' 0".
T.E.: 15,285 lb.
Allan straight link valve gear.

51537

Total 1

## 2-8-0                                      7F

Introduced 1914. Fowler design for
  S. & D.J.
(All taken into L.M.S. stock, 1930.)
Weight: Loco. 64 tons 15 cwt.
Pressure: 190 lb. Su.
Cyls.: (O) 21" × 28".
Driving Wheels: 4' 8½".
T.E.: 35,295 lb.
Walschaerts valve gear.  P.V.

| | | | |
|---|---|---|---|
| 53801 | 53805 | 53807 | 53809 |
| 53803 | 53806 | 53808 | 53810 |
| 53804 | | | |

Total 9

## 0-6-0                                      3F

Introduced 1889. Aspinall L. & Y. Class
  27. Nos. 52515–26 built superheated
  with roundtop firebox and extended
  smokebox, later rebuilt with satu-
  rated boiler and short smokebox.
*Introduced 1911. Rebuilt with Belpaire
  firebox and extended smokebox.
Weight: Loco. 42 tons 3 cwt.
Pressure: 180 lb.
Cyls.: 18" × 26".
Driving Wheels: 5' 1"
T.E.: 21,130 lb.
Joy valve gear.

## 4-4-0                                      3P

Introduced 1916. Pickersgill Caledonian
  " 113 " and " 928 " classes.
Weight: Loco. 61 tons 5 cwt.
Pressure: 180 lb. Su.
Cyls.: 20" × 26".
Driving Wheels: 6' 6".
T.E.: 20,400 lb.
P.V.

| | | | |
|---|---|---|---|
| 54463 | 54465 | 54466 | 54475 |
| 54464 | | | |

Total 5

## 4-4-0      3P

Introduced 1920. Pickersgill Caledonian
" 72 " class.
Weight: Loco. 61 tons 5 cwt.
Pressure: 180 lb. Su.
Cyls.: 20½" × 26".
Driving Wheels: 6' 6".
T.E.: 21,435 lb.
P.V.

| | | | |
|---|---|---|---|
| 54478 | 54487 | 54493 | 54502 |
| 54482 | 54488 | 54495 | 54505 |
| 54483 | 54489 | 54500 | 54506 |
| 54485 | 54491 | 54501 | 54507 |
| 54486 | 54492 | | |

Total 18

## 0-4-4T      2P

*Introduced 1895. McIntosh Cale-
donian " 19 " class, with railed coal
bunker.
†Introduced 1897. McIntosh " 92 "
class, developed from " 29 " class
with larger tanks and highsided
coal bunker (both classes originally
fitted for condensing on Glasgow
Central Low Level lines).
Weight: {53 tons 16 cwt.*
        {53 tons 19 cwt.†
Pressure: 180 lb.
Cyls.: 18" × 26".
Driving Wheels: 5' 9".
T.E.: 18,680 lb.

55124*    55126†

Total 2

## 0-4-4T      2P

Introduced 1900. McIntosh Caledonian
" 439 " or " Standard Passenger "
class.
*Introduced 1915. Pickersgill locos.
with detail alterations.
Weight: {53 tons 19 cwt.
        {57 tons 12 cwt.*
Pressure: 180 lb.
Cyls.: 18" × 26".
Driving Wheels: 5' 9".
T.E.: 18,680 lb.

| | | | |
|---|---|---|---|
| 55165 | 55202 | 55216 | 55227* |
| 55167 | 55203 | 55217 | 55228* |
| 55169 | 55204 | 55219 | 55229* |
| 55173 | 55206 | 55220 | 55230* |
| 55185 | 55207 | 55221 | 55231* |
| 55189 | 55208 | 55222 | 55232* |
| 55195 | 55209 | 55223 | 55233* |
| 55198 | 55210 | 55225 | 55234* |
| 55199 | 55211 | 55226 | 55235* |
| 55200 | 55214 | | 55236* |
| 55201 | 55215 | | |

Total 42

## 0-4-4T      2P

Introduced 1922. Pickersgill Caledonian
" 431 " class (developed from " 439 "
class) with cast-iron front buffer
beam for banking.
Weight: 57 tons 17 cwt.
Pressure: 180 lb.
Cyls.: 18½" × 26".
Driving Wheels: 5' 9".
T.E.: 19,200 lb.

55237    55238    55239    55240

Total 4

## 0-4-4T      2P

Introduced 1925. Post-Grouping devel-
opment of Caledonian " 439 " class.
Weight: 59 tons 12 cwt.
Pressure: 180 lb.
Cyls.: 18½ × 26".
Driving Wheels: 5' 9".
T.E.: 19,200 lb.

| | | | |
|---|---|---|---|
| 55260 | 55263 | 55266 | 55268 |
| 55261 | 55264 | 55267 | 55269 |
| 55262 | 55265 | | |

Total 10

## 0-4-0ST      0F

Introduced 1885. Drummond and
McIntosh Caledonian " Pugs."
Weight: 27 tons 7 cwt.
Pressure: 160 lb.
Cyls.: (O) 14" × 20".
Driving Wheels: 3' 8"
T.E.: 12,115 lb.

56029    56031    56039

Total 3

| DO NOT TRESPASS |
| ON THE RAILWAY |

## 0-6-0T 2F

Introduced 1911. McIntosh Caledonian dock shunters, " 498 " class.
Weight: 47 tons 15 cwt.
Pressure: 160 lb.
Cyls.: (O) 17″ × 22″.
Driving Wheels: 4′ 0″.
T.E.: 18,015 lb.

| 56151 | 56159 | 56168 | 56171 |
| 56158 | 56167 | 56169 | 56173 |

Total 8

## 0-6-0T 3F

Introduced 1895. McIntosh Caledonian " 29 " and " 782 " classes (56232–9 originally condensing).
Weight: 47 tons 15 cwt.
Pressure: 160 lb.
Cyls.: 18″ × 26″.
Driving Wheels: 4′ 6″.
T.E.: 21,215 lb.

| 56232 | 56298 | 56325 | 56356 |
| 56239 | 56302 | 56326 | 56360 |
| 56240 | 56305 | 56336 | 56362 |
| 56242 | 56309 | 56337 | 56368 |
| 56246 | 56312 | 56338 | 56370 |
| 56256 | 56313 | 56341 | 56372 |
| 56278 | 56324 | 56347 | 56376 |
| 56282 | | | |

Total 29

## 0-6-0 2F

Introduced 1883. Drummond Caledonian " Standard Goods "; later additions by Lambie and McIntosh.

*Some rebuilt with L.M.S. boiler.

Weight: Loco. $\begin{cases} 41 \text{ tons } 6 \text{ cwt.} \\ 42 \text{ tons } 4 \text{ cwt.*} \end{cases}$

Pressure: 180 lb.
Cyls.: 18″ × 26″.
Driving Wheels: 5′ 0″
T.E.: 21,480 lb.

| 57232 | 57269 | 57331 | 57383 |
| 57233 | 57270 | 57335 | 57384 |
| 57236 | 57271 | 57336 | 57385 |
| 57237 | 57274 | 57338 | 57386 |
| 57238 | 57275 | 57340 | 57389 |
| 57239 | 57278 | 57341 | 57392 |
| 57240 | 57284 | 57345 | 57398 |
| 57242 | 57285 | 57347 | 57404 |
| 57244 | 57287 | 57348 | 57411 |
| 57245 | 57288 | 57349 | 57416 |
| 57246 | 57291 | 57350 | 57417 |
| 57249 | 57292 | 57353 | 57418 |
| 57250 | 57295 | 57355 | 57426 |
| 57251 | 57296 | 57356 | 57429 |
| 57252 | 57299 | 57357 | 57431 |
| 57253 | 57300 | 57359 | 57432 |
| 57254 | 57302 | 57360 | 57434 |
| 57256 | 57303 | 57362 | 57436 |
| 57257 | 57309 | 57363 | 57441 |
| 57258 | 57311 | 57364 | 57445 |
| 57259 | 57314 | 57365 | 57446 |
| 57261 | 57317 | 57366 | 57447 |
| 57262 | 57319 | 57367 | 57451 |
| 57263 | 57321 | 57369 | 57461 |
| 57264 | 57324 | 57370 | 57463 |
| 57265 | 57325 | 57373 | 57470 |
| 57266 | 57326 | 57375 | 57472 |
| 57267 | 57328 | 57377 | 57473 |
| 57268 | 57329 | 57378 | |

Total 115

## 0-6-0 3F

Introduced 1899. McIntosh Caledonian "812" (Nos. 57550–57623) and "652" (remainder) classes.
Weight: Loco. 45 tons 14 cwt.
Pressure: 180 lb.
Cyls.: 18½″ × 26″.
Driving Wheels: 5′ 0″.
T.E.: 22,690 lb.

| | | | |
|---|---|---|---|
| 57550 | 57579 | 57602 | 57623 |
| 57555 | 57580 | 57603 | 57625 |
| 57557 | 57581 | 57604 | 57626 |
| 57559 | 57583 | 57607 | 57627 |
| 57560 | 57585 | 57608 | 57630 |
| 57562 | 57586 | 57611 | 57631 |
| 57563 | 57587 | 57612 | 57632 |
| 57564 | 57590 | 57613 | 57633 |
| 57565 | 57591 | 57614 | 57634 |
| 57566 | 57592 | 57615 | 57635 |
| 57568 | 57593 | 57617 | 57637 |
| 57569 | 57594 | 57618 | 57640 |
| 57570 | 57596 | 57619 | 57642 |
| 57571 | 57597 | 57620 | 57643 |
| 57572 | 57600 | 57621 | 57644 |
| 57576 | 57601 | 57622 | 57645 |
| 57577 | | | |

**Total 65**

## 0-6-0 2F

†Introduced 1917. Johnson Midland 4′ 11″ design of 1875 rebuilt with Belpaire firebox.
§Introduced 1917. Johnson Midland 5′ 3″ design rebuilt with Belpaire firebox.
Weight: Loco. Various—
37 tons 12 cwt. to 40 tons 3 cwt.
Pressure: 160 lb.
Cyls.: 18″ × 26″.
Driving Wheels: $\begin{cases} 4' 11''.† \\ 5' 3''.§ \end{cases}$
T.E.: $\begin{cases} 19,420 \text{ lb.†} \\ 18,185 \text{ lb.§} \end{cases}$

| | | | |
|---|---|---|---|
| 58115† | 58137† | 58174† | 58215§ |
| 58120† | 58138† | 58175† | 58218§ |
| 58122† | 58143† | 58177† | 58221§ |
| 58123† | 58148† | 58181† | 58228§ |
| 58124† | 58160† | 58182† | 58271§ |
| 58128† | 58163† | 58185† | 58283§ |
| 58131† | 58166† | 58186† | 58291§ |
| 58135† | 58169† | 58214§ | 58305§ |

**Total 32**

## 0-6-0 3F

Introduced 1918. Pickersgill Caledonian "294" class (superheated) and "670" classes.
Weight: Loco. 50 tons 13 cwt.
Pressure: 180 lb. Su.
Cyls.: 18½″ × 26″.
Driving Wheels: 5′ 0″.
T.E.: 22,690 lb.
P.V.

| | | | |
|---|---|---|---|
| 57650 | 57661 | 57670 | 57682 |
| 57651 | 57663 | 57671 | 57684 |
| 57652 | 57665 | 57672 | 57686 |
| 57654 | 57666 | 57673 | 57688 |
| 57655 | 57667 | 57674 | 57689 |
| 57658 | 57668 | 57679 | 57690 |
| 57659 | 57669 | 57681 | 57691 |

**Total 28**

# PRESERVED LOCOS IN WORKING ORDER

## 4-4-0 (3-Cyl. Compd.) 4P

Introduced 1902. Johnson Midland design, rebuilt by Deeley in 1914. Withdrawn 1951 for preservation. Restored to 1914 condition and returned to service for special use 1959.
Weight: Loco. 61 tons 14 cwt.
Pressure: 200 lb.
Cyls.: $\begin{cases} \text{L.P. (2) } 21'' \times 26''. \\ \text{H.P. (1) } 19'' \times 26''. \end{cases}$
Driving Wheels: 7′ 0″.
T.E. (of L.P. cyls. at 80% boiler pressure): 21,840 lb.

1000

## 4-2-2

Introduced 1886. Neilson & Co. design for the Caledonian Railway incorporating Drummond details. Withdrawn as L.M.S. No. 14010 in 1935. Restored to Caledonian livery and returned to service for special use 1958.
Weight: Engine and Tender: 75 tons.
Pressure: 150 lb.
Cyls.: 18″ × 26″.
Driving Wheels: 7′ 0″.
T.E.: 12,785 lb.

123

## 4-6-0

Introduced 1894. Jones Highland goods design. Withdrawn 1934 as L.M.S. No. 17916 for preservation. Restored to original condition and returned to service for special use 1959.
Weight: Loco. 56 tons.
Pressure: 175 lb.
Cyls.: 20″ × 26″.
Driving Wheels: 5′ 3″.
T.E.: 24,555 lb.

103

# SERVICE LOCOS.

Details of Diesel Service Locomotives are shown in ABC of British Railways Diesels and the Diesel section of the Combined Volume of ABC of British Railways Locomotives.

## 0-4-0        Diesel

| E.D.1 | E.D.4 | E.D.6 |
|-------|-------|-------|
| E.D.2 | E.D.5 | E.D.7 |
| E.D.3 | | |

## 0-4-0 (3′ 0″ gauge)   Diesel

E.D.10

## 0-4-0 (1′ 6″ gauge)   Diesel

ZM 32

## 0-4-0 ST (1′ 6″ gauge)

Wren

## 0-6-0ST          2F

For details see Nos. 51371-51496.

11304   11305   11324   11368

# CHIEF MECHANICAL ENGINEERS

## BRITISH RAILWAYS (L.M. Region)

H. G. Ivatt ... 1943–1951

## L.M.S.

| | | | | | |
|---|---|---|---|---|---|
| George Hughes ... ... | 1923–1925 | | Sir William Stanier ... | 1932–1944 |
| Sir Henry Fowler ... | 1925–1931 | | Charles E. Fairburn ... | 1944–1945 |
| E. H. J. Lemon | 1931–1932 | | H. G. Ivatt ... ... ... | 1945–1947 |
| (Sir Ernest Lemon) | | | | |

## LOCOMOTIVE SUPERINTENDENTS AND C.M.E.'S—L.M.S. CONSTITUENT COMPANIES

### CALEDONIAN RAILWAY

| | |
|---|---|
| Robert Sinclair | |
| (First loco. engineer)* | 1847–1856 |
| Benjamin Connor ... | 1856–1876 |
| George Brittain ... | 1876–1882 |
| Dugald Drummond ... | 1882–1890 |
| Hugh Smellie ... | 1890 |
| J. Lambie ... ... | 1890–1895 |
| J. F. McIntosh ... | 1895–1914 |
| William Pickersgill | 1914–1923 |

### FURNESS RAILWAY

| | |
|---|---|
| R. Mason ... ... ... | 1890–1897 |
| W. F. Pettigrew ... | 1897–1918 |
| D. J. Rutherford ... | 1918–1923 |

### GLASGOW AND SOUTH WESTERN RAILWAY

| | |
|---|---|
| Patrick Stirling ... | 1853–1866 |
| James Stirling ... | 1866–1878 |
| Hugh Smellie ... | 1878–1890 |
| James Manson ... | 1890–1912 |
| Peter Drummond ... | 1912–1918 |
| R. H. Whitelegg ... | 1918–1923 |

### HIGHLAND RAILWAY

| | |
|---|---|
| William Stroudley | |
| (First loco. engineer) ... | 1866–1869 |
| David Jones ... ... | 1869–1896 |
| Peter Drummond ... | 1896–1911 |
| F. G. Smith... ... | 1912–1915 |
| C. Cumming ... ... | 1915–1923 |

### L. & Y.R.

| | |
|---|---|
| Sir John Hawkshaw (Consultant),* | |
| Hurst and Jenkins successively to 1868 | |
| W. Hurst ... ... | 1868–1876 |
| W. Barton Wright ... | 1876–1886 |
| John A. F. Aspinall ... | 1886–1899 |
| H. A. Hoy ... ... | 1899–1904 |
| George Hughes ... | 1904–1921 |

The L. & Y. amalgamated with L.N.W.R. as from January 1st, 1922.

### L.N.W.R.

| | |
|---|---|
| Francis Trevithick and J. E. McConnell, first loco. engineers, 1846, with Alexander Allan largely responsible for design at Crewe.* | |
| John Ramsbottom... ... | 1857–1871 |
| Francis William Webb ... | 1871–1903 |
| George Whale ... ... | 1903–1909 |
| Charles John Bowen-Cooke ... | 1909–1920 |
| Capt. Hewitt Pearson Montague Beames ... | 1920–1921 |
| George Hughes ... ... | 1922 |

### L.T. & S.R.

| | |
|---|---|
| Thomas Whitelegg ... | 1880–1910 |
| Robert Harben Whitelegg | 1910–1912 |

(L.T. & S.R. absorbed by M.R., control of locos. transferred to Derby as from August, 1912.)

* Exclusive of previous service with constituent company.

# LOCOMOTIVE SUPERINTENDENTS
## AND C.M.E.'S (continued)

### MARYPORT & CARLISLE

| | | |
|---|---|---|
| Hugh Smellie | ... ... | 1870–1878 |
| J. Campbell | ... ... | 1878– |
| William Coulthard | ... * | –1904 |
| J. B. Adamson | ... ... | 1904–1923 |

### MIDLAND RAILWAY

| | | |
|---|---|---|
| Matthew Kirtley (First loco. engineer) | ... | 1844–1873 |
| Samuel Waite Johnson | ... | 1873–1903 |
| Richard Mountford Deeley | | 1903–1909 |
| Henry Fowler | ... ... | 1909–1923 |

### SOMERSET AND DORSET JOINT RAILWAY

Until leased by Mid. and L. & S.W. (as from 1st November, 1875) locomotives were bought from outside builders, principally George England of Hatcham Iron Works, S.E. After the above date, Derby and its various Loco. Supts. and C.M.E.'s have acted for S. & D.J. aided by a resident Loco. Supt. stationed at Highbridge Works.

### NORTH STAFFORDSHIRE RAILWAY

| | | |
|---|---|---|
| L. Clare | ... ... | 1876–1882 |
| L. Longbottom | ... ... | 1882–1902 |
| J. H. Adams | ... ... | 1902–1915 |
| J. A. Hookham | ... ... | 1915–1923 |

W. Angus was Loco. Supt. at Stoke prior to 1876. No earlier records can be traced.

### WIRRAL

| | | |
|---|---|---|
| Eric G. Barker | ... ... | 1892–1902 |
| T. B. Hunter | ... ... | 1903–1923 |

Barker of the Wirral Railway is noteworthy for originating the 4-4-4 tank type in this country (1896).

### NORTH LONDON RAILWAY

(Worked by L. & N.W. by agreement dated December, 1908.)

| | | |
|---|---|---|
| William Adams | ... ... | 1853–1873 |
| J. C. Park | ... ... | 1873–1893 |
| Henry J. Pryce | ... ... | 1893–1908 |

\* Date of actual entry into office not known.

## HISTORIC LOCOMOTIVES PRESERVED IN STORE

| Type | Originating Company | Pre-Grouping No. | L.M.S. No. | Name | Place of Preservation |
|---|---|---|---|---|---|
| 4-2-2 | M.R. | 118 | (673) | — | Derby |
| 2-4-0 | M.R. | 158A | — | — | Derby |
| 4-4-2T | L.T. & S. | 80 | (2148) | Thundersley | Derby |
| 2-2-2 | L.N.W. | (49) | — | Columbine | York Museum |
| 2-2-2 | L.N.W. | 3020 | — | Cornwall | Crewe |
| 2-4-0 | L.N.W. | 790 | (5031) | Hardwicke | Crewe |
| 0-4-0ST | L.N.W. | 1439 | — | — | Crewe |
| †0-4-0T | L.N.W. | — | — | Pet | Crewe |
| 2-4-2T | L. & Y. | 1008 | (10621) | — | Horwich |
| 0-4-0 | F.R. | 3 | — | Coppernob | Horwich |
| 0-4-2 | Liverpool & Manchester | — | — | Lion | Crewe |
| ‡4-4-0 | H.R. | (2) | (14398) | Ben Alder | Boat of Garten |

The unbracketed numbers are the ones at present carried by the locos.
† 18 in. gauge works shunter.
‡ Present number 54398.

# NUMERICAL LIST OF ENGINES

The code given in smaller bold type at the head of each class, e.g. " 4MT ", denotes its British Railways power classification.

The numbers of locomotives in service have been checked in E. & N.E.R. to February 18th, 1961, L.M.R. to January 28th, 1961, and Sc.R. to January 14th, 1961.

---

## 4-6-2   8P6F   Class A4

Introduced 1935. Gresley streamlined design with corridor tender (except those marked †). All fitted with double blastpipe and chimney.
*Inside cylinder reduced to 17".
Weight: Loco.   102 tons 19 cwt.
Tender $\begin{cases} 64 \text{ tons } 19 \text{ cwt.} \\ 60 \text{ tons } 7 \text{ cwt.†} \end{cases}$
Pressure: 250 lb. Su.
Cyls.: $\begin{cases} (3) \ 18\frac{1}{2}'' \times 26''. \\ (2) \ 18\frac{1}{2}'' \times 26'' \ (1) \ 17'' \times 26''.* \end{cases}$
Driving Wheels: 6' 8"
T.E.: $\begin{cases} 35,455 \text{ lb.} \\ 33,616 \text{ lb.*} \end{cases}$
Walschaerts valve gear and derived motion. P.V.

| | |
|---|---|
| 60001† | Sir Ronald Matthews |
| 60002† | Sir Murrough Wilson |
| 60003† | Andrew K. McCosh |
| 60004 | William Whitelaw |
| 60005† | Sir Charles Newton |
| 60006† | Sir Ralph Wedgwood |
| 60007 | Sir Nigel Gresley |
| 60008† | Dwight D. Eisenhower |
| 60009 | Union of South Africa |
| 60010 | Dominion of Canada |
| 60011 | Empire of India |
| 60012* | Commonwealth of Australia |
| 60013 | Dominion of New Zealand |
| 60014 | Silver Link |
| 60015 | Quicksilver |
| 60016† | Silver King |
| 60017 | Silver Fox |
| 60018† | Sparrow Hawk |
| 60019† | Bittern |
| 60020*† | Guillemot |
| 60021 | Wild Swan |
| 60022 | Mallard |
| 60023† | Golden Eagle |
| 60024 | Kingfisher |
| 60025 | Falcon |
| 60026† | Miles Beevor |
| 60027 | Merlin |
| 60028 | Walter K. Whigham |
| 60029 | Woodcock |
| 60030 | Golden Fleece |
| 60031 | Golden Plover |
| 60032 | Gannet |
| 60033 | Seagull |
| 60034 | Lord Faringdon |

Total 34

---

## 4-6-2   7P6F   Class A3

Introduced 1927. Development of Gresley G.N. 180 lb. Pacific (introduced 1922, L.N.E.R. A1, later A10) with 220 lb. pressure (prototype and others rebuilt from A10). Some have G.N.-type tender with coal rails†, remainder L.N.E.R. pattern. All fitted with double blastpipe and chimney.
Weight: Loco.   96 tons 5 cwt.
Tender $\begin{cases} 56 \text{ tons } 6 \text{ cwt.†} \\ 57 \text{ tons } 18 \text{ cwt.} \end{cases}$
Pressure: 220 lb. Su.
Cyls.: (3) 19" × 26".
Driving Wheels: 6' 8".
T.E.: 32,910 lb.
Walschaerts valve gear and derived motion. P.V.

| | |
|---|---|
| 60035 | Windsor Lad |
| 60036 | Colombo |
| 60037 | Hyperion |
| 60038 | Firdaussi |

| | |
|---|---|
| 60039 | Sandwich |
| 60040 | Cameronian |
| 60041 | Salmon Trout |
| 60042 | Singapore |
| 60043 | Brown Jack |
| 60044 | Melton |
| 60045 | Lemberg |
| 60046 | Diamond Jubilee |
| 60047 | Donovan |
| 60048 | Doncaster |
| 60049 | Galtee More |
| 60050 | Persimmon |
| 60051 | Blink Bonny |
| 60052 | Prince Palatine |
| 60053 | Sansovino |
| 60054 | Prince of Wales |
| 60055 | Woolwinder |
| 60056 | Centenary |
| 60057 | Ormonde |
| 60058 | Blair Athol |
| 60059 | Tracery |
| 60060 | The Tetrarch |
| 60061 | Pretty Polly |
| 60062 | Minoru |
| 60063 | Isinglass |
| 60064 | Tagalie |
| 60065 | Knight of Thistle |
| 60066 | Merry Hampton |
| 60067 | Ladas |
| 60068 | Sir Visto |
| 60069 | Sceptre |
| 60070 | Gladiateur |
| 60071 | Tranquil |
| 60072 | Sunstar |
| 60073 | St. Gatien |
| 60074 | Harvester |
| 60075 | St. Frusquin |
| 60076 | Galopin |
| 60077 | The White Knight |
| 60078 | Night Hawk |
| 60079 | Bayardo |
| 60080 | Dick Turpin |
| 60081 | Shotover |
| 60082 | Neil Gow |
| 60083 | Sir Hugo |
| 60084 | Trigo |
| 60085 | Manna |

| | |
|---|---|
| 60086 | Gainsborough |
| 60087 | Blenheim |
| 60088 | Book Law |
| 60089 | Felstead |
| 60090 | Grand Parade |
| 60091 | Captain Cuttle |
| 60092 | Fairway |
| 60093 | Coronach |
| 60094 | Colorado |
| 60095 | Flamingo |
| 60096 | Papyrus |
| 60097 | Humorist |
| 60098 | Spion Kop |
| 60099 | Call Boy |
| 60100 | Spearmint |
| 60101 | Cicero |
| 60102 | Sir Frederick Banbury |
| 60103 | Flying Scotsman |
| 60105 | Victor Wild |
| 60106 | Flying Fox |
| 60107 | Royal Lancer |
| 60108 | Gay Crusader |
| 60109 | Hermit |
| 60110 | Robert the Devil |
| 60111 | Enterprise |
| 60112 | St. Simon |

Total 77

## 4-6-2　8P6F　Class A1

A1/1* Introduced 1945. Thompson rebuild of A10.
A1 Peppercorn development of A1/1 for new construction.
A1† Fitted with roller bearings.
Weight: Loco. { 101 tons.*
　　　　　　　 { 104 tons 2 cwt.
　　　　　　 Tender 60 tons 7 cwt.
Pressure: 250 lb. Su.
Cyls.: (3) 19" × 26".
Driving Wheels: 6' 8".
T.E.: 37,400 lb.
Walschaerts valve gear. P.V.

| | |
|---|---|
| 60113* | Great Northern |
| 60114 | W. P. Allen |
| 60115 | Meg Merrilies |
| 60116 | Hal o' the Wynd |

| | |
|---|---|
| 60117 | Bois Roussel |
| 60118 | Archibald Sturrock |
| 60119 | Patrick Stirling |
| 60120 | Kittiwake |
| 60121 | Silurian |
| 60122 | Curlew |
| 60123 | H. A. Ivatt |
| 60124 | Kenilworth |
| 60125 | Scottish Union |
| 60126 | Sir Vincent Raven |
| 60127 | Wilson Worsdell |
| 60128 | Bongrace |
| 60129 | Guy Mannering |
| 60130 | Kestrel |
| 60131 | Osprey |
| 60132 | Marmion |
| 60133 | Pommern |
| 60134 | Foxhunter |
| 60135 | Madge Wildfire |
| 60136 | Alcazar |
| 60137 | Redgauntlet |
| 60138 | Boswell |
| 60139 | Sea Eagle |
| 60140 | Balmoral |
| 60141 | Abbotsford |
| 60142 | Edward Fletcher |
| 60143 | Sir Walter Scott |
| 60144 | King's Courier |
| 60145 | Saint Mungo |
| 60146 | Peregrine |
| 60147 | North Eastern |
| 60148 | Aboyeur |
| 60149 | Amadis |
| 60150 | Willbrook |
| 60151 | Midlothian |
| 60152 | Holyrood |
| 60153† | Flamboyant |
| 60154† | Bon Accord |
| 60155† | Borderer |
| 60156† | Great Central |
| 60157† | Great Eastern |
| 60158 | Aberdonian |
| 60159 | Bonnie Dundee |
| 60160 | Auld Reekie |
| 60161 | North British |
| 60162 | Saint Johnstoun |

Total 50

## 4-6-2 (A2/1: 7P6F) 8P7F Class A2

**A2/2\*** Introduced 1943. Thompson rebuild of Gresley Class P2 2-8-2 (introduced 1934).

Weight: Loco. 101 tons 10 cwt.
Pressure: 225 lb. Su.
Cyls.: (3) 20″ x 26″.
Driving Wheels: 6′ 2″.
T.E.: 40,320 lb.

**A2/1†** Introduced 1944. Development of Class A2/2, incorporating Class V2 2-6-2 boiler.

Weight: Loco 98 tons.
Pressure: 225 lb. Su.
Cyls.: (3) 19″ x 26″.
Driving Wheels: 6′2″.
T.E.: 36,385 lb.

**A2/3‡** Introduced 1946. Development of Class A2/2 for new construction.

Weight: Loco. 101 tons 10 cwt.
Pressure: 250 lb. Su.
Cyls.: (3) 19″ x 26″.
Driving Wheels: 6′ 2″.
T.E.: 40,430 lb.

**A2§** Introduced 1947. Peppercorn development of Class A2/2 with shorter wheelbase. (No. 60539 built with double blast pipe.)

**A2\*\*** Rebuilt with double blast pipe and multiple valve regulator.

Weight: Loco. 101 tons.
Pressure: 250 lb. Su.
Cyls.: (3) 19″ x 26″.
Driving Wheels: 6′ 2″.
T.E.: 40,430 lb.
Tender weight (all parts): 60 tons 7 cwt.
Walschaerts valve gear. P.V.

| | |
|---|---|
| 60500‡ | Edward Thompson |
| 60502\* | Earl Marischal |
| 60506\* | Wolf of Badenoch |
| 60508† | Duke of Rothesay |
| 60511‡ | Airborne |
| 60512‡ | Steady Aim |
| 60513‡ | Dante |
| 60514‡ | Chamossaire |
| 60515‡ | Sun Stream |
| 60516‡ | Hycilla |
| 60517‡ | Ocean Swell |

| | |
|---|---|
| 60518‡ Tehran | 60802 |
| 60519‡ Honeyway | 60803 |
| 60520‡ Owen Tudor | 60804 |
| 60521‡ Watling Street | 60805 |
| 60522‡ Straight Deal | 60806 |
| 60523‡ Sun Castle | 60807 |
| 60524‡ Herringbone | 60808 |
| 60525§ A. H. Peppercorn | 60809 The Snapper, The East Yorkshire Regiment, The Duke of York's Own |
| 60526**Sugar Palm | |
| 60527§ Sun Chariot | |
| 60528§ Tudor Minstrel | 60810 |
| 60529**Pearl Diver | 60811 |
| 60530§ Sayajirao | 60812 |
| 60531§ Bahram | 60813 |
| 60532**Blue Peter | 60814 |
| 60533**Happy Knight | 60815 |
| 60534§ Irish Elegance | 60816 |
| 60535§ Hornet's Beauty | 60817 |
| 60536§ Trimbush | 60818 |
| 60537§ Bachelor's Button | 60819 |
| 60538**Velocity | 60820 |
| 60539§ Bronzino | 60821 |
| | 60822 |
| **Total** | 60823 |
| **Class A2** 15 **Class A2/2** 3 | 60824 |
| **Class A2/1** 1 **Class A2/3** 15 | 60825 |
| | 60826 |
| | 60827 |
| | 60828 |
| | 60829 |
| | 60830 |
| | 60831 |
| | 60832 |
| | 60833 |
| | 60834 |

## 2-6-2  7P6F  Class V2

Introduced 1936. Gresley design.
*Fitted with double chimney.
Weight: Loco.   93 tons 2 cwt.
Tender 52 tons.
Pressure: 220 lb. Su.
Cyls.: (3) 18½" × 26".
Driving Wheels: 6' 2".
T.E.: 33,730 lb.
Walschaerts valve gear and derived motion. P.V.

| | |
|---|---|
| | 60835 The Green Howard, Alexandra, Princess of Wales's Own Yorkshire Regiment |
| 60800  Green Arrow | |
| 60801 | |
| | 60836 |
| | 60837 |
| | 60838 |
| | 60839 |
| | 60840 |
| | 60841 |
| | 60842 |
| | 60843 |

103

| | | | |
|---|---|---|---|
| 60844 | 60934 | 60942 | 60949 | 60956 |
| 60845 | 60935 | 60943 | 60950 | 60957 |
| 60846 | 60936 | 60944 | 60951 | 60958 |
| 60847 St. Peter's School York | 60937 | 60945 | 60952 | 60959 |
| A.D. 627 | 60938 | 60946 | 60953 | 60960 |
| 60848 | 60939 | 60947 | 60954 | 60961 |
| 60849 | 60940 | 60948 | 60955 | 60962 |
| 60850 | 60941 | | | |
| 60851 | 60963* | | | |

**60964 The Durham Light Infantry**

| | | | |
|---|---|---|---|
| 60852 | 60965 | 60970 | 609/5 | 60980 |
| 60853 | 60966 | 60971 | 60976 | 60981 |
| 60854 | 60967 | 60972 | 60977 | 50982 |
| 60855 | 60968 | 60973 | 60978 | 60983 |
| 60856 | 60969 | 60974 | 60979 | |
| 60857 | | | | |

Total 184

| | |
|---|---|
| 60858 | |
| 60859 | |
| 60860 | Durham School |
| 60861 | |
| 60862 | |
| 60863 | |

## 4-6-0  5MT  Class BI

Introduced 1942. Thompson design.
Weight: Loco. 71 tons 3 cwt.
Tender 52 tons.
Pressure: 225 lb. Su.
Cyls.: (O) 20" x 26".
Driving Wheels: 6' 2".
T.E.: 26,880 lb.
Walschaerts valve gear.  P.V.

| | |
|---|---|
| 60864 | |
| 60865 | |
| 60866 | |
| 60867 | |
| 60868 | |
| 60869 | |
| 60870 | |
| 60871 | |
| 60872 King's Own Yorkshire | 61000 Springbok |
| Light Infantry | 61001 Eland |
| 60873 Coldstreamer | 61002 Impala |

| | | | | |
|---|---|---|---|---|
| 60874 | 60889 | 60904 | 60919 | 61003 Gazelle |
| 60875 | 60890 | 60905 | 60920 | 61004 Oryx |
| 60876 | 60891 | 60906 | 60921 | 61005 Bongo |
| 60877 | 60892 | 60907 | 60922 | 61006 Blackbuck |
| 60878 | 60893 | 60908 | 60923 | 61007 Klipspringer |
| 60879 | 60894 | 60909 | 60924 | 61008 Kudu |
| 60880 | 60895 | 60910 | 60925 | 61009 Hartebeeste |
| 60881* | 60896 | 60911 | 60926 | 61010 Wildebeeste |
| 60882 | 60897 | 60912 | 60927 | 61011 Waterbuck |
| 60883 | 60898 | 60913 | 60928 | 61012 Puku |
| 60884 | 60899 | 60914 | 60929 | 61013 Topi |
| 60885 | 60900 | 60915 | 60930 | 61014 Oribi |
| 60886 | 60901 | 60916 | 60931 | 61015 Duiker |
| 60887 | 60902 | 60917 | 60932 | 61016 Inyala |
| 60888 | 60903 | 60918 | 60933 | 61017 Bushbuck |

| | | | | | | | |
|---|---|---|---|---|---|---|---|
| 61018 | Gnu | | | 61138 | 61151 | 61164 | 61177 |
| 61019 | Nilghal | | | 61139 | 61152 | 61165 | 61178 |
| 61020 | Gemsbok | | | 61140 | 61153 | 61166 | 61179 |
| 61021 | Reitbok | | | 61141 | 61154 | 61167 | 61180 |
| 61022 | Sassaby | | | 61142 | 61155 | 61168 | 61181 |
| 61023 | Hirola | | | 61143 | 61156 | 61169 | 61182 |
| 61024 | Addax | | | 61141 | 61157 | 61170 | 61183 |
| 61025 | Pallah | | | 61145 | 61158 | 61171 | 61184 |
| 61026 | Ourebi | | | 61146 | 61159 | 61172 | 61185 |
| 61027 | Madoqua | | | 61147 | 61160 | 61173 | 61186 |
| 61028 | Umseke | | | 61148 | 61161 | 61174 | 61187 |
| 61029 | Chamois | | | 61149 | 61162 | 61175 | 61188 |
| 61030 | Nyala | | | 6 150 | 61163 | 61176 | |
| 61031 | Reedbuck | | | 61189 | Sir William Gray | | |
| 61032 | Stembok | | | 61190 | | | |
| 61033 | Dibatag | | | 61191 | | | |
| 61034 | Chiru | | | 61192 | | | |
| 61035 | Pronghorn | | | 61193 | | | |
| 61036 | Ralph Assheton | | | 61194 | | | |
| 61037 | Jairou | | | 61195 | | | |
| 61038 | Blacktail | | | 61196 | | | |
| 61039 | Steinbok | | | 61197 | | | |
| 61040 | Roedeer | | | 61198 | | | |
| 61041 | 61066 | 61090 | 61114 | 61199 | | | |
| 61042 | 61067 | 61091 | 61115 | 61200 | | | |
| 61043 | 61068 | 61092 | 61116 | 61201 | | | |
| 61044 | 61069 | 61093 | 61117 | 61202 | | | |
| 61045 | 61070 | 61094 | 61118 | 61203 | | | |
| 61046 | 61071 | 61095 | 61119 | 61204 | | | |
| 61047 | 61072 | 61096 | 61120 | 61205 | | | |
| 61048 | 61073 | 61097 | 61121 | 61206 | | | |
| 61049 | 61074 | 61098 | 61122 | 61207 | | | |
| 61050 | 61075 | 61099 | 61123 | 61208 | | | |
| 61051 | 61076 | 61100 | 61124 | 61209 | | | |
| 61052 | 61077 | 61101 | 61125 | 61210 | | | |
| 61053 | 61078 | 61102 | 61126 | 61211 | | | |
| 61054 | 61079 | 61103 | 61127 | 61212 | | | |
| 61055 | 61080 | 61104 | 61128 | 61213 | | | |
| 61056 | 61081 | 61105 | 61129 | 61214 | | | |
| 61058 | 61082 | 61106 | 61130 | 61215 | William Henton Carver | | |
| 61059 | 61083 | 61107 | 61131 | 61216 | | | |
| 61060 | 61084 | 61108 | 61132 | 61217 | | | |
| 61061 | 61085 | 61109 | 61133 | 61218 | | | |
| 61062 | 61086 | 61110 | 61134 | 61219 | | | |
| 61063 | 61087 | 61111 | 61135 | 61220 | | | |
| 61064 | 61088 | 61112 | 61136 | 61221 | Sir Alexander Erskine-Hill | | |
| 61065 | 61089 | 61113 | 61137 | | | | |

| | |
|---|---|
| 61222 | |
| 61223 | |
| 61224 | |
| 61225 | |
| 61226 | |
| 61227 | |
| 61228 | |
| 61229 | |
| 61230 | |
| 61231 | |
| 61232 | |
| 61233 | |
| 61234 | |
| 61235 | |
| 61236 | |
| 61237 | Geoffrey H. Kitson |
| 61238 | Leslie Runciman |
| 61239 | |
| 61240 | Harry Hinchcliffe |
| 61241 | Viscount Ridley |
| 61242 | Alexander Reith Gray |
| 61243 | Sir Harold Mitchell |
| 61244 | Strang Steel |
| 61245 | Murray of Elibank |
| 61246 | Lord Balfour of Burleigh |
| 61247 | Lord Burghley |
| 61248 | Geoffrey Gibbs |
| 61249 | FitzHerbert Wright |
| 61250 | A. Harold Bibby |
| 61251 | Oliver Bury |

| | | | |
|---|---|---|---|
| 61252 | 61269 | 61286 | 61303 |
| 61253 | 61270 | 61287 | 61304 |
| 61254 | 61271 | 61288 | 61305 |
| 61255 | 61272 | 61289 | 61306 |
| 61256 | 61273 | 61290 | 61307 |
| 61257 | 61274 | 61291 | 61308 |
| 61258 | 61275 | 61292 | 61309 |
| 61259 | 61276 | 61293 | 61310 |
| 61260 | 61277 | 61294 | 61311 |
| 61261 | 61278 | 61295 | 61312 |
| 61262 | 61279 | 61296 | 61313 |
| 61263 | 61280 | 61297 | 61314 |
| 61264 | 61281 | 61298 | 61315 |
| 61265 | 61282 | 61299 | 61316 |
| 61266 | 61283 | 61300 | 61317 |
| 61267 | 61284 | 61301 | 61318 |
| 61268 | 61285 | 61302 | 61319 |

| | | | |
|---|---|---|---|
| 61320 | 61335 | 61350 | 61365 |
| 61321 | 61336 | 61351 | 61366 |
| 61322 | 61337 | 61352 | 61367 |
| 61323 | 61338 | 61353 | 61368 |
| 61324 | 61339 | 61354 | 61369 |
| 61325 | 61340 | 61355 | 61370 |
| 61326 | 61341 | 61356 | 61371 |
| 61327 | 61342 | 61357 | 61372 |
| 61328 | 61343 | 61358 | 61373 |
| 61329 | 61344 | 61359 | 61374 |
| 61330 | 61345 | 61360 | 61375 |
| 61331 | 61346 | 61361 | 61376 |
| 61332 | 61347 | 61362 | 61377 |
| 61333 | 61348 | 61363 | 61373 |
| 61334 | 61349 | 61364 | |

| | | |
|---|---|---|
| 61379 | Mayflower | |

| | | | |
|---|---|---|---|
| 61380 | 61388 | 61396 | 61404 |
| 61381 | 61389 | 61397 | 61405 |
| 61382 | 61390 | 61398 | 61406 |
| 61383 | 61391 | 61399 | 61407 |
| 61384 | 61392 | 61400 | 61408 |
| 61385 | 61393 | 61401 | 61409 |
| 61386 | 61394 | 61402 | |
| 61387 | 61395 | 61403 | |

**Total 409**

## 4-6-0    5MT    Class B16

**B16/1** Introduced 1920. Raven N.E. design with Stephenson valve gear.

**B16/2\*** Introduced 1937. Gresley rebuild of B16/1 with Walschaerts valve gear and derived motion for inside cylinder.

**B16/3†** Introduced 1944. Thompson rebuild of B16/1 with individual sets of Walschaerts valve gear for each cylinder.

Weight: Loco. $\begin{cases} 77 \text{ tons } 14 \text{ cwt.} \\ 79 \text{ tons } 4 \text{ cwt.*} \\ 78 \text{ tons } 19 \text{ cwt.†} \end{cases}$

Tender 46 tons 12 cwt.
Pressure: 180 lb. Su.
Cyls.: (3) 18½" × 26".
Driving Wheels: 5' 8".
T.E.: 30,030 lb.        P.V.

| 61411 | 61425 | 61445 | 61460 |
|-------|-------|--------|--------|
| 61412 | 61429 | 61447 | 61461† |
| 61413 | 61431 | 61448† | 61462 |
| 61414 | 61432 | 61449† | 61453† |
| 61415 | 61434† | 61450 | 61454† |
| 61416 | 61435* | 61451 | 61466 |
| 61417† | 61436 | 61452 | 61467† |
| 61418† | 61437* | 61453† | 61468† |
| 61419 | 61438* | 61454† | 61472† |
| 61420† | 61439† | 61455* | 61473 |
| 61421* | 61443 | 61457* | 61475* |
| 61422 | 61444† | 61459 | 61476† |
| 61423 |  |  |  |

**Total: Class B16/1 25**

**Class B16/3 17 Class B16/2 7**

---

**4-6-0**    4P3F    **Class B12**

B12/3 Introduced 1932. Gresley rebuild of Holden G.E. design of 1911 with large boiler, round-topped firebox and long-travel valves.
Weight: Loco. 69 tons 10 cwt.
         Tender 39 tons 6 cwt.
Pressure: 180 lb. Su.
Cyls.: 20″ × 28″.

Driving Wheels: 6′ 6″.
T.E.: 21,970 lb.
P.V.

61572

                 **Total 1**

---

**2-6-0**    4MT    **Class K2**

K2/2 Introduced 1914. Gresley G.N. design.
*Fitted with side-window cab.
Weight: Loco. 64 tons 8 cwt.
         Tender 43 tons 2 cwt.
Pressure: 180 lb. Su.
Cyls.: (O) 20″ × 26″.
Driving Wheels: 5′ 8″.
T.E.: 23,400 lb.
Walschaerts valve gear. P.V.

61742
61756
61764* Loch Arkaig
61784*
61788* Loch Rannoch

                 **Total 5**

---

## 2-6-0    5P6F    Class K3

**K3/2** Introduced 1924. Development of Gresley G.N. design, built to L.N.E.R. loading gauge.

**K3/3*** Introduced 1929. Differ in details only, such as springs, from K3/2.

‡K3/2 fitted with G.N. tender.

(K3/1 were G.N. locos. (introduced 1920), with G.N. cabs, and K3/4, K3/5 and K3/6 were variations of K3/2 differing in weight and details These locos. have now been modified to K3/2.)

Weight: Loco.    72 tons 12 cwt.

Tender $\begin{cases} 52 \text{ tons.} \\ 43 \text{ tons 2 cwt.‡} \end{cases}$

Pressure: 180 lb. Su.

Cyls.: (3) 18½″ × 26″.

Driving Wheels: 5′ 8″

T.E.: 30,030 lb.

Walschaerts valve gear and derived motion. P.V.

| | | | |
|---|---|---|---|
| 61800 | 61832 | 61864 | 61899 |
| 61801 | 61833 | 61865 | 61901 |
| 61803 | 61834 | 61866 | 61902 |
| 61804 | 61835 | 61867 | 61903 |
| 61805 | 61837 | 61868 | 61904 |
| 61807 | 61839 | 61869 | 61905 |
| 61808 | 61840 | 61870* | 61906 |
| 61809 | 61841‡ | 61871* | 61907 |
| 61810 | 61842 | 61872* | 61908 |
| 61811 | 61843 | 61873* | 61910 |
| 61812‡ | 61844 | 61874* | 61912 |
| 61813 | 61845 | 61875* | 61913 |
| 61814 | 61846 | 61877* | 61914 |
| 61816 | 61847 | 61880* | 61915 |
| 61817 | 61848 | 61883* | 61917 |
| 61818 | 61849 | 61884* | 61918 |
| 61819 | 61850 | 61886* | 61919 |
| 61820 | 61851 | 61887* | 61920 |
| 61821 | 61852 | 61888* | 61921 |
| 61822 | 61853 | 61889* | 61922 |
| 61824 | 61854‡ | 61890 | 61923 |
| 61825 | 61856‡ | 61891 | 61925 |
| 61826 | 61857‡ | 61892 | 61926 |
| 61827 | 61858‡ | 61893 | 61927 |
| 61828 | 61859‡ | 61894 | 61929 |
| 61829 | 61860 | 61895 | 61930 |
| 61830 | 61861 | 61896 | 61932 |
| 61831 | 61862 | 61897 | 61934 |

| | | | |
|---|---|---|---|
| 61935 | 61949 | 61963 | 61976 |
| 61936 | 61950 | 61964 | 61977 |
| 61938 | 61951 | 61965 | 61978 |
| 61939 | 61952 | 61966 | 61979 |
| 61940 | 61953 | 61967 | 61980 |
| 61941 | 61954 | 61968 | 61981 |
| 61942 | 61956 | 61969 | 61982 |
| 61943 | 61957 | 61970 | 61984 |
| 61944 | 61958 | 61971 | 61985 |
| 61945 | 61959 | 61972 | 61986 |
| 61946 | 61960 | 61973 | 61987 |
| 61947 | 61961 | 61974 | 61989 |
| 61948 | 61962 | 61975 | |

### Total

**Class K3/2 149    Class K3/3 14**

## 2-6-0    5P6F    Classes K1 & K4

**K4*** Introduced 1937. Gresley locos. for West Highland line.

Weight: Loco.    68 tons 8 cwt.

Tender 44 tons 4 cwt.

Pressure: 200 lb. Su.

Cyls.: (3) 18½″ × 26″.

Driving Wheels: 5′ 2″.

T.E.: 36,600 lb.

Walschaerts valve gear and derived motion. P.V.

**K1/1†** Introduced 1945. Thompson 2-cyl. loco. Rebuilt from K4.

**K1** Introduced 1949. Peppercorn development of Thompson K1/1 (No. 61997) for new construction, with increased length.

Weight: Loco.    66 tons 17 cwt.

Tender 44 tons 4 cwt.

Pressure: 225 lb. Su.

Cyls.: (O) 20″ × 26″.

Driving Wheels: 5′ 2″.

T.E.: 32,080 lb.

Walschaerts valve gear. P.V.

| | | | |
|---|---|---|---|
| 61993* | Loch Long | | |
| 61994* | The Great Marquess | | |
| 61995* | Cameron of Lochiel | | |
| 61996* | Lord of the Isles | | |
| 61997† | MacCailin Mor | | |
| 61993* | Macleod of Macleod | | |

| | | | |
|---|---|---|---|
| 62001 | 62019 | 62037 | 62054 |
| 62002 | 62020 | 62038 | 62055 |
| 62003 | 62021 | 62039 | 62056 |
| 62004 | 62022 | 62040 | 62057 |
| 62005 | 62023 | 62041 | 62058 |
| 62006 | 62024 | 62042 | 62059 |
| 62007 | 62025 | 62043 | 62060 |
| 62008 | 62026 | 62044 | 62061 |
| 62009 | 62027 | 62045 | 62062 |
| 62010 | 62028 | 62046 | 62063 |
| 62011 | 62029 | 62047 | 62064 |
| 62012 | 62030 | 62048 | 62065 |
| 62013 | 62031 | 62049 | 62066 |
| 62014 | 62032 | 62050 | 62067 |
| 62015 | 62033 | 62051 | 62068 |
| 62016 | 62034 | 62052 | 62069 |
| 62017 | 62035 | 62053 | 62070 |
| 62018 | 62036 | | |

**Total**

Class K1   70        Class K4   5

Class K1/1   1

DO NOT
TRESPASS
ON THE
RAILWAY

## 4-4-0   3P   Class D34

Introduced 1913. Reid N.B. " Glen " class.

Weight: Loco.   57 tons   4 cwt.
Tender   46 tons 13 cwt.

Pressure: 165 lb. Su.

Cyls.: 20″ × 26″.

Driving Wheels: 6′ 0″.

T.E.: 20,260 lb.

P.V.

| 62474 | Glen Croe |
| 62479 | Glen Sheil |
| 62484 | Glen Lyon |
| 62495 | Glen Luss |
| 62496 | Glen Loy |

**Total 5**

## 4-4-0   3P2F   Class D11

D11/2 Introduced 1924. Post-grouping locos. Robinson G.C. " Large Director " development of D10 (introduced 1913). Built to Scottish loading gauge. From 1938 the class has been rebuilt with long-travel valves.

Weight: Loco.   61 tons 3 cwt.
Tender   48 tons 6 cwt.

Pressure: 180 lb. Su.

Cyls.: 20″ × 26″.

Driving Wheels: 6′ 9″.

T.E.: 19,645 lb.

P.V.

| 62671 | Bailie MacWheeble |
| 62672 | Baron of Bradwardine |
| 62674 | Flora MacIvor |
| 62680 | Lucy Ashton |
| 62681 | Captain Craigengelt |
| 62682 | Haystoun of Bucklaw |
| 62685 | Malcolm Graeme |
| 62686 | The Fiery Cross |
| 62687 | Lord James of Douglas |
| 62688 | Ellen Douglas |

| 62689 | Maid of Lorn |
| 62690 | The Lady of the Lake |
| 62691 | Laird of Balmawhapple |
| 62693 | Roderick Dhu |

**Total 14**

## 4-4-0    4P    Class D49

**D49/1\*** Introduced 1927. Gresley design with piston valves. Walschaerts valve gear and derived motion.

**D49/2†** Introduced 1928. Development of D49/1 with Lentz Rotary Cam poppet valves.

(D49/3 comprised locos. 62720–5 as built with Lentz Oscillating Cam poppet valves. From 1938 these locos. were converted to D49/1. 62751–75 have larger valves than the earlier D49/2, and were at first classified D49/4).

[1]Fitted with G.C. tender.
[2]Fitted with N.E. tender.
[3]The remainder have L.N.E.R. tenders.
Weight: Loco.    66 tons.\*†
Tender $\begin{cases} 48 \text{ tons } 6 \text{ cwt.}[1] \\ 44 \text{ tons } 2 \text{ cwt.}[3] \\ 52 \text{ tons.}[3] \end{cases}$

Pressure: 180 lb. Su.
Cyls.: (3) 17″ × 26″.
Driving Wheels: 6′ 8″.
T.E.: 21,555 lb.

| 62711\*[1] | Dumbartonshire |
| 62712\*[1] | Morayshire |
| 62716\*[1] | Kincardineshire |
| 62718\*[1] | Kinross-shire |
| 62729\*[1] | Rutlandshire |
| 62733\*[1] | Northumberland |
| 62734\*[2] | Cumberland |
| 62747†[3] | The Percy |

**Total**
**Class D49/1 7    Class D49/2 1**

## 0-8-0    6F    Class Q6

Introduced 1913. Raven N.E. design.
\*Some locos. are fitted with tender from withdrawn B15 locos.
Weight: Loco.    65 tons 18 cwt.
Tender $\begin{cases} 44 \text{ tons } 2 \text{ cwt.} \\ 44 \text{ tons.}\* \end{cases}$
Pressure: 180 lb. Su.

Cyls.: (O) 20″ × 26″.
Driving Wheels: 4′ 7¼″.
T.E.: 28,800 lb.
P.V.

| 63340 | 63370 | 63401 | 63431 |
|-------|-------|-------|-------|
| 63341 | 63371 | 63402 | 63432 |
| 63342 | 63373 | 63403 | 63433 |
| 63343 | 63374 | 63404 | 63434 |
| 63344 | 63375 | 63405 | 63435 |
| 63345 | 63376 | 63406 | 63436 |
| 63346 | 63377 | 63407 | 63437 |
| 63347 | 63378 | 63408 | 63438 |
| 63348 | 63379 | 63409 | 63439 |
| 63349 | 63380 | 63410 | 63440 |
| 63350 | 63381 | 63411 | 63441 |
| 63351 | 63382 | 63412 | 63442 |
| 63352 | 63383 | 63413 | 63443 |
| 63353 | 63384 | 63414 | 63444 |
| 63354 | 63385 | 63415 | 63445 |
| 63355 | 63386 | 63416 | 63446 |
| 63356 | 63387 | 63417 | 63447 |
| 63357 | 63388 | 63418 | 63448 |
| 63358 | 63389 | 63419 | 63449 |
| 63359 | 63390 | 63420 | 63450 |
| 63360 | 63391 | 63421 | 63451 |
| 63361 | 63392 | 63422 | 63452 |
| 63362 | 63393 | 63423 | 63453 |
| 63363 | 63394 | 63424 | 63454 |
| 63364 | 63395 | 63425 | 63455 |
| 63365 | 63396 | 63426 | 63456 |
| 63366 | 63397 | 63427 | 63457 |
| 63367 | 63398 | 63428 | 63458 |
| 63368 | 63399 | 63429 | 63459 |
| 63369 | 63400 | 63430 |       |

**Total 119**

## 0-8-0   8F   Class Q7

Introduced 1919. Raven N.E. design.
Weight: Loco.   71 tons 12 cwt.
            Tender 44 tons 2 cwt.
Pressure: 180 lb. Su.
Cyls.: (3) 18½″ × 26″.
Driving Wheels: 4′ /½″.
T.E.: 36,965 lb.
P.V.

| 63460 | 63464 | 63468 | 63472 |
|-------|-------|-------|-------|
| 63461 | 63465 | 63469 | 63473 |
| 63462 | 63466 | 63470 | 63474 |
| 63463 | 63467 | 63471 |       |

**Total 15**

## Classes
## 2-8-0   8F (O1)   O1 & O4
##          7F (O4)

**O4/1**[1] Introduced 1911. Robinson
G.C. design with small boiler,
Belpaire firebox, steam and vacuum
brakes and water scoop.

**O4/3**[2] Introduced 1917. R.O.D. locos.
with steam brake only and no scoop.

**O4/2**[3] Introduced 1925. O4/3 with
cabs and boiler mountings reduced.

**O4/6**[4] Introduced 1924. Rebuilt from
O5 retaining higher cab (63914–20
with side windows).

**O4/7**[5] Introduced 1939. Rebuilt with
shortened O2-type boiler, retaining
G.C. smokebox.

**O4/8**[6] Introduced 1944. Rebuilt with
100A (B1) boiler, retaining origina
cylinders.

(O4/4 were rebuilds with O2 boilers,
since rebuilt again; O5 was a G.C.
development of O4 with larger
boiler and Belpaire firebox.)

Weight: Loco. {
73 tons 4 cwt.[1]
73 tons 4 cwt.[2]
73 tons 4 cwt.[3]
74 tons 13 cwt.[4]
73 tons 4 cwt.[5]
73 tons 17 cwt.[6]
72 tons 10 cwt.[7]
}

Tender {
48 tons 6 cwt. (with scoop)
47 tons 6 cwt. (without scoop)
}

Pressure: 180 lb. Su.
Cyls.: (O) 21″ × 26″.
Driving Wheels: 4′ 8″.
T.E.: 31,325 lb.
P.V.

**O1**[1] Introduced 1944. Thompson re-
build with 100A boiler, Walschaerts
valve gear and new cylinders.
Weight: Loco.   73 tons 6 cwt.
            Tender as O4.
Pressure: 225 lb. Su.
Cyls.: (O) 20″ × 26″.
Driving Wheels: 4′ 8″.
T.E.: 35,520 lb.
Walschaerts valve gear.   P.V.

| | | | | | | | |
|---|---|---|---|---|---|---|---|
| 63570[8] | 63624[6] | 63686[2] | 63743[1] | 63800[6] | 63836[6] | 63863[7] | 63890[7] |
| 63571[7] | 63626[1] | 63687[7] | 63744[2] | 63801[6] | 63837[6] | 63864[6] | 63891[5] |
| 63573[6] | 63628[6] | 63688[6] | 63746[7] | 63802[6] | 63838[7] | 63865[7] | 63893[6] |
| 63574[1] | 63630[7] | 63689[7] | 63747[8] | 63803[7] | 63840[6] | 63867[7] | 63895[6] |
| 63575[6] | 63631[6] | 63690[3] | 63748[6] | 63805[6] | 63841[6] | 63868[7] | 63897[6] |
| 63576[1] | 63632[1] | 63691[6] | 63750[6] | 63806[7] | 63842[2] | 63869[7] | 63898[6] |
| 63577[1] | 63633[6] | 63692[1] | 63752[7] | 63807[6] | 63843[5] | 63870[2] | 63899[6] |
| 63578[7] | 63634[5] | 63693[1] | 63754[6] | 63808[7] | 63845[2] | 63872[7] | 63900[2] |
| 63579[1] | 63635[1] | 63695[2] | 63755[7] | 63813[2] | 63846[2] | 63873[7] | 63901[7] |
| 63584[1] | 63636[6] | 63697[6] | 63757[1] | 63816[6] | 63848[5] | 63874[7] | 63902[4] |
| 63585[1] | 63637[2] | 63698[1] | 63759[5] | 63817[7] | 63850[6] | 63877[6] | 63904[4] |
| 63586[1] | 63639[6] | 63701[2] | 63759[2] | 63818[6] | 63852[6] | 63878[6] | 63906[4] |
| 63587[1] | 63641[6] | 63702[2] | 63760[7] | 63819[6] | 63853[6] | 63879[7] | 63907[4] |
| 63588[6] | 63644[6] | 63703[6] | 63762[1] | 63821[2] | 63854[7] | 63880[5] | 63908[4] |
| 63589[7] | 63645[6] | 63704[6] | 63763[6] | 63822[6] | 63856[7] | 63881[6] | 63911[4] |
| 63590[7] | 63646[7] | 63705[6] | 63764[2] | 63823[6] | 63857[6] | 63882[6] | 63912[4] |
| 63591[7] | 63647[6] | 63706[6] | 63765[6] | 63824[6] | 63858[5] | 63883[2] | 63913[4] |
| 63592[7] | 63648[3] | 63707[1] | 63766[2] | 63827[6] | 63859[2] | 63884[6] | 63914[6] |
| 63593[1] | 63649[6] | 63708[5] | 63767[2] | 63828[6] | 63860[5] | 63885[6] | 63915[6] |
| 63594[7] | 63650[7] | 63709[6] | 63768[7] | 63829[6] | 63861[6] | 63886[7] | 63917[4] |
| 63595[6] | 63651[6] | 63711[7] | 63770[5] | 63832[6] | 63862[6] | 63887[7] | 63920[4] |
| 63596[7] | 63652[7] | 63712[6] | 63771[2] | 63833[2] | | | |
| 63597[1] | 63653[6] | 63713[2] | 63772[5] | | | | |
| 63598[1] | 63655[5] | 63715[6] | 63773[7] | | | | |
| 63599[1] | 63656[2] | 63716[6] | 63774[2] | | | | |
| 63600[8] | 63657[7] | 63718[6] | 63775[5] | | | | |
| 63601[1] | 63658[1] | 63719[1] | 63776[6] | | | | |
| 63602[1] | 63659[2] | 63720[6] | 63777[7] | | | | |
| 63603[5] | 63662[5] | 63721[6] | 63779[2] | | | | |
| 63604[6] | 63662[6] | 63722[1] | 63780[7] | | | | |
| 63605[1] | 63663[6] | 63724[2] | 63781[6] | | | | |
| 63606[6] | 63664[6] | 63725[7] | 63782[2] | | | | |
| 63607[6] | 63665[2] | 63726[6] | 63783[2] | | | | |
| 63608[1] | 63666[2] | 63727[1] | 63784[7] | | | | |
| 63609[1] | 63670[7] | 63728[6] | 63785[6] | | | | |
| 63610[7] | 63671[1] | 63730[6] | 63786[7] | | | | |
| 63611[8] | 63672[6] | 63731[6] | 63787[2] | | | | |
| 63612[6] | 63674[6] | 63732[6] | 63788[6] | | | | |
| 63613[6] | 63675[6] | 63734[6] | 63789[7] | | | | |
| 63615[6] | 63676[7] | 63735[2] | 63791[6] | | | | |
| 63616[6] | 63677[1] | 63736[1] | 63792[2] | | | | |
| 63617[1] | 63678[6] | 63737[2] | 63793[6] | | | | |
| 63618[1] | 63679[6] | 63738[6] | 63794[6] | | | | |
| 63619[7] | 63681[2] | 63739[6] | 63795[7] | | | | |
| 63621[1] | 63683[6] | 63740[7] | 63796[7] | | | | |
| 63622[1] | 63684[1] | 63741[6] | 63798[2] | | | | |
| 63623[1] | 63685[2] | 63742[6] | 63799[1] | | | | |

Total

| | | | |
|---|---|---|---|
| Class O1 | 58 | Class O4/6 | 10 |
| Class O4/1 | 42 | Class O4/7 | 23 |
| Class O4/2 | 2 | Class O4/8 | 100 |
| Class O4/3 | 38 | | | |

**2-8-0**  8F  **Class O2**

O2/1* Introduced 1921. Development of experimental Gresley G.N. 3-cyl. loco. (L.N.E.R. 3921). Subsequently rebuilt with side-window cab, and reduced boiler mountings.

O2/2† Introduced 1924. Development of O2/1 with detail differences.

O2/3 Introduced 1932. Development of O2/2 with side-window cab and reduced boiler mountings.

O2/4‡ Introduced 1943. Rebuilt with 100A (B1 type) boiler and smokebox extended backwards (63924 retaining G.N. tender).

Weight: Loco. { 75 tons 16 cwt.*†
78 tons 13 cwt.
74 tons 2 cwt.‡

Tender { 43 tons 2 cwt.
(63922–46)
52 tons (63947–87).

Pressure: 180 lb. Su.
Cyls.: (3) 18½″ × 26″.
Driving Wheels: 4′ 8″.
T.E.: 36,740 lb.
Walschaerts valve gear and derived
motion. P.V.

**Total**

Class O2/1  7    Class O2/3  28
Class O2/2  10   Class O2/4  17

| | | | |
|---|---|---|---|
| 63922* | 63938‡ | 63956 | 63973 |
| 63923* | 63939† | 63957 | 63974 |
| 63924‡ | 63940† | 63958 | 63975 |
| 63925‡ | 63941† | 63960 | 63976 |
| 63926* | 63942† | 63961‡ | 63977 |
| 63927* | 63943† | 63962‡ | 63978 |
| 63928* | 63944† | 63963 | 63979 |
| 63929* | 63945‡ | 63964 | 63980 |
| 63930‡ | 63946† | 63965‡ | 63981 |
| 63931* | 63947 | 63966‡ | 63982‡ |
| 63932‡ | 63948‡ | 63967 | 63983‡ |
| 63933‡ | 63949‡ | 63968 | 63984 |
| 63934† | 63951 | 63969 | 63985 |
| 63935‡ | 63952 | 63971 | 63986 |
| 63936† | 63954 | 63972 | 63987 |
| 63937† | 63955‡ | | |

**0-6-0    2P3F    Class J6**

Introduced 1911. Gresley G.N. design.
Weight: Loco.  50 tons 10 cwt.
Tender 43 tons 2 cwt.
Pressure: 170 lb. Su.
Cyls.: 19″ × 26″.
Driving Wheels: 5′ 2″.
T.E.: 21,875 lb.
P.V.

| | | | |
|---|---|---|---|
| 64170 | 64191 | 64226 | 64260 |
| 64171 | 64203 | 64233 | 64265 |
| 64174 | 64208 | 64236 | 64277 |
| 64177 | 64219 | 64245 | 64278 |
| 64185 | 64223 | 64253 | |

**Total 19**

| HISTORIC LOCOMOTIVES PRESERVED IN STORE | | | | | |
|---|---|---|---|---|---|
| Type | Originating Company | Pre-Grouping No. | L.N.E.R. No. | Name | Place of Preservation |
| 4-2-2 | G.N.R. | 1 | — | — | York Museum |
| 4-4-2 | G.N.R. | 990 | (3990) | Henry Oakley | York Museum |
| 4-4-2 | G.N.R. | 251 | (3251) | — | York Museum |
| 2-2-4T | N.E.R. | 66 | 66 | Aerolite | York Museum |
| 2-4-0 | N.E.R. | 910 | 910 | — | York Museum |
| 2-4-0 | N.E.R. | 1463 | 1463 | — | York Museum |
| 4-4-0 | N.E.R. | 1621 | 1621 | — | York Museum |

The unbracketed numbers are the ones at present carried by the locos.

## 0-6-0    2P3F    Class J11

Introduced 1901. Robinson G.C. design. Parts 1 and 4 have 3,250-gallon tenders; Parts 2 and 5, 4,000-gallon. Parts 1 and 2 have high boiler mountings; Parts 4 and 5 low. All of Parts 4 and 5 are superheated, and some of Parts 1 and 2. There are frequent changes between parts.

J11/3* Introduced 1942. Rebuilt with long-travel piston valves and boiler higher pitched.

Weight: Loco. $\begin{cases} 51 \text{ tons } 19 \text{ cwt. (Sat.)} \\ 52 \text{ tons } 2 \text{ cwt. (Su.)} \\ 53 \text{ tons } 6 \text{ cwt.*} \end{cases}$

Tender $\begin{cases} 44 \text{ tons } 3 \text{ cwt. (3,250 gall.)} \\ 48 \text{ tons } 6 \text{ cwt. (4,000 gall.)} \end{cases}$

Pressure: 180 lb. SS.
Cyls.: $18\frac{1}{2}'' \times 26''$.
Driving Wheels: 5' 2".
T.E.: 21,960 lb.

| | | | |
|---|---|---|---|
| 64284* | 64333* | 64377 | 64420* |
| 64292 | 64337 | 64379* | 64423 |
| 64305 | 64341 | 64384 | 64427* |
| 64308 | 64346* | 64385 | 64435 |
| 64310 | 64352* | 64386* | 64437 |
| 64313 | 64354* | 64393* | 64439* |
| 64314* | 64355 | 64394* | 64442* |
| 64316* | 64359* | 64395* | 64443 |
| 64317* | 64362* | 64402* | 64444 |
| 64318* | 64363 | 64406* | 64445 |
| 64324* | 64364* | 64417* | 64446 |
| 64329 | 64373* | 64418* | 64447 |
| 64332* | 64375* | 64419 | 64450* |

### Total
Class J11 3   30
Class J11 (other parts) 22

## 0-6-0    3F    Class J35

J35/5* Introduced 1906. Reid N.B. design with piston valves.

J35/4 Introduced 1908. Slide valves. (Parts 1, 2 and 3 were variations of Parts 4 and 5 before superheating.)

Weight: Loco. $\begin{cases} 51 \text{ tons.*} \\ 50 \text{ tons } 15 \text{ cwt.} \end{cases}$

Tender $\begin{cases} 38 \text{ tons } 1 \text{ cwt.*} \\ 37 \text{ tons } 15 \text{ cwt.} \end{cases}$

Pressure: 180 lb. Su.
Cyls.: $18\frac{1}{2}'' \times 26''$.
Driving Wheels: 5' 0".
T.E.: 22,080 lb.

| | | | |
|---|---|---|---|
| 64461* | 64480 | 64505 | 64524 |
| 64470* | 64482 | 64507 | 64525 |
| 64471* | 64488 | 64510 | 64527 |
| 64472* | 64489 | 64514 | 64531 |
| 64474* | 64491 | 64515 | 64532 |
| 64476* | 64494 | 64518 | 64533 |
| 64477* | 64497 | 64519 | 64534 |
| 64478 | 64499 | 64523 | 64535 |
| 64479 | 64500 | | |

### Total
Class J35/4 27     Class J35/5 7

## 0-6-0    5F    Class J37

Introduced 1914. Reid N.B. design. Superheated development of J35.
Weight: Loco. 54 tons 14 cwt.
         Tender 40 tons 19 cwt.
Pressure: 180 lb. Su.
Cyls.: $19\frac{1}{2}'' \times 26''$.
Driving Wheels: 5' 0".
T.E.: 25,210 lb.
P.V.

| | | | |
|---|---|---|---|
| 64537 | 64551 | 64564 | 64578 |
| 64539 | 64552 | 64565 | 64579 |
| 64540 | 64553 | 64566 | 64580 |
| 64541 | 64554 | 64568 | 64581 |
| 64542 | 64555 | 64569 | 64582 |
| 64543 | 64556 | 64570 | 64583 |
| 64544 | 64557 | 64571 | 64585 |
| 64545 | 64558 | 64572 | 64586 |
| 64546 | 64559 | 64573 | 64587 |
| 64547 | 64560 | 64574 | 64588 |
| 64548 | 64561 | 64575 | 64589 |
| 64549 | 64562 | 64576 | 64590 |
| 64550 | 64563 | 64577 | 64591 |

| 64592 | 64604 | 64616 | 64628 |
|-------|-------|-------|-------|
| 64593 | 64605 | 64617 | 64629 |
| 64594 | 64606 | 64618 | 64630 |
| 64595 | 64607 | 64619 | 64631 |
| 64596 | 64608 | 64620 | 64632 |
| 64597 | 64609 | 64621 | 64633 |
| 64598 | 64610 | 64622 | 64634 |
| 64599 | 64611 | 64623 | 64635 |
| 64600 | 64612 | 64624 | 64636 |
| 64601 | 64613 | 64625 | 64637 |
| 64602 | 64614 | 64626 | 64638 |
| 64603 | 64615 | 64627 | 64639 |

**Total 100**

Weight: Loco. 54 tons 15 cwt.
Tender 38 tons 5 cwt.
Pressure: 180 lb. Su.
Cyls.: 20″ × 28″.
Driving Wheels: 4′ 11″.
T.E.: 29,045 lb.
P.V.

| 64676 | 64690 | 64696 | 64698 |
|-------|-------|-------|-------|
| 64677 | 64691 | 64697 | 64699 |
| 64687 | 64692 | | |

**Total 10**

## 0-6-0  3P5F  Class J19

Introduced 1916. Hill G.E. design
rebuilt with round-topped firebox
from 1934.
*Rebuilt with 19″ cyls. and 180 lb.
pressure.
Weight: Loco. 50 tons 7 cwt.
Tender 38 tons 5 cwt.
Pressure: { 170 lb. Su.
{ 180 lb. Su.*
Cyls.: { 20″ × 26″.
{ 19″ × 26″.*
Driving Wheels: 4′ 11″.
T.E.: { 27,430 lb.
{ 26,215 lb.*

| 64643 | 64657 | 64667 | 64671* |
|-------|-------|-------|--------|
| 64646 | 64664* | 64669 | 64673 |
| 64655 | | | |

**Total 9**

## 0-6-0  5F  Class J20

J20/1 Introduced 1943. Hill G.E.
design with Belpaire firebox (introduced 1920) rebuilt with B12/1-type
boiler with round-topped firebox.

## 0-6-0  4P5F  Class J39

Introduced 1926. Gresley design.
J39/1 Standard 3,500-gallon tender.
J39/2* Standard 4,200-gallon tender.
J39/3† Various N.E. tenders (3,940-
gallon on 64843-5 4,125-gallon on
64855-9).
Weight: Loco. 57 tons 17 cwt.
Tender { 44 tons 4 cwt.
{ 52 tons 13 cwt.*
and others.
Pressure: 180 lb. Su.
Cyls.: 20″ × 26″.
Driving Wheels: 5′ 2″.
T.E.: 25,665 lb.
P.V.

| 64700 | 64720 | 64746 | 64792* |
|-------|-------|-------|--------|
| 64701 | 64723 | 64747 | 64794* |
| 64703 | 64725 | 64748 | 64795* |
| 64704 | 64727 | 64749 | 64796 |
| 64705 | 64729 | 64754 | 64798 |
| 64706 | 64730 | 64756 | 64801 |
| 64707 | 64732 | 64757 | 64804 |
| 64709 | 64733 | 64758 | 64806 |
| 64710 | 64736 | 64760 | 64808 |
| 64711 | 64739 | 64772 | 64809 |
| 64713 | 64740 | 64779 | 64810 |
| 64716 | 64742 | 64786* | 64811 |
| 64718 | 64744 | 64790* | 64812 |
| 64719 | 64745 | 64791* | 64813 |

115

| | | | |
|---|---|---|---|
| 64814 | 64854 | 64895* | 64931* |
| 64815 | 64855† | 64897* | 64932* |
| 64816 | 64856† | 64899* | 64933 |
| 64817 | 64857† | 64901* | 64934 |
| 64818 | 64858† | 64903* | 64935 |
| 64819 | 64859† | 64904* | 64936 |
| 64820* | 64860 | 64906* | 64938 |
| 64821* | 64861 | 64907* | 64939 |
| 64822* | 64862 | 64908* | 64940 |
| 64825 | 64863 | 64909* | 64941 |
| 64831 | 64864 | 64910* | 64942 |
| 64833 | 64865 | 64911* | 64943 |
| 64835 | 64866 | 64914* | 64944 |
| 64836 | 64867 | 64915* | 64945* |
| 64837 | 64868 | 64916* | 64946* |
| 64839* | 64869 | 64917* | 64947* |
| 64840* | 64870 | 64918* | 64949* |
| 64842* | 64871 | 64919* | 64955* |
| 64843† | 64872* | 64920* | 64963* |
| 64844† | 64874* | 64921* | 64964* |
| 64845† | 64875* | 64922* | 64969* |
| 64846 | 64877* | 64923* | 64970* |
| 64847 | 64879* | 64924* | 64971† |
| 64848 | 64880* | 64925* | 64975* |
| 64849 | 64882* | 64926 | 64978† |
| 64850 | 64884* | 64927* | 64979† |
| 64851 | 64886* | 64928* | 64982† |
| 64852 | 64888* | 64929* | 64986* |
| 64853 | 64892* | 64930* | 64987† |

Total

Class J39/1 95  Class J39/3 15
Class J39/2 63

## 0-6-0     2F     Class J21

Introduced 1886. T. W. Worsdell N.E. design. Majority built as 2-cyl. compounds and later rebuilt as simple locos., subsequently rebuilt with superheater and piston valves, superheater later removed.

Weight : Loco. 42 tons 9 cwt.
          Tender 36 tons 19 cwt.

Pressure: 160 lb. SS.
Cyls.: 19″ × 24″.
Driving Wheels. 5′ 1¼″.
T.E.: 17,240 lb.

65033     65099

Total 2

## 0-6-0     2F     Class J10

J10/4* Introduced 1896. Pollitt development of J10/2 with larger bearings and large tender.

J10/6 Introduced 1901. Robinson locos. with larger bearings and small tender.

Weight: Loco.    41 tons 6 cwt.
          Tender { 37 tons 6 cwt.
                  { 43 tons.*

Pressure: 160 lb.
Cyls.: 18″ × 26″.
Driving Wheels: 5′ 1″.
T.E.: 18,780 lb.

65157*    65198

Total

Class J10/4 1    Class J10/6 1

## 0-6-0     2F     Class J36

Introduced 1888. Holmes N.B. design.
Weight: Loco.  41 tons 19 cwt.
          Tender 33 tons 9 cwt.
Pressure: 165 lb.
Cyls.: 18½″ × 26″.
Driving Wheels: 5′ 0″.
T.E.: 19,690 lb.

| | |
|---|---|
| 65210 | |
| 65211 | |
| 65214 | |
| 65216 | Byng |
| 65217 | French |
| 65218 | |

| | | | |
|---|---|---|---|
| 65222 Somme | | | |
| 65224 Mons | | | |
| 65227 | | | |
| 65228 | | | |
| 65230 | | | |
| 65232 | | | |
| 65234 | | | |
| 65235 Gough | | | |
| 65237 | | | |
| 65241 | | | |
| 65243 Maude | | | |
| 65246 | | | |
| 65251 | | | |
| 65253 Joffre | | | |
| 65257 | 65260 | 65265 | 65267 |
| 65258 | 65261 | 65266 | |
| 65268 Allenby | | | |
| 65273 | 65282 | 65295 | 65305 |
| 65275 | 65285 | 65296 | 65306 |
| 65276 | 65287 | 65297 | 65307 |
| 65277 | 65288 | 65300 | 65309 |
| 65280 | 65290 | 65303 | 65310 |
| 65281 | 65293 | 65304 | |
| 65311 Haig | | | |
| 65312 | 65320 | 65330 | 65339 |
| 65313 | 65321 | 65331 | 65341 |
| 65315 | 65323 | 65334 | 65344 |
| 65316 | 65325 | 65335 | 65345 |
| 65318 | 65327 | 65338 | 65346 |
| 65319 | 65329 | | |

Total 74

| | | | |
|---|---|---|---|
| 65361 | 65450 | 65460 | 65469 |
| 65389 | 65453 | 65462 | 65476 |
| 65420 | 65457 | 65464 | 65478 |
| 65445 | 65458 | 65465 | |

Total 15

## 0-6-0    2P4F    Class J17

Introduced 1901. J. Holden G.E.
    design. Many rebuilt from round-top
    firebox J16, introduced 1900.
*Fitted with small tender.
Weight: Loco.    45 tons 8 cwt.
    Tender $\begin{cases} 38 \text{ tons } 5 \text{ cwt.} \\ 30 \text{ tons } 12 \text{ cwt.*} \end{cases}$
Pressure: 180 lb. Su.
Cyls.: 19″ × 26″.
Driving Wheels: 4′ 11″.
T.E.: 24,340 lb.

| | | | |
|---|---|---|---|
| 65507* | 65532 | 65567 | 65582 |
| 65513* | 65541 | 65576 | 65583 |
| 65520 | 65554 | 65577 | 65586 |
| 65521 | 65556 | 65578 | 65588 |
| 65528* | 65560 | 65581 | |

Total 19

## 0-6-0    3F    Class J25

Introduced 1898. W. Worsdell N.E.
    design.
*Original design, saturated, with slide
    valves.
†Rebuilt with superheater and piston
    valves.
Weight: Loco. $\begin{cases} 39 \text{ tons } 11 \text{ cwt.*} \\ 41 \text{ tons } 14 \text{ cwt.†} \end{cases}$
    Tender 36 tons 19 cwt.
Pressure: 160 lb. SS.
Cyls.: 18½″ × 26″.
Driving Wheels: 4′ 7¼″.
T.E.: 21,905 lb.

## 0-6-0    1P2F    Class J15

Introduced 1883. Worsdell G.E. design,
    modified by J. Holden.
Weight: Loco.    37 tons 2 cwt.
    Tender 30 tons 13 cwt.
Pressure: 160 lb.
Cyls.: 17½″ × 24″.
Driving Wheels: 4′ 11″.
T.E.: 16,940 lb.

| 65645† | 65691* | 65695* | 65726* |
|--------|--------|--------|--------|
| 65663* | 65693* | 65720* | 65728* |
| 65670* |        |        |        |

Total 9

## 0-6-0    5F    Class J26

Introduced 1904. W. Worsdell N.E. design.
Weight: Loco.    46 tons 16 cwt.
Tender 36 tons 19 cwt.
Pressure: 180 lb.
Cyls.: 18½″ × 26″.
Driving Wheels: 4′ 7½″.
T.E.: 24,640 lb.

| 65731 | 65747 | 65760 | 65773 |
|-------|-------|-------|-------|
| 65735 | 65751 | 65761 | 65774 |
| 65736 | 65753 | 65763 | 65776 |
| 65741 | 65755 | 65768 | 65778 |
| 65743 | 65756 | 65769 | 65779 |
| 65745 | 65757 | 65772 |       |

Total 23

## 0-6-0    5F    Class J27

Introduced 1906. W. Worsdell N.E. design developed from J26.
*Introduced 1921. Raven locos. Superheated, with piston valves.
†Introduced 1943. Piston valves, but superheater removed.
Weight: Loco. { 47 tons Sat.
{ 49 tons 10 cwt. Su.
Tender 36 tons 19 cwt.
Pressure: 180 lb. SS.
Cyls.: 18½″ × 26″.
Driving Wheels: 4′ 7½″.
T.E.: 24,640 lb.

| 65782 | 65813 | 65844  | 65871* |
|-------|-------|--------|--------|
| 65786 | 65814 | 65845  | 65872† |
| 65787 | 65815 | 65846  | 65873† |
| 65788 | 65817 | 65849  | 65874† |
| 65789 | 65818 | 65850  | 65875† |
| 65790 | 65819 | 65851  | 65876† |
| 65791 | 65820 | 65852  | 65877† |
| 65792 | 65821 | 65853  | 65878† |
| 65794 | 65822 | 65854  | 65879† |
| 65795 | 65823 | 65855  | 65880* |
| 65796 | 65825 | 65857  | 65881* |
| 65797 | 65828 | 65858  | 65882† |
| 65799 | 65830 | 65859  | 65883† |
| 65800 | 65831 | 65860† | 65884† |
| 65801 | 65832 | 65861† | 65885† |
| 65802 | 65833 | 65862† | 65887* |
| 65804 | 65834 | 65863† | 65888† |
| 65805 | 65835 | 65864† | 65889† |
| 65807 | 65837 | 65865† | 65890* |
| 65808 | 65838 | 65867† | 65891† |
| 65809 | 65839 | 65868† | 65892† |
| 65810 | 65841 | 65869† | 65893* |
| 65811 | 65842 | 65870† | 65894* |
| 65812 |       |        |        |

Total 93

## 0-6-0    6F    Class J38

Introduced 1926. Gresley design. Predecessor of J39, with 4′ 8″ wheels, boiler 6″ longer than J39 and smokebox 6″ shorter.
*Rebuilt with J39 boiler.
Weight: Loco.    58 tons 19 cwt.
Tender 44 tons 4 cwt.
Pressure: 180 lb. Su.
Cyls.: 20″ × 26″.
Driving Wheels: 4′ 8″.
T.E.: 28,415 lb.
P.V.

| 65900 | 65905  | 65910 | 65915  |
|-------|--------|-------|--------|
| 65901 | 65906* | 65911 | 65916  |
| 65902 | 65907  | 65912 | 65917* |
| 65903* | 65908* | 65913 | 65918* |
| 65904 | 65909  | 65914 | 65919  |

| | | | |
|---|---|---|---|
| 65920 | 65924 | 65928 | 65932 |
| 65921 | 65925 | 65929 | 65933 |
| 65922 | 65926* | 65930 | 65934 |
| 65923 | 65927* | 65931 | |

Total 35

| | | | |
|---|---|---|---|
| 67629 | 67645* | 67661* | 67678* |
| 67630 | 67646* | 67662* | 67679* |
| 67631 | 67647* | 67663* | 67680 |
| 67632* | 67648* | 67664 | 67681* |
| 67633* | 67649 | 67665 | 67682* |
| 67634* | 67650* | 67666 | 67683* |
| 67635* | 67651* | 67667* | 67684* |
| 67636* | 67652* | 67668* | 67685* |
| 67637 | 67653* | 67669* | 67686* |
| 67638* | 67654* | 67670* | 67687* |
| 67639 | 67655 | 67672* | 67688* |
| 67640* | 67656* | 67673 | 67689* |
| 67641 | 67657* | 67674* | 67690* |
| 67642* | 67658* | 67675* | 67691* |
| 67643* | 67659 | 67676* | |
| 67644* | 67660* | 67677* | |

Total

Class V1 21    Class V3 69

## 4-4-2T    2P    Class C16

Introduced 1915. Reid N.B. design, superheated development of C15.
Weight: 72 tons 10 cwt.
Pressure: 165 lb. Su.
Cyls.: 19″ × 26″.
Driving Wheels: 5′ 9″.
T.E.: 19,080 lb.
P.V.

67485    67489    67494

Total 3

## Classes
## 2-6-2T    V1 (3MT)    V1 & V3
##            V3 (4MT)

V1 Introduced 1930. Gresley design.
V3* Introduced 1939. Development of V1 with higher pressure (locos. numbered below 67682 rebuilt from V1).
Weight: {84 tons.
        {86 tons 16 cwt.*
Pressure: {180 lb. Su.
          {200 lb. Su.*
Cyls.: (3) 16″ × 26″.
Driving Wheels: 5′ 8″.
T.E.: {22,465 lb.
      {24,960 lb.*
Walschaerts valve gear and derived motion. P.V.

| | | | |
|---|---|---|---|
| 67600* | 67607* | 67614* | 67621* |
| 67601 | 67608 | 67615* | 67622 |
| 67602 | 67609* | 67616 | 67623* |
| 67603 | 67610 | 67617* | 67625* |
| 67604* | 67611* | 67618* | 67626* |
| 67605* | 67612* | 67619* | 67627* |
| 67606* | 67613* | 67620* | 67628* |

## 2-6-4T    4MT    Class L1

Introduced 1945. Thompson design.
*Introduced 1954. Cylinder diameter reduced.
Weight: 89 tons 9 cwt.
Pressure: 225 lb.
Cyls.: {(O) 20″  × 26″.
       {(O) 18¾″ × 26″.*
Driving Wheels: 5′ 2″.
T.E.: {32,080 lb.
      {28,180 lb.*
Walschaerts valve gear. P.V.

| | | | |
|---|---|---|---|
| 67703 | 67717 | 67724 | 67733 |
| 67707 | 67718 | 67727 | 67734 |
| 67710 | 67719 | 67728 | 67735 |
| 67712 | 67720 | 67729 | 67737 |
| 67713 | 67721 | 67730 | 67738 |
| 67715 | 67722 | 67731 | 67739 |
| 67716 | 67723 | 67732 | 67740 |

119

| | | | |
|---|---|---|---|
| 67741 | 67756 | 67771* | 67786 |
| 67742 | 67757 | 67772* | 67787 |
| 67743 | 67758 | 67773 | 67788 |
| 67744 | 67759 | 67774 | 67789 |
| 67745 | 67760 | 67775 | 67791 |
| 67746 | 67761 | 67776* | 67792 |
| 67747 | 67762 | 67777 | 67793 |
| 67748 | 67763 | 67778 | 67794 |
| 67749 | 67764 | 67779* | 67795 |
| 67750 | 67765 | 67780 | 67796 |
| 67751 | 67766 | 67781 | 67797 |
| 67752 | 67767 | 67782 | 67798 |
| 67753 | 67768 | 67783 | 67799 |
| 67754 | 67769 | 67784 | 67800 |
| 67755 | 67770* | 67785 | |

Total 87

## 0-4-0ST 0F Class Y9

Introduced 1882. Holmes N.B. design.
*Locos. running permanently attached
to wooden tender.
Weight: Loco. 27 tons 16 cwt.
 Tender 6 tons.*
Pressure: 130 lb.
Cyls.: (O) 14" × 20".
Driving Wheels: 3' 8".
T.E.: 9,845 lb.

| | | | |
|---|---|---|---|
| 68095 | 68104 | 68117* | 68119* |
| 68101 | 68110 | | |

Total 6

## 0-6-0ST 4F Class J94

Introduced 1943. Riddles M.o.S. design.
 (Bought from M.o.S., 1946.)
Weight: 48 tons 5 cwt.
Pressure: 170 lb.
Cyls.: 18" × 26".
Driving Wheels: 4' 3".
T.E.: 23,870 lb.

| | | | |
|---|---|---|---|
| 68006 | 68025 | 68045 | 68062 |
| 68007 | 68026 | 68046 | 68063 |
| 68008 | 68029 | 68047 | 68064 |
| 68009 | 68030 | 68048 | 68065 |
| 68010 | 68031 | 68049 | 68066 |
| 68011 | 68032 | 68050 | 68067 |
| 68012 | 68034 | 68051 | 68068 |
| 68013 | 68035 | 68052 | 68069 |
| 68014 | 68036 | 68053 | 68070 |
| 68015 | 68037 | 68054 | 68071 |
| 68016 | 68038 | 68055 | 68073 |
| 68017 | 68039 | 68056 | 68074 |
| 68018 | 68040 | 68057 | 68075 |
| 68019 | 68041 | 68058 | 68077 |
| 68020 | 68042 | 68059 | 68078 |
| 68021 | 68043 | 68060 | 68079 |
| 68023 | 68044 | 68061 | 68080 |
| 68024 | | | |

Total 69

## 0-6-0T Unclass. Class J71

Introduced 1886. T. W. Worsdell N.E.
 design.
Weight: 37 tons 12 cwt.
Pressure: 140 lb.
Driving Wheels 4' 7½".
Cyls.: 16" × 22".
T.E.: 12,130 lb.

68233

Total 1

## 0-6-0T 0F Class J88

Introduced 1904. Reid N.B. design
 with short wheelbase.
Weight: 38 tons 14 cwt.
Pressure: 130 lb.
Cyls.: (O) 15" × 22".
Driving Wheels: 3' 9".
T.E.: 12,155 lb.

| | | | |
|---|---|---|---|
| 68325 | 68338 | 68345 | 68350 |
| 68335 | 68342 | 68346 | 68353 |
| 68336 | 68344 | | |

Total 10

Class 3 (Fowler) 2-6-2T No 40063          [I. E. Wilkinson

Class 3 (Fowler) 2-6-2T No. 40031 (fitted with condensing apparatus)     [P. H. Groom

Class 3 (Stanier) 2-6-2T No. 40080          [J. B. Bucknall

Class 4 (Fairburn) 2-6-4T No. 42115         [J. B. Bucknall

Class 2P (ex-Midland) 4-4-0 No. 40396         [P. H. Groom

Class 2P (ex-L.M.S.) 4-4-0 No. 40621         [P. H. Groom

Class 4 (Stanier 3-cyl.) 2-6-4T No. 42524 (with full-height cab door) [J. B. Bucknall

Class 4 (Stanier 3-cyl.) 2-6-4T No. 42525 [A. R. Carpenter

Class 4 (Stanier) 2-6-4T No. 42601 [P. H. Groom

Class 2 (Ivatt) 2-6-2T No. 41284 (push and pull fitted)

[P. H. Groom

Standard Class 2 2-6-2T No. 84019

[J. B. Bucknall

Class 2 (Ivatt) 2-6-0 No. 46474

[P. J. Sharpe

Class 4 (Ivatt) 2-6-0 No. 43089      [R. K. Evans

Class 6P (Hughes-Fowler) 2-6-0 No. 42712      [J. E. Wilkinson

Class 6P (Stanier) 2-6-0 No. 42948      [J. E. Wilkinson

Class 5 (Stanier) 4-6-0 No. 44738 (with Caprotti valve gear) [J. E. Wilkinson

Class 5 (Stanier) 4-6-0 No. 45253 [D. Penney

Class 5 (Stanier) 4-6-0 No. 45158 Glasgow Yeomanry (with domeless boiler)
[C. W. Woodhead

Class 6P 4-6-0 No. 45500 *Patriot*                                    [J. E. Wilkinson

Class 6P 4-6-0 No. 45505 *The Royal Army Ordnance Corps* (with high-sided tender)
[J. R. Carter

Class 7P 4-6-0 No. 45545 *Planet*                                     [I. J. McIntosh

Class 7P 4-6-0 No. 46170 *British Legion* (Stanier rebuild of experimental loco. No. 6399 *Fury*)
[J. B. Bucknall

Class 7P 4-6-0 No. 46156 *The South Wales Borderer*
[R. A. Panting

Class 7P 4-6-0 No. 45735 *Comet*
[J. B. Bucknall

Class 6P (Stanier) 4-6-0 No. 45666 *Cornwallis* [K. L. Cook

Class 8P (Stanier) 4-6-2 No. 46207 *Princess Arthur of Connaught*

Class 8P 4-6-2 No. 46245 *City of London* [P. H. Groom

Class 8F 2-8-0 No. 48253 [J. E. Wilkinson]

Class 8F 2-8-0 No. 48762 (with Fowler type tender) [J. B. Bucknall]

Class 7F (Fowler) 2-8-0 No. 53809 [R. C. Riley]

Class 3F (ex-L. & Y.) 0-6-0 No. 52093                    *[A. Trickett*

Class 3F (ex-L. & Y.) 0-6-0 No. 52201 (with Belpaire firebox and extended smokebox)          *[R S. Greenwood*

Class 2F 0-6-0ST No. 51412                   *[P. J. Sharpe*

Top :
Class 0F 0-4-0ST
No. 47007 (with
extended side tanks)
[H. J. Buckley

Centre :
Class 0F 0-4-0ST
No. 47004
[J. B. Bucknall

Right :
Class 0F 0-4-0T
No. 41535
[P. J. Sharpe

Class 2F 0-6-0 No. 58122                                 *[P. J. Sharpe*

Class 3P (ex-Caledonian) 4-4-0 No. 54495                  *[P. Hutchinson*

Class 4F (Pickersgill) 0-6-0 No. 57684                     *[P. J. Hughes*

*Above :*
Class 0F
(ex-Caledonian)
0-4-0ST No. 56039
[*B. A. Hill*

*Left :*
Class 2F (McIntosh
dock shunter) 0-6-0T
No. 56158
[*P. J. Sharpe*

*Below :*
Class 3F (McIntosh)
0-6-0T No. 56239
[*H. Stevenson*

Above :
Class A4 4-6-2
No. 60029 *Woodcock*
[*K. R. Pirt*

Right : Class A3 4-6-2
No. 60049 *Galtee More*
(with German-type
smoke deflectors)
[*Dr. P. R. Westall*

Below :
Class A3 4-6-2
No. 60048 *Doncaster*
(with wing-type smoke
deflectors) [*K. R. Pirt*

Class A1 4-6-2 No. 60159 *Bonnie Dundee*                    [N. Preedy

Class A2/2 4-6-2 No. 60502 *Earl Marischal*                 [P. N. Townend

Class A2 4-6-2 No. 60529 *Pearl Diver* (with double blast-pipe and multiple-valve regulator)
[J. R. Paterson

## 0-6-0T 2F Class J77

Introduced 1899. W. Worsdell N.E. rebuild of Fletcher 0-4-4T originally built 1874–84.
Weight: 43 tons.
Pressure: 160 lb.
Cyls.: 17″ × 22″.
Driving Wheels: 4′ 1¼″.
T.E.: 17,560 lb.

68408

Total 1

## 0-6-0T 2F Class J83

Introduced 1900. Holmes N.B. design.
Weight: 45 tons 5 cwt.
Pressure: 150 lb.
Cyls.: 17″ × 26″.
Driving Wheels: 4′ 6″.
T.E.: 17,745 lb.

| | | | |
|---|---|---|---|
| 68442 | 68448 | 68458 | 68472 |
| 68443 | 68453 | 68459 | 68477 |
| 68445 | 68454 | 68470 | 68479 |
| 68447 | 68456 | 68471 | 68481 |

Total 16

## 0-6-0T 2F Class J69

J69/1 Introduced 1902. Development of Holden J67 with 180 lb. pressure, larger tanks and larger firebox (some rebuilt from J67).

J69/2* Introduced 1950. J67/1 rebuilt with 180 lb. boiler and larger firebox.
Weight: 40 tons 9 cwt.
Pressure: 180 lb.
Cyls.: 16½″ × 22″.
Driving Wheels: 4′ 0″.
T.E.: 19,090 lb.
(See also E.R. Departmental Locos.)

| | | | |
|---|---|---|---|
| 68499 | 68550 | 68566 | 68613 |
| 68522* | 68552 | 68570 | 68619 |
| 68538 | 68554 | 68600 | 68621 |
| 68542 | 68556 | 68609 | 68626 |
| 68549 | 68565 | 68612 | 68635 |

Total

Class J69/2 1 Class J69/1 21

## 0-6-0T 2F Class J63

Introduced 1912. Hill G.E. development of J69 with side-window cab.
Weight: 42 tons 9 cwt.
Pressure: 180 lb.
Cyls.: 16½″ × 22″.
Driving Wheels: 4′ 0″.
T.E.: 19,090 lb.

68642      68646      68649

Total 3

## 0-6-0T  2F  Class J72

Introduced 1898. W. Worsdell N.E. design.
Weight: 38 tons 12 cwt.
Pressure: 140 lb.
Cyls.: 17" × 24".
Driving Wheels: 4' 1¼".
T.E.: 16,760 lb.

| | | | |
|---|---|---|---|
| 68672 | 68690 | 68713 | 68733 |
| 68673 | 68692 | 68715 | 68734 |
| 68674 | 68693 | 68716 | 68736 |
| 68675 | 68695 | 68717 | 68737 |
| 68677 | 68698 | 68719 | 68740 |
| 68678 | 68702 | 68720 | 68742 |
| 68680 | 68703 | 68721 | 68743 |
| 68683 | 68704 | 68723 | 68744 |
| 68684 | 68707 | 68726 | 68745 |
| 68686 | 68708 | 68728 | 68747 |
| 68687 | 68709 | 68729 | 68750 |
| 68688 | 68711 | 68732 | 68754 |
| 68689 | | | |

*(Class continued with No. 69001)*

## 0-6-0ST  3F  Class J52

J52/2 Introduced 1897. Ivatt G.N. saddletank with domed boiler.
Weight: 51 tons 14 cwt.
Pressure: 170 lb.
Cyls.: 18" × 26".
Driving Wheels: 4' 8".
T.E.: 21,735 lb.

*(See also E.R. Departmental Locos.)*

68869    68875

**Total 4**

## 0-6-0T  4F  Class J50

J50/2* Introduced 1922. Gresley G.N. design (68900–19 rebuilt from smaller J51, built 1915–22).

J50/3† Introduced 1926. Post-grouping development with detail differences.

J50/1‡ Introduced 1929. Rebuilt from smaller J51, built 1913–14.

J50/4§ Introduced 1937. Development of J50/3 with larger bunker.

Weight: $\begin{cases} 57 \text{ tons.*} \\ 56 \text{ tons 6 cwt.‡} \\ 58 \text{ tons 3 cwt.†§} \end{cases}$

Pressure: 175 lb.
Cyls.: 18½" × 26".
Driving Wheels: 4' 8".
T.E.: 23,635 lb.

| | | | |
|---|---|---|---|
| 68890‡ | 68922* | 68943† | 68970† |
| 68891‡ | 68923* | 68945† | 68971† |
| 68892‡ | 68925* | 68946† | 68972† |
| 68894‡ | 68926* | 68947† | 68975† |
| 68896‡ | 68927* | 68948† | 68976† |
| 68900* | 68928* | 68950† | 68977† |
| 68903* | 68929* | 68951† | 68981§ |
| 68904* | 68931* | 68959† | 68982§ |
| 68907* | 68932* | 68960† | 68983§ |
| 68908* | 68933* | 68961† | 68984§ |
| 68910* | 68934* | 68962† | 68986§ |
| 68916* | 68935* | 68963† | 68987§ |
| 68917* | 68936* | 68964† | 68988§ |
| 68918* | 68937* | 68965† | 68989§ |
| 68920* | 68939* | 68966† | 68990§ |
| 68921* | 68941† | 68968† | 68991§ |

Total

Class J50/1  5    Class J50/3  23

Class J50/2  26    Class J50/4  10

## 0-6-0T    2F    Class J72

*(Continued from 68754)*

| | | | |
|---|---|---|---|
| 69001 | 69008 | 69015 | 69022 |
| 69002 | 69009 | 69016 | 69023 |
| 69003 | 69010 | 69017 | 69024 |
| 69004 | 69011 | 69018 | 69025 |
| 69005 | 69012 | 69019 | 69026 |
| 69006 | 69013 | 69020 | 69027 |
| 69007 | 69014 | 69021 | 69028 |

**Total 77**

| | | | |
|---|---|---|---|
| 69150 | 69180 | 69196 | 69216 |
| 69155 | 69181 | 69199 | 69218 |
| 69156 | 69183 | 69204 | 69219 |
| 69159 | 69188 | 69211 | 69221 |
| 69163 | 69191 | 69212 | 69224 |
| 69178 | | | |

**Total**

**Class N15/1 26   Class N15/2 3**

## 0-6-2T    3F    Class N10

Introduced 1902. W. Worsdell N.E. design.
Weight: 57 tons 14 cwt.
Pressure: 160 lb.
Cyls.: $18\frac{1}{4}'' \times 26''$.
Driving Wheels: $4' 7\frac{1}{4}''$.
T.E.: 21,905 lb.

| | | | |
|---|---|---|---|
| 69097 | 69101 | 69105 | 69109 |

**Total 4**

## 0-6-2T    3MT    Class N15

N15/2* Introduced 1910. Reid N.B. design developed from N14. Cowlairs Incline banking locos.

N15/1 Introduced 1910. Development of N15/2 with smaller bunker for normal duties.

Weight: $\begin{cases} 62 \text{ tons } 1 \text{ cwt.*} \\ 60 \text{ tons } 18 \text{ cwt.} \end{cases}$
Pressure: 175 lb.
Cyls.: $18'' \times 26''$.
Driving Wheels: $4' 6''$.
T.E.: 23,205 lb.

| | | | |
|---|---|---|---|
| 69126* | 69131* | 69135 | 69137 |
| 69128* | 69134 | 69136 | 69138 |

## 0-6-2T    3P2F    Class N2

N2/2* Introduced 1925. Post-grouping development of Gresley G.N. N2/1, introduced 1920, which class is now included in N2/2. Built with condensing apparatus and small chimney.

N2/2† Condensing apparatus removed.

N2/3‡ Introduced 1925. Locos. built non-condensing, originally fitted with large chimney. Some now with small chimney.

N2/4§ Introduced 1928. Development of N2/2, slightly heavier. Built with condensing apparatus and small chimney.

The small chimneys are to suit the Metropolitan loading gauge, for working to Moorgate. Condensing apparatus has been removed from or added to certain locos. transferred from or to the London area.)

Weight: $\begin{cases} 70 \text{ tons } 5 \text{ cwt.*†} \\ 70 \text{ tons } 8 \text{ cwt.‡} \\ 71 \text{ tons } 9 \text{ cwt.§} \end{cases}$

Pressure: 170 lb. Su.
Cyls.: $19'' \times 26''$.
Driving Wheels: $5' 8''$
T.E.: 19,945 lb.
P.V.

| | | | | | | | |
|---|---|---|---|---|---|---|---|
| 69498* | 69523* | 69549* | 69579§ | 69692² | 69690² | 69713¹ | 69725¹ |
| 69504* | 69529* | 69561† | 69580§ | 69693² | 69702¹ | 69714¹ | 69728¹ |
| 69506* | 69531* | 69564‡ | 69583§ | 69696² | 69707¹ | 69723¹ | 69730¹ |
| 69512* | 69533* | 69568§ | 69585§ | 69697² | 69710¹ | 69724¹ | 69732¹ |
| 69513* | 69535* | 69571§ | 69586§ | | | | |
| 69518† | 69538* | 69572§ | 69592§ | | | | |
| 69520* | 69543* | 69574§ | 69593§ | | | | |
| 69521* | 69546* | 69575§ | | | | | |

**Total**

**Class N7/3 21  Class N7/4  2**

**Class N7/5  1 9**

**Total**

**Class N2/2 13  Class N2/4 11**

**Class N2/3  1**

## 4-8-0T  5F  Class T1

Introduced 1909. W. Worsdell N.E. design.
Weight: 85 tons 8 cwt.
Pressure: 175 lb.
Cyls.: (3) 18" x 26".
Driving Wheels: 4' 7¼".
T.E.: 34,080 lb.
P.V.

69921

**Total  1**

## 0-6-2T  3MT  Class N7

**N7/3**¹ Introduced 1927. Doncaster-built version of N7/2 (see below) but with round-topped firebox.

**N7/3**¹ Introduced 1943. N7/2 post-grouping development of Hill G.E. design (N7) with long-travel valves rebuilt with round-topped firebox.

**N7/4**³ Introduced 1940. Pre-grouping G.E. design (N7), rebuilt with round-topped firebox, retaining short-travel valves.

**N7/5** Introduced 1943. Post-grouping development of G.E. design N7/1, rebuilt with round-topped firebox, retaining short-travel valves.

Weight: $\begin{cases} 64 \text{ tons.}^{1 \cdot 4} \\ 61 \text{ tons 16 cwt.}^5 \end{cases}$
Pressure: 180 lb. Su.
Cyls.: 18" x 24".
Driving Wheels: 4' 10".
T.E.: 20,515 lb.
Walschaerts valve gear.  P.V.

## PRESERVED LOCOS IN WORKING ORDER

### 4-4-0

Introduced 1920. Heywood G. N. of S. superheated development of Pickersgill 1899 design. Withdrawn 1958 as B.R. No 62277 and restored to original condition, being returned to service for special use in 1959. (L.N.E.R. Class D40)

Weight : Loco.  48 tons 13 cwt.
Tender 37 tons 8 cwt.
Pressure: 165 lb. Su.
Cyls.: 18" x 26".
Driving Wheels : 6' 1".
T.E.: 16,185 lb.

**49 Gordon Highlander**

| | | | |
|---|---|---|---|
| 69618³ | 69646⁴ | 69669⁴ | 69674² |
| 69621³ | 69653⁴ | 69670⁴ | 69675² |
| 69632⁴ | 69656⁴ | 69671⁴ | 69678² |
| 69640⁴ | 69658⁴ | 69673² | 69686² |

**4-4-0**

Introduced 1913. Reid N.B. "Glen"
class. Withdrawn 1959 as B.R. No.
62469 and restored to original livery.
Returned to service for special use
1959. (L.N.E.R. Class D34)
Weight: Loco.  57 tons  4 cwt.
         Tender  46 tons 13 cwt.

Pressure: 165 lb. Su.
Cyls.: 20″ × 26″.
Driving Wheels: 6′ 0″
T.E.: 20,260 lb.
P.V.

256 Glen Douglas

# DEPARTMENTAL LOCOMOTIVES

**(Former running no. in brackets)**

## 0-6-0ST  3F  Class J52/2

2 (68858)      9 (68840)

## 0-4-0T  Un-class.  Class Y3

Introduced 1927.
Sentinel Wagon Works design.
Two-speed Geared Sentinel locos.
Sprocket gear ratio 15 : 19.
Weight: 20 tons 16 cwt.
Pressure: 275 lb. Su.
Cyls.: $6\frac{3}{4}'' \times 9''$.
Driving Wheels: 2' 6".
T.E.: $\begin{cases} \text{Low Gear: } 15,960 \text{ lb.} \\ \text{High Gear: } 5,960 \text{ lb.} \end{cases}$
Poppet valves.

7 (68166)      41 (68177)
40 (68173)

Total 3

## 0-6-0T  2F  Class J66

Introduced 1886. J. Holden G.E.
design.
Weight: 40 tons 6 cwt.
Pressure: 160 lb.
Cyls.: $16\frac{1}{2}'' \times 22''$.
Driving Wheels: 4' 0".
T.E.: 16,970 lb.

32 (68370)

Total 1

## 0-6-0T  2F  Class J69

44 (68498)      45 (68543)

## 0-4-0T  Un-class.  Class Y1/1

Sentinel Wagon Works design.
Single-speed Geared Sentinel
locomotives. The parts of this
class differ in details, including size
of boiler and fuel capacity.

Y1/1* Introduced 1925.
Y1/2† Introduced 1927.
Sprocket gear ratio 11 : 25.
Weight: $\begin{cases} 20 \text{ tons } 17 \text{ cwt.}^* \\ 19 \text{ tons } 16 \text{ cwt.}† \end{cases}$
Pressure: 275 lb. Su.
Cyls.: $6\frac{3}{4}'' \times 9''$.
Driving Wheels: 2' 6".
T.E.: 7,260 lb.*†
Poppet valves.

39*(68131)      54†(68153)

**Total**
Class Y1/1 1  Class Y1/2 1

## 0-4-0T  Dock Tank  Class Y4

Introduced 1913. Hill G.E. design.
Weight: 38 tons 1 cwt.
Pressure: 180 lb.
Cyls.: (O) $17'' \times 20''$.
Driving Wheels: 3' 10".
T.E.: 19,225 lb.
Walschaerts valve gear.

33 (68129)      Total 1

## 0-4-0 Diesel Mechanical

52 (11104)

## 0-4-0 Diesel Mechanical

56      82      84      85
81      83

## 0-6-0 Diesel Mechanical

88      91      92

## Bo-Bo  EB1 Electric

100 (26510)

**NOTE.** (For details of Departmental diesel and electric locomotives, see ABC British Railways Diesel and Electric
locomotives and Diesel and Electric Section of combined volume.)

# ROUTE AVAILABILITY OF LOCOMOTIVES

## CLASSES OF LOCOMOTIVES

| R.A. No. | Ex-L.N.E.R. including Electric Locomotives | Ex-L.M.S. | B.R. including Diesel Locomotives |
|---|---|---|---|
| 1 | J15, J71, Y1, Y3 | 2MT (2-6-2T) | DJ12, DJ13, DJ14, DJ15, DY1, DY2, DY5, DY11 |
| 2 | J72, J77, Y9 | 2MT (2-6-0) | — |
| 3 | J10, J21, J25, J36, J66, J63, J69, J88, N10 | 2F (0-6-0), 1F (0-6-0T), 3MT (2-6-2T P.B.), 3MT (2-6-2T T.B.) | 2MT (2-6-0), 2MT (2-6-2T) |
| 4 | B12/3, J17, J26, J55, J83, N14, EM2 (Co-Co) | 3F (0-6-0 L. & Y.), 3F (0-6-0 Mid.), 4MT (2-6-0), 1P (0-4-4T), 2P (0-4-4T), 4MT (2-6-4T 2-cyl. T.B.) | 3MT (2-6-0), 4MT (2-6-0), 3MT (2-6-2T), DE1 (800 h.p. N.B.) |
| 5 | B1, J6, J11, J19, J20, J27, K2, J52, J94, N7, EB1 (Bo-Bo) | 2P (4-4-0), 4F (0-6-0), 7F (0-8-0 Std.), 3F (0-6-0T), 4MT (2-6-4T P.B.), 3F (0-6-2T) | DE2 (1,000 h.p. N.B.), DE2 (1,100 h.p. E.E.), 4MT (2-6-4T), DEJ1, DEJ2, DEJ3, DEJ4, DEJ5, DEJ6 |
| 6 | C16, D11, D34, J35, J39, K1, K4, N15 O1, O2, O4, WD8, Q6, I50, N2, V1, Y4. | 8F (2-8-0 Std.), 7F (0-8-0 L.N.W.) | DE1 (1,000 h.p. E.E.), DE2 (1,160 h.p. B.R.), DE2 (1 250 h.p. Brush), DE2 (1,365 h.p. Brush) |
| 7 | Q7, L1, V3 | 5MT (4-6-0), 4P (4-4-0), 6P/5F (2-6-0 P.B.), 6P/5F (2-6-0 T.B.), 4MT (2-6-4T 3-cyl.) | 4MT (4-6-0), 5MT (4-6-0), DE2 (1,160 h.p. B.C.W.), DE4 (2,000 h.p. E.E.), DE4 (2,000 h.p. N.B.) |
| 8 | B16/1, B16/2, B16/3, D49, J37, J38, K3, T1 | 6P (4-6-0 " Jubilee "), 6P (4-6-0 " Patriot ") | 6MT (4-6-2), 7MT (4-6-2) |
| 9 | A1, A2, A3, A4, V2, EM1 (Bo-Bo) | 7P (4-6-0 Converted " Jubilee "), 7P (4-6-0 Converted " Patriot "), 7P (4-6-0 " Scot ") | 9F (2-10-0) |

# BRITISH RAILWAYS
## EASTERN & NORTH EASTERN REGIONS

### CHIEF MECHANICAL ENGINEER
A. H. Peppercorn ... 1948–1949
*(post abolished)*

---

## LOCOMOTIVE SUPERINTENDENTS AND CHIEF MECHANICAL ENGINEERS OF THE L.N.E.R.

| | | |
|---|---|---|
| Sir Nigel Gresley ... ... | 1923–1941 | E. Thompson ... ... 1941–1946 |
| A. H. Peppercorn ... | ... 1946–1947 | |

### GREAT NORTHERN RAILWAY

| | | | |
|---|---|---|---|
| A. Sturrock | ... | ... | 1850–1866 |
| P. Stirling ... | ... | ... | 1866–1895 |
| H. A. Ivatt ... | ... | ... | 1896–1911 |
| H. N. Gresley | ... | ... | 1911–1922 |

### NORTH EASTERN RAILWAY

| | | | |
|---|---|---|---|
| E. Fletcher ... | ... | ... | 1854–1883 |
| A. McDonnell* | ... | ... | 1883–1884 |
| T. W. Worsdell | ... | ... | 1885–1890 |
| W. Worsdell | ... | ... | 1890–1910 |
| Sir Vincent Raven | | ... | 1910–1922 |

### GREAT EASTERN RAILWAY

| | | | |
|---|---|---|---|
| R. Sinclair | ... | ... | 1862–1866 |
| S. W. Johnson | ... | ... | 1866–1873 |
| W. Adams | ... | ... | 1873–1878 |
| M. Bromley | ... | ... | 1878–1881 |
| T. W. Worsdell | ... | ... | 1881–1885 |
| J. Holden ... | ... | ... | 1885–1907 |
| S. D. Holden | ... | ... | 1908–1912 |
| A. J. Hill ... | ... | ... | 1912–1922 |

### LANCASHIRE, DERBYSHIRE AND EAST COAST RAILWAY

| | | | |
|---|---|---|---|
| R. A. Thom | ... | ... | 1902–1907 |

### MANCHESTER, SHEFFIELD AND LINCOLNSHIRE RAILWAY

| | | | |
|---|---|---|---|
| Richard Peacock ... | ... | ... | –1854 |
| W. G. Craig | ... | ... | 1854–1859 |

| | | | |
|---|---|---|---|
| Charles Sacré | ... | ... | 1859–1886 |
| T. Parker | ... | ... | 1886–1893 |
| H. Pollitt ... | ... | ... | 1893–1897 |

### GREAT CENTRAL RAILWAY

| | | | |
|---|---|---|---|
| H. Pollitt ... | ... | ... | 1897–1900 |
| J. G. Robinson | ... | ... | 1900–1922 |

### HULL AND BARNSLEY RAILWAY

| | | | |
|---|---|---|---|
| M. Stirling ... | ... | ... | 1885–1922 |

### MIDLAND AND GREAT NORTHERN JOINT RAILWAY

| | | | |
|---|---|---|---|
| W. Marriott | ... | ... | 1884–1924 |

### NORTH BRITISH RAILWAY

| | | | |
|---|---|---|---|
| T. Wheatley† | ... | ... | 1867–1874 |
| D. Drummond | ... | ... | 1875–1882 |
| M. Holmes ... | ... | ... | 1882–1903 |
| W. P. Reid | ... | ... | 1903–1919 |
| W. Chalmers | ... | ... | 1919–1922 |

### GREAT NORTH OF SCOTLAND RAILWAY

| | | | |
|---|---|---|---|
| D. K. Clark | ... | ... | 1853–1855 |
| J. F. Ruthven | ... | ... | 1855–1857 |
| W. Cowan ... | ... | ... | 1857–1883 |
| J. Manson ... | ... | ... | 1883–1890 |
| J. Johnson ... | ... | ... | 1890–1894 |
| W. Pickersgill | ... | ... | 1894–1914 |
| T. E. Heywood | ... | ... | 1914–1922 |

\* Between McDonnell and T. W. Worsdell there was an interval during which the office was covered by a Locomotive Committee.

† Previous to whom the records are indeterminate.

# BRITISH RAILWAYS STANDARD LOCOMOTIVES

## Chief Mechanical Engineer
## J. F. HARRISON

**4-6-2**　　　　　　　　　**7P6F**

Introduced 1951. Designed at Derby.
Weight: Loco. 94 tons 0 cwt.
Pressure: 250 lb. Su.
Cyls.: (O) 20″ × 28″.
Driving Wheels: 6′ 2″. T.E.: 32,150 lb.
Walschaerts valve gear.　P V.

| | |
|---|---|
| 70000 | Britannia |
| 70001 | Lord Hurcomb |
| 70002 | Geoffrey Chaucer |
| 70003 | John Bunyan |
| 70004 | William Shakespeare |
| 70005 | John Milton |
| 70006 | Robert Burns |
| 70007 | Coeur-de-Lion |
| 70008 | Black Prince |
| 70009 | Alfred the Great |
| 70010 | Owen Glendower |
| 70011 | Hotspur |
| 70012 | John of Gaunt |
| 70013 | Oliver Cromwell |
| 70014 | Iron Duke |
| 70015 | Apollo |
| 70016 | Ariel |
| 70017 | Arrow |
| 70018 | Flying Dutchman |
| 70019 | Lightning |
| 70020 | Mercury |
| 70021 | Morning Star |
| 70022 | Tornado |
| 70023 | Venus |
| 70024 | Vulcan |
| 70025 | Western Star |
| 70026 | Polar Star |
| 70027 | Rising Star |
| 70028 | Royal Star |
| 70029 | Shooting Star |
| 70030 | William Wordsworth |
| 70031 | Byron |
| 70032 | Tennyson |
| 70033 | Charles Dickens |
| 70034 | Thomas Hardy |
| 70035 | Rudyard Kipling |
| 70036 | Boadicea |
| 70037 | Hereward the Wake |
| 70038 | Robin Hood |
| 70039 | Sir Christopher Wren |
| 70040 | Clive of India |
| 70041 | Sir John Moore |
| 70042 | Lord Roberts |
| 70043 | Lord Kitchener |
| 70044 | Earl Haig |
| 70045 | Lord Rowallan |
| 70046 | Anzac |
| 70047 | |
| 70048 | The Territorial Army 1908-1958 |
| 70049 | Solway Firth |
| 70050 | Firth of Clyde |
| 70051 | Firth of Forth |
| 70052 | Firth of Tay |
| 70053 | Moray Firth |
| 70054 | Dornoch Firth |

**Total 55**

**4-6-2**　　　　　　　　　**8P**

Introduced 1954. Designed at Derby.
Weight: Loco. 101 tons 5 cwt.
Pressure: 250 lb. Su.
Cyls: (3) 18″ × 28″.
Driving Wheels: 6′ 2″. T.E.: 39,080 lb.
Caprotti valve gear.

| | |
|---|---|
| 71000 | Duke of Gloucester |

**Total 1**

**4-6-2**　　　　　　　　　**6P5F**

Introduced 1952. Designed at Derby.
Weight: Loco. 86 tons 19 cwt.
Pressure: 225 lb. Su.
Cyls.: (O) 19½″ × 28″.
Driving Wheels: 6′ 2″. T.E.: 27,520 lb.
Walschaerts valve gear.　P.V.

| | |
|---|---|
| 72000 | Clan Buchanan |
| 72001 | Clan Cameron |
| 72002 | Clan Campbell |

| 72003 | Clan Fraser |
|---|---|
| 72004 | Clan Macdonald |
| 72005 | Clan Macgregor |
| 72006 | Clan Mackenzie |
| 72007 | Clan Mackintosh |
| 72008 | Clan Macleod |
| 72009 | Clan Stewart **Total 10** |

## 4-6-0      5

Introduced 1951. Designed at Doncaster.
*Introduced 1956. Fitted with Caprotti valve gear.
Weight: Loco. 76 tons 4 cwt.
Pressure: 225 lb. Su.
Cyls.: (O) 19″ × 28″.
Driving Wheels: 6′ 2″. T.E.: 26,120 lb.
Walschaerts valve gear. P.V.

| 73000 | 73020 | 73040 | 73060 |
|---|---|---|---|
| 73001 | 73021 | 73041 | 73061 |
| 73002 | 73022 | 73042 | 73062 |
| 73003 | 73023 | 73043 | 73063 |
| 73004 | 73024 | 73044 | 73064 |
| 73005 | 73025 | 73045 | 73065 |
| 73006 | 73026 | 73046 | 73066 |
| 73007 | 73027 | 73047 | 73067 |
| 73008 | 73028 | 73048 | 73068 |
| 73009 | 73029 | 73049 | 73069 |
| 73010 | 73030 | 73050 | 73070 |
| 73011 | 73031 | 73051 | 73071 |
| 73012 | 73032 | 73052 | 73072 |
| 73013 | 73033 | 73053 | 73073 |
| 73014 | 73034 | 73054 | 73074 |
| 73015 | 73035 | 73055 | 73075 |
| 73016 | 73036 | 73056 | 73076 |
| 73017 | 73037 | 73057 | 73077 |
| 73018 | 73038 | 73058 | 73078 |
| 73019 | 73039 | 73059 | 73079 |

| 73080 | Merlin |
|---|---|
| 73081 | Excalibur |
| 73082 | Camelot |
| 73083 | Pendragon |
| 73084 | Tintagel |
| 73085 | Melisande |
| 73086 | The Green Knight |
| 73087 | Linette |
| 73088 | **Joyous Gard** |

| 73089 | Maid of Astolat |
|---|---|

| 73090 | 73095 | 73100 | 73105 |
|---|---|---|---|
| 73091 | 73096 | 73101 | 73106 |
| 73092 | 73097 | 73102 | 73107 |
| 73093 | 73098 | 73103 | 73108 |
| 73094 | 73099 | 73104 | 73109 |

| 73110 | The Red Knight |
|---|---|
| 73111 | King Uther |
| 73112 | Morgan le Fay |
| 73113 | Lyonnesse |
| 73114 | Etarre |
| 73115 | King Pellinore |
| 73116 | Iseult |
| 73117 | Vivien |
| 73118 | King Leodegrance |
| 73119 | Elaine |

| 73120 | 73133* | 73146* | 73159 |
|---|---|---|---|
| 73121 | 73134* | 73147* | 73160 |
| 73122 | 73135* | 73148* | 73161 |
| 73123 | 73136* | 73149* | 73162 |
| 73124 | 73137* | 73150* | 73163 |
| 73125* | 73138* | 73151* | 73164 |
| 73126* | 73139* | 73152* | 73165 |
| 73127* | 73140* | 73153* | 73166 |
| 73128* | 73141* | 73154* | 73167 |
| 73129* | 73142* | 73155 | 73168 |
| 73130* | 73143* | 73156 | 73169 |
| 73131* | 73144* | 73157 | 73170 |
| 73132* | 73145* | 73158 | 73171 |

**Total 172**

## 4-6-0      4

Introduced 1951. Designed at Brighton.
*Introduced 1957. Fitted with double chimney.
Weight: Loco. 69 tons 0 cwt.
Pressure: 225 lb. Su.
Cyls.: (O) 18″ × 28″.
Driving Wheels: 5′ 8″. T.E.: 25,100 lb.
Walschaerts valve gear. P.V.

| 75000 | 75008 | 75016 | 75024 |
|---|---|---|---|
| 75001 | 75009 | 75017 | 75025 |
| 75002 | 75010 | 75018 | 75026 |
| 75003 | 75011 | 75019 | 75027 |
| 75004 | 75012 | 75020 | 75028 |
| 75005 | 75013 | 75021 | 75029* |
| 75006* | 75014 | 75022 | 75030 |
| 75007 | 75015 | 75023 | 75031 |

| 75032 | 75044 | 75056 | 75068 |
| 75033 | 75045 | 75057 | 75069* |
| 75034 | 75046 | 75058 | 75070 |
| 75035 | 75047 | 75059 | 75071 |
| 75036 | 75048 | 75060 | 75072* |
| 75037 | 75049 | 75061 | 75073 |
| 75038 | 75050 | 75062 | 75074 |
| 75039 | 75051 | 75063 | 75075 |
| 75040 | 75052 | 75064 | 75076 |
| 75041 | 75053 | 75065 | 75077 |
| 75042 | 75054 | 75066 | 75078 |
| 75043 | 75055 | 75067* | 75079 |

Total 80

## 2-6-0      4

Introduced 1953. Designed at Doncaster.
Weight: Loco. 59 tons 2 cwt.
Pressure: 225 lb. Su.
Cyls.: (O) $17\frac{1}{2}'' \times 26''$.
Driving Wheels: 5' 3". T.E.: 24,170 lb.
Walschaerts valve gear. P.V.

| 76000 | 76026 | 76052 | 76078 |
| 76001 | 76027 | 76053 | 76079 |
| 76002 | 76028 | 76054 | 76080 |
| 76003 | 76029 | 76055 | 76081 |
| 76004 | 76030 | 76056 | 76082 |
| 76005 | 76031 | 76057 | 76083 |
| 76006 | 76032 | 76058 | 76084 |
| 76007 | 76033 | 76059 | 76085 |
| 76008 | 76034 | 76060 | 76086 |
| 76009 | 76035 | 76061 | 76087 |
| 76010 | 76036 | 76062 | 76088 |
| 76011 | 76037 | 76063 | 76089 |
| 76012 | 76038 | 76064 | 76090 |
| 76013 | 76039 | 76065 | 76091 |
| 76014 | 76040 | 76066 | 76092 |
| 76015 | 76041 | 76067 | 76093 |
| 76016 | 76042 | 76068 | 76094 |
| 76017 | 76043 | 76069 | 76095 |
| 76018 | 76044 | 76070 | 76096 |
| 76019 | 76045 | 76071 | 76097 |
| 76020 | 76046 | 76072 | 76098 |
| 76021 | 76047 | 76073 | 76099 |
| 76022 | 76048 | 76074 | 76100 |
| 76023 | 76049 | 76075 | 76101 |
| 76024 | 76050 | 76076 | 76102 |
| 76025 | 76051 | 76077 | 76103 |

| 76104 | 76107 | 76110 | 76113 |
| 76105 | 76108 | 76111 | 76114 |
| 76106 | 76109 | 76112 | |

Total 115

## 2-6-0      3

Introduced 1954. Designed at Swindon.
Weight: Loco. 57 tons 9 cwt.
Pressure: 200 lb. Su.
Cyls.: (O) $17\frac{1}{2}'' \times 26''$.
Driving Wheels: 5' 3". T.E.: 21,490 lb.
Walschaerts valve gear. P.V.

| 77000 | 77005 | 77010 | 77015 |
| 77001 | 77006 | 77011 | 77016 |
| 77002 | 77007 | 77012 | 77017 |
| 77003 | 77008 | 77013 | 77018 |
| 77004 | 77009 | 77014 | 77019 |

Total 20

## 2-6-0      2

Introduced 1953. Designed at Derby.
Weight: Loco. 49 tons 5 cwt.
Pressure: 200 lb. Su.
Cyls.: (O) $16\frac{1}{2}'' \times 24''$.
Driving Wheels: 5' 0". T.E.: 18,515 lb.
Walschaerts valve gear. P.V.

| 78000 | 78017 | 78033 | 78049 |
| 78001 | 78018 | 78034 | 78050 |
| 78002 | 78019 | 78035 | 78051 |
| 78003 | 78020 | 78036 | 78052 |
| 78004 | 78021 | 78037 | 78053 |
| 78005 | 78022 | 78038 | 78054 |
| 78006 | 78023 | 78039 | 78055 |
| 78007 | 78024 | 78040 | 78056 |
| 78008 | 78025 | 78041 | 78057 |
| 78009 | 78026 | 78042 | 78058 |
| 78010 | 78027 | 78043 | 78059 |
| 78011 | 78028 | 78044 | 78060 |
| 78012 | 78029 | 78045 | 78061 |
| 78013 | 78030 | 78046 | 78062 |
| 78014 | 78031 | 78047 | 78063 |
| 78015 | 78032 | 78048 | 78064 |
| 78016 | | | |

Total 65

## 2-6-4T                    4

Introduced 1951. **Designed at Brighton.**
Weight: 88 tons 10 cwt.
Pressure: 225 lb. Su.
Cyls.: (O) 18″ × 28″.
Driving Wheels: 5′ 8″. T.E.: 25,100 lb.
Walschaerts valve gear.  P.V.

| | | | |
|---|---|---|---|
| 80000 | 80039 | 80078 | 80117 |
| 80001 | 80040 | 80079 | 80118 |
| 80002 | 80041 | 80080 | 80119 |
| 80003 | 80042 | 80081 | 80120 |
| 80004 | 80043 | 80082 | 80121 |
| 80005 | 80044 | 80083 | 80122 |
| 80006 | 80045 | 80084 | 80123 |
| 80007 | 80046 | 80085 | 80124 |
| 80008 | 80047 | 80086 | 80125 |
| 80009 | 80048 | 80087 | 80126 |
| 80010 | 80049 | 80088 | 80127 |
| 80011 | 80050 | 80089 | 80128 |
| 80012 | 80051 | 80090 | 80129 |
| 80013 | 80052 | 80091 | 80130 |
| 80014 | 80053 | 80092 | 80131 |
| 80015 | 80054 | 80093 | 80132 |
| 80016 | 80055 | 80094 | 80133 |
| 80017 | 80056 | 80095 | 80134 |
| 80018 | 80057 | 80096 | 80135 |
| 80019 | 80058 | 80097 | 80136 |
| 80020 | 80059 | 80098 | 80137 |
| 80021 | 80060 | 80099 | 80138 |
| 80022 | 80061 | 80100 | 80139 |
| 80023 | 80062 | 80101 | 80140 |
| 80024 | 80063 | 80102 | 80141 |
| 80025 | 80064 | 80103 | 80142 |
| 80026 | 80065 | 80104 | 80143 |
| 80027 | 80066 | 80105 | 80144 |
| 80028 | 80067 | 80106 | 80145 |
| 80029 | 80068 | 80107 | 80146 |
| 80030 | 80069 | 80108 | 80147 |
| 80031 | 80070 | 80109 | 80148 |
| 80032 | 80071 | 80110 | 80149 |
| 80033 | 80072 | 80111 | 80150 |
| 80034 | 80073 | 80112 | 80151 |
| 80035 | 80074 | 80113 | 80152 |
| 80036 | 80075 | 80114 | 80153 |
| 80037 | 80076 | 80115 | 80154 |
| 80038 | 80077 | 80116 | |

**Total 155**

## 2-6-2T                    3

Introduced 1952. Designed at Swindon.
Weight: 73 tons 10 cwt.
Pressure: 200 lb. Su.
Cyls.: (O) 17½″ × 26″.
Driving Wheels: 5′ 3″. T.E.: 21,490 lb.
Walschaerts valve gear.  P.V.

| | | | |
|---|---|---|---|
| 82000 | 82012 | 82024 | 82036 |
| 82001 | 82013 | 82025 | 82037 |
| 82002 | 82014 | 82026 | 82038 |
| 82003 | 82015 | 82027 | 82039 |
| 82004 | 82016 | 82028 | 82040 |
| 82005 | 82017 | 82029 | 82041 |
| 82006 | 82018 | 82030 | 82042 |
| 82007 | 82019 | 82031 | 82043 |
| 82008 | 82020 | 82032 | 82044 |
| 82009 | 82021 | 82033 | |
| 82010 | 82022 | 82034 | |
| 82011 | 82023 | 82035 | |

**Total 45**

## 2-6-2T                    2

Introduced 1953.  Designed at Derby.
Weight: 63 tons 5 cwt.
Pressure: 200 lb. Su.
Cyls.: (O) 16½″ × 24″.
Driving Wheels: 5′ 0″. T.E.: 18,515 lb.
Walschaerts valve gear.  P.V.

| | | | |
|---|---|---|---|
| 84000 | 84008 | 84016 | 84023 |
| 84001 | 84009 | 84017 | 84024 |
| 84002 | 84010 | 84018 | 84025 |
| 84003 | 84011 | 84019 | 84026 |
| 84004 | 84012 | 84020 | 84027 |
| 84005 | 84013 | 84021 | 84028 |
| 84006 | 84014 | 84022 | 84029 |
| 84007 | 84015 | | |

**Total 30**

## 2-8-0          8F          WD

Ministry of Supply " Austerity " 2-8-0
  locomotives purchased by British
  Railways, 1948.
Introduced 1943. Riddles M.o.S. design.
Weight: Loco.  70 tons  5 cwt.
        Tender 55 tons 10 cwt.
Pressure: 225 lb. Su.
Cyls.: (O) 19″ × 28″.
Driving Wheels: 4′ 8½″. T.E.: 34,215 lb.
Walschaerts valve gear.  P.V.

| | | | | | | | |
|---|---|---|---|---|---|---|---|
| 90000 | 90047 | 90096 | 90143 | 90190 | 90238 | 90285 | 90332 |
| 90001 | 90048 | 90097 | 90144 | 90192 | 90239 | 90286 | 90333 |
| 90002 | 90049 | 90098 | 90145 | 90193 | 90240 | 90287 | 90334 |
| 90003 | 90050 | 90099 | 90146 | 90194 | 90241 | 90288 | 90335 |
| 90004 | 90051 | 90100 | 90147 | 90195 | 90242 | 90289 | 90336 |
| 90005 | 90052 | 90101 | 90148 | 90196 | 90243 | 90290 | 90337 |
| 90006 | 90053 | 90102 | 90149 | 90197 | 90244 | 90291 | 90338 |
| 90007 | 90054 | 90103 | 90150 | 90198 | 90245 | 90292 | 90339 |
| 90008 | 90055 | 90104 | 90151 | 90199 | 90246 | 90293 | 90340 |
| 90009 | 90056 | 90105 | 90152 | 90200 | 90247 | 90294 | 90341 |
| 90010 | 90057 | 90106 | 90153 | 90201 | 90248 | 90295 | 90342 |
| 90011 | 90058 | 90107 | 90154 | 90202 | 90249 | 90296 | 90?43 |
| 90012 | 90059 | 90108 | 90155 | 90203 | 90250 | 90297 | 90344 |
| 90013 | 90060 | 90109 | 90156 | 90204 | 90251 | 90298 | 90345 |
| 90014 | 90061 | 90110 | 90157 | 90205 | 90252 | 90299 | 90346 |
| 90015 | 90063 | 90111 | 90158 | 90206 | 90253 | 90300 | 90347 |
| 90016 | 90064 | 90112 | 90159 | 90207 | 90254 | 90301 | 90348 |
| 90017 | 90065 | 90113 | 90160 | 90208 | 90255 | 90302 | 90349 |
| 90018 | 90066 | 90114 | 90161 | 90209 | 90256 | 90303 | 90350 |
| 90019 | 90067 | 90115 | 90162 | 90210 | 90257 | 90304 | 90351 |
| 90020 | 90068 | 90116 | 90163 | 90211 | 90258 | 90305 | 90352 |
| 90021 | 90069 | 90117 | 90164 | 90212 | 90259 | 90306 | 90353 |
| 90022 | 90070 | 90118 | 90165 | 90213 | 90260 | 90307 | 90354 |
| 90023 | 90071 | 90119 | 90166 | 90214 | 90261 | 90308 | 90355 |
| 90024 | 90072 | 90120 | 90167 | 90215 | 90262 | 90309 | 90356 |
| 90025 | 90073 | 90121 | 90168 | 90216 | 90263 | 90310 | 90357 |
| 90026 | 90074 | 90122 | 90169 | 90217 | 90264 | 90311 | 90358 |
| 90027 | 90075 | 90123 | 90170 | 90218 | 90265 | 90312 | 90359 |
| 90028 | 90076 | 90124 | 90171 | 90219 | 90266 | 90313 | 90360 |
| 90029 | 90077 | 90125 | 90172 | 90220 | 90267 | 90314 | 90361 |
| 90030 | 90078 | 90126 | 90173 | 90221 | 90268 | 90315 | 90362 |
| 90031 | 90079 | 90127 | 90174 | 90222 | 90269 | 90316 | 90363 |
| 90032 | 90080 | 90128 | 90175 | 90223 | 90270 | 90317 | 90364 |
| 90033 | 90081 | 90129 | 90176 | 90224 | 90271 | 90318 | 90365 |
| 90034 | 90082 | 90130 | 90177 | 90225 | 90272 | 90319 | 90366 |
| 90035 | 90084 | 90131 | 90178 | 90226 | 90273 | 90320 | 90367 |
| 90036 | 90085 | 90132 | 90179 | 90227 | 90274 | 90321 | 90368 |
| 90037 | 90086 | 90133 | 90180 | 90228 | 90275 | 90322 | 90369 |
| 90038 | 90087 | 90134 | 90181 | 90229 | 90276 | 90323 | 90370 |
| 90039 | 90088 | 90135 | 90182 | 90230 | 90277 | 90324 | 90371 |
| 90040 | 90089 | 90136 | 90183 | 90231 | 90278 | 90325 | 90372 |
| 90041 | 90090 | 90137 | 90184 | 90232 | 90279 | 90326 | 90373 |
| 90042 | 90091 | 90138 | 90185 | 90233 | 90280 | 90327 | 90374 |
| 90043 | 90092 | 90139 | 90186 | 90234 | 90281 | 90328 | 90375 |
| 90044 | 90093 | 90140 | 90187 | 90235 | 90282 | 90329 | 90376 |
| 90045 | 90094 | 90141 | 90188 | 90236 | 90283 | 90330 | 90377 |
| 90046 | 90095 | 90142 | 90189 | 90237 | 90284 | 90331 | 90378 |

| | | | | | | | |
|---|---|---|---|---|---|---|---|
| 90379 | 90426 | 90473 | 90520 | 90567 | 90610 | 90653 | 90696 |
| 90380 | 90427 | 90474 | 90521 | 90568 | 90611 | 90654 | 90697 |
| 90381 | 90428 | 90475 | 90522 | 90569 | 90612 | 90655 | 90698 |
| 90382 | 90429 | 90476 | 90523 | 90570 | 90613 | 90656 | 90699 |
| 90383 | 90430 | 90477 | 90524 | 90571 | 90614 | 90657 | 90700 |
| 90384 | 90431 | 90478 | 90525 | 90572 | 90615 | 90658 | 90701 |
| 90385 | 90432 | 90479 | 90526 | 90573 | 90616 | 90659 | 90702 |
| 90386 | 90433 | 90480 | 90527 | 90574 | 90617 | 90660 | 90703 |
| 90387 | 90434 | 90481 | 90528 | 90575 | 90618 | 90661 | 90704 |
| 90388 | 90435 | 90482 | 90529 | 90576 | 90619 | 90662 | 90705 |
| 90389 | 90436 | 90483 | 90530 | 90577 | 90620 | 90663 | 90706 |
| 90390 | 90437 | 90484 | 90531 | 90578 | 90621 | 90664 | 90707 |
| 90391 | 90438 | 90485 | 90532 | 90579 | 90622 | 90665 | 90708 |
| 90392 | 90439 | 90486 | 90533 | 90580 | 90623 | 90666 | 90709 |
| 90393 | 90440 | 90487 | 90534 | 90581 | 90624 | 90667 | 90710 |
| 90394 | 90441 | 90488 | 90535 | 90582 | 90625 | 90668 | 90711 |
| 90395 | 90442 | 90489 | 90536 | 90583 | 90626 | 90669 | 90712 |
| 90396 | 90443 | 90490 | 90537 | 90584 | 90627 | 90670 | 90713 |
| 90397 | 90444 | 90491 | 90538 | 90585 | 90628 | 90671 | 90714 |
| 90398 | 90445 | 90492 | 90539 | 90586 | 90629 | 90672 | 90715 |
| 90399 | 90446 | 90493 | 90540 | 90587 | 90630 | 90673 | 90716 |
| 90400 | 90447 | 90494 | 90541 | 90588 | 90631 | 90674 | 90717 |
| 90401 | 90448 | 90495 | 90542 | 90589 | 90632 | 90675 | 90718 |
| 90402 | 90449 | 90496 | 90543 | 90590 | 90633 | 90676 | 90719 |
| 90403 | 90450 | 90497 | 90544 | 90591 | 90634 | 90677 | 90720 |
| 90404 | 90451 | 90498 | 90545 | 90592 | 90635 | 90678 | 90721 |
| 90405 | 90452 | 90499 | 90546 | 90593 | 90636 | 90679 | 90722 |
| 90406 | 90453 | 90500 | 90547 | 90594 | 90637 | 90680 | 90723 |
| 90407 | 90454 | 90501 | 90548 | 90595 | 90638 | 90681 | 90724 |
| 90408 | 90455 | 90502 | 90549 | 90596 | 90639 | 90682 | 90725 |
| 90409 | 90456 | 90503 | 90550 | 90597 | 90640 | 90683 | 90726 |
| 90410 | 90457 | 90504 | 90551 | 90598 | 90641 | 90684 | 90727 |
| 90411 | 90458 | 90505 | 90552 | 90599 | 90642 | 90685 | 90728 |
| 90412 | 90459 | 90506 | 90553 | 90600 | 90643 | 90686 | 90729 |
| 90413 | 90460 | 90507 | 90554 | 90601 | 90644 | 90687 | 90730 |
| 90414 | 90461 | 90508 | 90555 | 90602 | 90645 | 90688 | 90731 |
| 90415 | 90462 | 90509 | 90556 | 90603 | 90646 | 90689 | 90732 |
| 90416 | 90463 | 90510 | 90557 | 90604 | 90647 | 90690 | Vulcan |
| 90417 | 90464 | 90511 | 90558 | 90605 | 90648 | 90691 | |
| 90418 | 90465 | 90512 | 90559 | 90606 | 90649 | 90692 | |
| 90419 | 90466 | 90513 | 90560 | 90607 | 90650 | 90693 | |
| 90420 | 90467 | 90514 | 90561 | 90608 | 90651 | 90694 | |
| 90421 | 90468 | 90515 | 90562 | 90609 | 90652 | 90695 | |
| 90422 | 90469 | 90516 | 90563 | | | | |
| 90423 | 90470 | 90517 | 90564 | | | | Total 730 |
| 90424 | 90471 | 90518 | 90565 | | | | |
| 90425 | 90472 | 90519 | 90566 | | | | |

## 2-10-0           WD

Ministry of Supply " Austerity " 2-10-0 locomotives purchased by British Railways.
Introduced 1943. Riddles M.o.S. design.
Weight: Loco. 78 tons 6 cwt.
        Tender 55 tons 10 cwt.
Pressure: 225 lb. Su.
Cyls.: (O) 19″ × 28″.
Driving Wheels: 4′ 8½″. T.E.: 34,215 lb.
Walschaerts valve gear. P.V.

| | | | |
|---|---|---|---|
| 90750 | 90757 | 90763 | 90769 |
| 90751 | 90758 | 90764 | 90770 |
| 90752 | 90759 | 90765 | 90771 |
| 90753 | 90760 | 90766 | 90772 |
| 90754 | 90761 | 90767 | 90773 |
| 90755 | 90762 | 90768 | 90774 |
| 90756 | | | Total 25 |

## 2-10-0           9F

Introduced 1954. Designed at Brighton.
*Introduced 1955. Fitted with Crosti boiler, some engines later having Crosti pre-heater sealed off for orthodox working.
†Introduced 1957. Fitted with double chimney.
‡Introduced 1958. Fitted with Mechanical Stoker and double chimney.
§Introduced 1960. Fitted with Giesl oblong ejector.
Weight: Loco. { 86 tons 14 cwt.
              { 90 tons 4 cwt.*
Pressure: 250 lb. Su.
Cyls.: (O) 20″ × 28″.
Driving Wheels: 5′ 0″. T.E.: 39,670 lb.
Walschaerts valve gear. P.V.

| | | | |
|---|---|---|---|
| 92000† | 92018 | 92036 | 92054 |
| 92001 | 92019 | 92037 | 92055 |
| 92002 | 92020* | 92038 | 92056 |
| 92003 | 92021* | 92039 | 92057 |
| 92004 | 92022* | 92040 | 92058 |
| 92005 | 92023* | 92041 | 92059 |
| 92006 | 92024* | 92042 | 92060 |
| 92007 | 92025* | 92043 | 92061 |
| 92008 | 92026* | 92044 | 92062 |
| 92009 | 92027* | 92045 | 92063 |
| 92010 | 92028* | 92046 | 92064 |
| 92011 | 92029* | 92047 | 92065 |
| 92012 | 92030 | 92048 | 92066 |
| 92013 | 92031 | 92049 | 92067 |
| 92014 | 92032 | 92050 | 92068 |
| 92015 | 92033 | 92051 | 92069 |
| 92016 | 92034 | 92052 | 92070 |
| 92017 | 92035 | 92053 | 92071 |
| 92072 | 92117 | 92162 | 92207† |
| 92073 | 92118 | 92163 | 92208† |
| 92074 | 92119 | 92164 | 92209† |
| 92075 | 92120 | 92165‡ | 92210† |
| 92076 | 92121 | 92166‡ | 92211† |
| 92077 | 92122 | 92167‡ | 92212† |
| 92078 | 92123 | 92168 | 92213† |
| 92079† | 92124 | 92169 | 92214† |
| 92080 | 92125 | 92170 | 92215† |
| 92081 | 92126 | 92171 | 92216† |
| 92082 | 92127 | 92172 | 92217† |
| 92083 | 92128 | 92173 | 92218† |
| 92084 | 92129 | 92174 | 92219† |
| 92085 | 92130 | 92175 | 92220†¶ |
| 92086 | 92131 | 92176 | 92221† |
| 92087 | 92132 | 92177 | 92222† |
| 92088 | 92133 | 92178† | 92223† |
| 92089 | 92134 | 92179 | 92224† |
| 92090 | 92135 | 92180 | 92225† |
| 92091 | 92136 | 92181 | 92226† |
| 92092 | 92137 | 92182 | 92227† |
| 92093 | 92138 | 92183† | 92228† |
| 92094 | 92139 | 92184† | 92229† |
| 92095 | 92140 | 92185† | 92230† |
| 92096 | 92141 | 92186† | 92231† |
| 92097 | 92142 | 92187† | 92232† |
| 92098 | 92143 | 92188† | 92233† |
| 92099 | 92144 | 92189† | 92234† |
| 92100 | 92145 | 92190† | 92235† |
| 92101 | 92146 | 92191† | 92236† |
| 92102 | 92147 | 92192† | 92237† |
| 92103 | 92148 | 92193† | 92238† |
| 92104 | 92149 | 92194† | 92239† |
| 92105 | 92150 | 92195† | 92240† |
| 92106 | 92151 | 92196† | 92241† |
| 92107 | 92152 | 92197† | 92242† |
| 92108 | 92153 | 92198† | 92243† |
| 92109 | 92154 | 92199† | 92244† |
| 92110 | 92155 | 92200† | 92245† |
| 92111 | 92156 | 92201† | 92246† |
| 92112 | 92157 | 92202† | 92247† |
| 92113 | 92158 | 92203† | 92248† |
| 92114 | 92159 | 92204† | 92249† |
| 92115 | 92160 | 92205† | 92250† |
| 92116 | 92161 | 92206† | |

**Total 251**

¶ 92220 named *Evening Star.*

# NUMERICAL LIST OF

# DIESEL LOCOMOTIVES

*The lists of numbers include all locomotives on order at the time of going to press. For details of delivery, see the Locomotive Stock change list each month in* Trains Illustrated.

---

## ICo-Col 4
### "PEAK" CLASS

*Introduced:* 1959.

*Locomotive manufacturer:* B.R.

*Total b.h.p.:* $\begin{cases} 2,300.\ddagger \\ 2,500*\dagger \end{cases}$

*Engine:* ‡Sulzer 12LDA28 twin bank pressure charged, 12-cyl. type of 2,300 b.h.p. (12LDA28-B, with inter-cooling, of 2,500 b.h.p.*†) at 750 r.p.m

*Transmission:* **Electric.** Six Crompton Parkinson 305 h.p. axle-hung nose-suspended traction motors.*‡

**Electric:** Six Brush traction motors.†

*Weight:* 138 tons 2 cwt.

*Driving Wheels:* 3′ 9″.

*Maximum tractive effort:* 70,000 lb.

D1‡ Scafell Pike
D2* Helvellyn
D3‡ Skiddaw
D4‡ Great Gable
D5‡ Cross Fell
D6‡ Whernside
D7‡ Ingleborough
D8‡ Penyghent
D9‡ Snowdon
D10‡ Tryfan

| | | | |
|---|---|---|---|
| D11* | D15* | D19* | D23* |
| D12* | D16* | D20* | D24* |
| D13* | D17* | D21* | D25* |
| D14* | D18* | D22* | D26* |

| | | | |
|---|---|---|---|
| D27* | D58* | D89* | D120* |
| D28* | D59* | D90* | D121* |
| D29* | D60* | D91* | D122* |
| D30* | D61* | D92* | D123* |
| D31* | D62* | D93* | D124* |
| D32* | D63* | D94* | D125* |
| D33* | D64* | D95* | D126* |
| D34* | D65* | D96* | D127* |
| D35* | D66* | D97* | D128* |
| D36* | D67* | D98* | D129* |
| D37* | D68* | D99* | D130* |
| D38* | D69* | D100* | D131* |
| D39* | D70* | D101* | D132* |
| D40* | D71* | D102* | D133* |
| D41* | D72* | D103* | D134* |
| D42* | D73* | D104* | D135* |
| D43* | D74* | D105* | D136* |
| D44* | D75* | D106* | D137* |
| D45* | D76* | D107* | D138* |
| D46* | D77* | D108* | D139* |
| D47* | D78* | D109* | D140* |
| D48* | D79* | D110* | D141* |
| D49* | D80* | D111* | D142* |
| D50* | D81* | D112* | D143* |
| D51* | D82* | D113* | D144* |
| D52* | D83* | D114* | D145* |
| D53* | D84* | D115* | D146* |
| D54* | D85* | D116* | D147* |
| D55* | D86* | D117* | D148† |
| D56* | D87* | D118* | D149† |
| D57* | D88* | D119* | D150† |

| | | | |
|---|---|---|---|
| D151† | D164† | D177† | D190† |
| D152† | D165† | D178† | D191† |
| D153† | D166† | D179† | D192† |
| D154† | D167† | D180† | D193† |
| D155† | D168† | D181† | D194† |
| D156† | D169† | D182† | D195† |
| D157† | D170† | D183† | D196† |
| D158† | D171† | D184† | D197† |
| D159† | D172† | D185† | D198† |
| D160† | D173† | D186† | D199† |
| D161† | D174† | D187† | |
| D162† | D175† | D188† | |
| D163† | D176† | D189† | |

| | | | |
|---|---|---|---|
| D272 | D304 | D336 | D363 |
| D273 | D305 | D337 | D369 |
| D274 | D306 | D338 | D370 |
| D275 | D307 | D339 | D371 |
| D276 | D308 | D340 | D372 |
| D277 | D309 | D341 | D373 |
| D278 | D310 | D342 | D374 |
| D279 | D311 | D343 | D375 |
| D280 | D312 | D344 | D376 |
| D281 | D313 | D345 | D377 |
| D282 | D314 | D346 | D378 |
| D283 | D315 | D347 | D379 |
| D284 | D316 | D348 | D380 |
| D285 | D317 | D349 | D381 |
| D286 | D318 | D350 | D382 |
| D287 | D319 | D351 | D383 |
| D288 | D320 | D352 | D384 |
| D289 | D321 | D353 | D385 |
| D290 | D322 | D354 | D386 |
| D291 | D323 | D355 | D387 |
| D292 | D324 | D356 | D388 |
| D293 | D325 | D357 | D389 |
| D294 | D326 | D358 | D390 |
| D295 | D327 | D359 | D391 |
| D296 | D328 | D360 | D392 |
| D297 | D329 | D361 | D393 |
| D298 | D330 | D362 | D394 |
| D299 | D331 | D363 | D395 |
| D300 | D332 | D364 | D396 |
| D301 | D333 | D365 | D397 |
| D302 | D334 | D366 | D398 |
| D303 | D335 | D367 | D399 |

## |Co-Co| 4

*Introduced:* 1958.
*Locomotive manufacturer:* English Electric.
*Total b.h.p.:* 2,000.
*Engine:* English Electric 16SVT. Mk. II of 2,000 b.h.p. at 850 r.p.m.
*Transmission:* **Electric.** Six English Electric nose-suspended traction motors.
*Weight:* 133 tons.
*Driving Wheels:* 3′ 9″.
*Maximum tractive effort:* 52,000 lb.

| | | | |
|---|---|---|---|
| D200 | D218 | D236 | D254 |
| D201 | D219 | D237 | D255 |
| D202 | D220 | D238 | D256 |
| D203 | D221 | D239 | D257 |
| D204 | D222 | D240 | D258 |
| D205 | D223 | D241 | D259 |
| D206 | D224 | D242 | D260 |
| D207 | D225 | D243 | D261 |
| D208 | D226 | D244 | D262 |
| D209 | D227 | D245 | D263 |
| D210* | D228 | D246 | D264 |
| D211* | D229 | D247 | D265 |
| D212* | D230 | D248 | D266 |
| D213 | D231 | D249 | D267 |
| D214 | D232 | D250 | D268 |
| D215 | D233 | D251 | D269 |
| D216 | D234 | D252 | D270 |
| D217 | D235 | D253 | D271 |

\* D210 "Empress of Britain."
  D211 " Mauretania."
  D212 " Aureol."

## AIA-AIA 4
### "WARSHIP" CLASS

*Introduced:* 1958.
*Locomotive manufacturer:* North British Locomotive Co.
*Total b.h.p.:* 2,000.
*Engines:* Two N.B.L./M.A.N. type L12V 18/21S 12-cyl. of 1,000 b.h.p.
*Transmission:* **Hydraulic.** Two Hardy Spicer cardan shafts to Voith-North British type L306r hydraulic transmissions each containing three torque converters.

Weight: 117 tons 8 cwt.
Driving Wheels: 3' 7".
Maximum tractive effort: 50,000 lb.

D600 Active
D601 Ark Royal
D602 Bulldog
D603 Conquest
D604 Cossack

# B-B 4

### "WARSHIP" CLASS

Introduced: 1958.

Locomotive manufacturer: Swindon Works, B.R.

Total b.h.p.: 2,000*
2,200.
2,400†

Engines: Two Bristol Siddeley-Maybach MD 650 V-type of 1,152 b.h.p. at 1,530 r.p.m. (*1,056 b.h.p. at 1,400 r.p.m.)

†Two Paxman 12-cyl. high-speed 12YJXL of 1,200 b.h.p. at 1,500 r.p.m.

Transmission: **Hydraulic.** Two Mekydro type K104 hydraulic transmissions containing permanently filled single torque converter and four-speed automatic gearbox.

Weight: 78 tons.
Driving Wheels: 3' 3½".
Maximum tractive effort: 52,400 lb.

D800* Sir Brian Robertson
D801* Vanguard
D802* Formidable
D803 Albion
D804 Avenger
D805 Benbow
D806 Cambrian
D807 Caradoc
D808 Centaur
D809 Champion
D810 Cockade
D811 Daring
D812 Royal Naval Reserve 1859-1959
D813 Diadem
D814 Dragon
D815 Druid

D816 Eclipse
D817 Foxhound
D818 Glory
D819 Goliath
D820 Grenville
D821 Greyhound
D822 Hercules
D823 Hermes
D824 Highflyer
D825 Intrepid
D826 Jupiter
D827 Kelly
D828 Magnificent
D829 Magpie
D830† Majestic
D831 Monarch
D832 Onslaught

# B-B 4

### "WARSHIP" CLASS

Introduced: 1960.
Locomotive manufacturer: North British Locomotive Co.
Total b.h.p.: 2,200.
Engines:
Transmission: **Hydraulic.**
Weight:
Driving Wheels:
Maximum tractive effort:

D833 Panther
D834 Pathfinder
D835 Pegasus
D836 Powerful
D837 Ramillies
D838 Rapid
D839 Relentless
D840 Resistance
D841 Roebuck
D842 Royal Oak
D843 Sharpshooter
D844 Spartan
D845 Sprightly
D846 Steadfast
D847 Strongbow
D848 Sultan
D849 Superb

| D850 | Swift |
| D851 | Temeraire |
| D852 | Tenacious |
| D853 | Thruster |
| D854 | Tiger |
| D855 | Triumph |
| D856 | Trojan |
| D857 | Undaunted |
| D858 | Valorous |
| D859 | Vanquisher |
| D860 | Victorious |
| D861 | Vigilant |
| D862 | Viking |
| D863 | Warrior |
| D864 | Zealous |
| D865 | Zenith |

## B-B      4

D866-70 for particulars see Nos.
D800-32

D866
D867
D868
D869
D870

## C-C      4

*To be introduced:*
*Locomotive manufacturer:* B.R.
*Total b.h.p.:* 2,700.
*Engines:* Two Maybach M.D. 655.
*Transmission:* **Hydraulic** Voith.
*Weight:*
*Driving Wheels:*
*Maximum tractive effort:*

| D1000 | D1007 | D1014 | D1021 |
| D1001 | D1008 | D1015 | D1022 |
| D1002 | D1009 | D1016 | D1023 |
| D1003 | D1010 | D1017 | D1024 |
| D1004 | D1011 | D1018 | D1025 |
| D1005 | D1012 | D1019 | D1026 |
| D1006 | D1013 | D1020 | D1027 |

| D1028 | D1040 | D1052 | D1064 |
| D1029 | D1041 | D1053 | D1065 |
| D1030 | D1042 | D1054 | D1066 |
| D1031 | D1043 | D1055 | D1067 |
| D1032 | D1044 | D1056 | D1068 |
| D1033 | D1045 | D1057 | D1069 |
| D1034 | D1046 | D1058 | D1070 |
| D1035 | D1047 | D1059 | D1071 |
| D1036 | D1048 | D1060 | D1072 |
| D1037 | D1049 | D1061 | D1073 |
| D1038 | D1050 | D1062 | |
| D1039 | D1051 | D1063 | |

## ICo-Col      4

### "PEAK" CLASS

D1500-12 for particulars see Nos.
D1-199.

| D1500† | D1504† | D1508† | D1512† |
| D1501† | D1505† | D1509† | |
| D1502† | D1506† | D1510† | |
| D1503† | D1507† | D1511† | |

## 0-6-0      Shunter

*Introduced:* 1957.
*Locomotive manufacturer:* B.R.
*Total b.h.p.:* 204
*Engine:* Gardner type 8L3 of 204 b.h.p.
  at 1,200 r.p.m.
*Transmission:* **Mechanical.** Vulcan-
  Sinclair type 23 fluid coupling.
  Wilson-Drewry C.A.5 type five-speed
  epicyclic gearbox. Type RF II spiral
  bevel reverse and final drive unit.
*Weight:* 30 tons 16 cwt.
*Driving Wheels:* 3' 7".
*Maximum tractive effort:* 15,650 lb.

**(Original numbers in brackets)**

| D2000 (11187) | D2006 (11193) |
| D2001 (11188) | D2007 (11194) |
| D2002 (11189) | D2008 (11195) |
| D2003 (11190) | D2009 (11196) |
| D2004 (11191) | D2010 (11197) |
| D2005 (11192) | D2011 (11198) |

| | |
|---|---|
| D2012 (11199) | D2018 (11205) |
| D2013 (11200) | D2019 (11206) |
| D2014 (11201) | D2020 (11207) |
| D2015 (11202) | D2021 (11208) |
| D2016 (11203) | D2022 (11209) |
| D2017 (11204) | |

| | | | |
|---|---|---|---|
| D2023 | D2062 | D2101 | D2139 |
| D2024 | D2063 | D2102 | D2140 |
| D2025 | D2064 | D2103 | D2141 |
| D2026 | D2065 | D2104 | D2142 |
| D2027 | D2066 | D2105 | D2143 |
| D2028 | D2067 | D2106 | D2144 |
| D2029 | D2068 | D2107 | D2145 |
| D2030 | D2069 | D2108 | D2146 |
| D2031 | D2070 | D2109 | D2147 |
| D2032 | D2071 | D2110 | D2148 |
| D2033 | D2072 | D2111 | D2149 |
| D2034 | D2073 | D2112 | D2150 |
| D2035 | D2074 | D2113 | D2151 |
| D2036 | D2075 | D2114 | D2152 |
| D2037 | D2076 | D2115 | D2153 |
| D2038 | D2077 | D2116 | D2154 |
| D2039 | D2078 | D2117 | D2155 |
| D2040 | D2079 | D2118 | D2156 |
| D2041 | D2080 | D2119 | D2157 |
| D2042 | D2081 | D2120 | D2158 |
| D2043 | D2082 | D2121 | D2159 |
| D2044 | D2083 | D2122 | D2160 |
| D2045 | D2084 | D2123 | D2161 |
| D2046 | D2085 | D2124 | D2162 |
| D2047 | D2086 | D2125 | D2163 |
| D2048 | D2087 | D2126 | D2164 |
| D2049 | D2088 | D2127 | D2165 |
| D2050 | D2089 | D2128 | D2166 |
| D2051 | D2090 | D2129 | D2167 |
| D2052 | D2091 | D2130 | D2168 |
| D2053 | D2092 | D2131 | D2169 |
| D2054 | D2093 | D2132 | D2170 |
| D2055 | D2094 | D2133 | D2171 |
| D2056 | D2095 | D2134 | D2172 |
| D2057 | D2096 | D2135 | D2173 |
| D2058 | D2097 | D2136 | D2174 |
| D2059 | D2098 | D2137 | D2175 |
| D2060 | D2099 | D2138 | D2176 |
| D2061 | D2100 | | |

## 0-6-0      Shunter

*Introduced: 1952.*
*Locomotive manufacturer: Drewry.*
*Total b.h.p.: 204.*
*Engine: Gardner type 8L3 of 204 b.h.p. at 1,200 r.p.m.*
*Transmission:* **Mechanical.** *Vulcan-Sinclair type 23 fluid coupling. Wilson-Drewry C.A.5 type five-speed epicyclic gearbox. Type RF 11 spiral bevel reverse and final drive unit.*
*Weight: 29 tons 15 cwt.*
*Driving Wheels: 3' 3".*
*Maximum tractive effort: 16,850 lb.*

### (Original numbers in brackets)

| | |
|---|---|
| D2200 (11100) | D2208 (11109) |
| D2201 (11101) | D2209 (11110) |
| D2202 (11102) | D2210 (11111) |
| D2203 (11103) | D2211 (11112) |
| D2204 (11105) | D2212 (11113) |
| D2205 (11106) | D2213 (11114) |
| D2206 (11107) | D2214 (11115) |
| D2207 (11108) | |

## 0-6-0      Shunter

*Introduced: 1955.*
*Locomotive manufacturer: Drewry.*
*Total b.h.p.: 204.*
*Engine: Gardner type 8L3 of 204 b.h.p. at 1,200 r.p.m.*
*Transmission:* **Mechanical.** *Vulcan-Sinclair type 23 fluid coupling. Wilson-Drewry C.A.5 type five-speed epicyclic gearbox. Type RF 11 spiral bevel reverse and final drive unit.*
*Weight: 29 tons 15 cwt.*
*Driving Wheels: 3' 6".*
*Maximum tractive effort: 15,650 lb.*

### (Original numbers in brackets)

| | |
|---|---|
| D2215 (11121) | D2223 (11129) |
| D2216 (11122) | D2224 (11130) |
| D2217 (11123) | D2225 (11131) |
| D2218 (11124) | D2226 (11132) |
| D2219 (11125) | D2227 (11133) |
| D2220 (11126) | D2228 (11134) |
| D2221 (11127) | D2229 (11135) |
| D2222 (11128) | D2230 (11149) |

| | |
|---|---|
| D2231 (11150) | D2237 (11156) |
| D2232 (11151) | D2238 (11157) |
| D2233 (11152) | D2239 (11158) |
| D2234 (11153) | D2240 (11159) |
| D2235 (11154) | D2241 (11160) |
| D2236 (11155) | |

## 0-6-0 Shunter

D2242-D2295, FOR PARTICULARS
SEE D2200-D2214.
(Original numbers in brackets)

| | |
|---|---|
| D2242 (11212) | D2251 (11221) |
| D2243 (11213) | D2252 (11222) |
| D2244 (11214) | D2253 (11223) |
| D2245 (11215) | D2254 (11224) |
| D2246 (11216) | D2255 (11225) |
| D2247 (11217) | D2256 (11226) |
| D2248 (11218) | D2257 (11227) |
| D2249 (11219) | D2258 (11228) |
| D2250 (11220) | D2259 (11229) |

| | | | |
|---|---|---|---|
| D2260 | D2281 | D2301 | D2321 |
| D2261 | D2282 | D2302 | D2322 |
| D2262 | D2283 | D2303 | D2323 |
| D2263 | D2284 | D2304 | D2324 |
| D2264 | D2285 | D2305 | D2325 |
| D2265 | D2286 | D2306 | D2326 |
| D2266 | D2287 | D2307 | D2327 |
| D2267 | D2288 | D2308 | D2328 |
| D2268 | D2289 | D2309 | D2329 |
| D2269 | D2290 | D2310 | D2330 |
| D2270 | D2291 | D2311 | D2331 |
| D2271 | D2292 | D2312 | D2332 |
| D2272 | D2293 | D2313 | D2333 |
| D2273 | D2294 | D2314 | D2334 |
| D2274 | D2295 | D2315 | D2335 |
| D2275 | D2296 | D2316 | D2336 |
| D2276 | D2297 | D2317 | D2337 |
| D2277 | D2298 | D2318 | D2338 |
| D2278 | D2299 | D2319 | D2339 |
| D2279 | D2300 | D2320 | D2340 |
| D2280 | | | |

## 0-6-0 Shunter

Introduced: 1956.
Locomotive manufacturer: Barclay.
Total b.h.p.: 204.

Engine: Gardner type 8L3 or 204 b.h.p.
at 1,200 r.p.m.
Transmission: **Mechanical.** Vulcan-
Sinclair type 23 fluid coupling.
Wilson C.A.4 type four-speed epi-
cyclic gearbox. Wiseman type 15
RLGB reverse and final drive unit.
Weight: 32 tons 0 cwt.
Driving Wheels: 3' 6".
Maximum tractive effort: 15,340 lb.

(Original numbers in brackets)

| | |
|---|---|
| D2400 (11177) | D2405 (11182) |
| D2401 (11178) | D2406 (11183) |
| D2402 (11179) | D2407 (11184) |
| D2403 (11180) | D2408 (11185) |
| D2404 (11181) | D2409 (11186) |

## 0-4-0 Shunter

Introduced: 1958.
Locomotive manufacturer: Barclay.
Total b.h.p.: 204.
Engine: Gardner type 8L3 of 204 b.h.p.
at 1,200 r.p.m.
Transmission: **Mechanical.** Vulcan-
Sinclair type 23 fluid coupling.
Wilson-Drewry C.A.5 type five-speed
epicyclic gearbox. Wiseman type 15.
R.L.G.B. reverse and final drive unit.
Weight: 35 tons.
Driving Wheels: 3' 7".
Maximum tractive effort: 20,000 lb.

| | | | |
|---|---|---|---|
| D2410 | D2419 | D2428 | D2437 |
| D2411 | D2420 | D2429 | D2438 |
| D2412 | D2421 | D2430 | D2439 |
| D2413 | D2422 | D2431 | D2440 |
| D2414 | D2423 | D2432 | D2441 |
| D2415 | D2424 | D2433 | D2442 |
| D2416 | D2425 | D2434 | D2443 |
| D2417 | D2426 | D2435 | D2444 |
| D2418 | D2427 | D2436 | |

## 0-6-0 Shunter

Introduced: 1956.
Locomotive manufacturer. Hudswell-
Clarke.
Total b.h.p.: 204.
Engine: Gardner type 8L3 of 204 b.h.p.
at 1,200 r.p.m.
Transmission: **Mechanical.** S.C.R.5
type, size 23 scoop control fluid
coupling. Three-speed " SSS Power-

flow " double synchro-type gearbox and final drive.
*Weight:* 36 tons 7 cwt.
*Driving Wheels:* 3′ 6″.
*Maximum tractive effort:* 16,100 lb.

### (Original numbers in brackets)

| | |
|---|---|
| D2500 (11116) | D2505 (11144) |
| D2501 (11117) | D2506 (11145) |
| D2502 (11118) | D2507 (11146) |
| D2503 (11119) | D2508 (11147) |
| D2504 (11120) | D2509 (11148) |

| | | | |
|---|---|---|---|
| D2510 | D2513 | D2516 | D2518 |
| D2511 | D2514 | D2517 | D2519 |
| D2512 | D2515 | | |

## 0-6-0                     Shunter
*Introduced:* 1955.
*Locomotive manufacturer:* Hunslet.
*Total b.h.p.:* 204.
*Engine:* Gardner type 8L3 of 204 b.h.p. at 1,200 r.p.m.
*Transmission:* **Mechanical.** Hunslet patent friction clutch. Hunslet four-speed gearbox incorporating reverse and final drive gears.
*Weight:* 30 tons 0 cwt.
*Driving Wheels:* 3′ 4″.
*Maximum tractive effort:* 14,500 lb.

### (Original numbers in brackets)

| | |
|---|---|
| D2550 (11136) | D2562 (11165) |
| D2551 (11137) | D2563 (11166) |
| D2552 (11138) | D2564 (11167) |
| D2553 (11139) | D2565 (11168) |
| D2554 (11140) | D2566 (11169) |
| D2555 (11141) | D2567 (11170) |
| D2556 (11142) | D2568 (11171) |
| D2557 (11143) | D2569 (11172) |
| D2558 (11161) | D2570 (11173) |
| D2559 (11162) | D2571 (11174) |
| D2560 (11163) | D2572 (11175) |
| D2561 (11164) | D2573 (11176) |

| | | | |
|---|---|---|---|
| D2574 | D2580 | D2586 | D2592 |
| D2575 | D2581 | D2587 | D2593 |
| D2576 | D2582 | D2588 | D2594 |
| D2577 | D2583 | D2589 | D2595 |
| D2578 | D2584 | D2590 | D2596 |
| D2579 | D2585 | D2591 | D2597 |

| | | | |
|---|---|---|---|
| D2598 | D2604 | D2609 | D2614 |
| D2599 | D2605 | D2610 | D2615 |
| D2600 | D2606 | D2611 | D2616 |
| D2601 | D2607 | D2612 | D2617 |
| D2602 | D2608 | D2613 | D2618 |
| D2603 | | | |

## 0-4-0                     Shunter
*Introduced:* 1953.
*Locomotive manufacturer:* North British Locomotive Co.
*Total b.h.p.:* 200.
*Engine:* Paxman type 6RPH of 200 b.h.p. at 1,000 r.p.m.
*Transmission:* **Hydraulic.** Voith-North British hydraulic torque converter type L33YU. North British bevel gears and reversing dog clutch coupled through reduction gearing to jackshaft.
*Weight:* 32 tons.
*Driving Wheels:* 3′ 6″.
*Maximum tractive effort:* 21,500 lb.

### (Original numbers in brackets)

| | |
|---|---|
| D2700 (11700) | D2704 (11704) |
| D2701 (11701) | D2705 (11705) |
| D2702 (11702) | D2706 (11706) |
| D2703 (11703) | D2707 (11707) |

## 0-4-0                     Shunter
*Introduced:* 1957.
*Locomotive manufacturer:* North British Locomotive Co.
*Total b.h.p.:* 225.
*Engine:* North British type M.A.N. W6V 17.5/22A of 225 b.h.p. at 1,100 r.p.m. (12 hr. rating).
*Transmission:* **Hydraulic.** Voith-North British hydraulic torque converter type LCCYU. North British bevel gears and reversing dog clutch coupled through reduction gearing to jackshaft.
*Weight:* 30 tons.
*Driving Wheels:* 3′ 6″.
*Maximum tractive effort:* 20,080 lb.

### (Original numbers in brackets)

| | |
|---|---|
| D2708 (11708) | D2714 (11714) |
| D2709 (11709) | D2715 (11715) |
| D2710 (11710) | D2716 (11716) |
| D2711 (11711) | D2717 (11717) |
| D2712 (11712) | D2718 (11718) |
| D2713 (11713) | D2719 (11719) |

| | | | | | | | |
|---|---|---|---|---|---|---|---|
| D2720 | D2735 | D2750 | D2765 | D2900 | D2906 | D2912 | D2918 |
| D2721 | D2736 | D2751 | D2766 | D2901 | D2907 | D2913 | D2919 |
| D2722 | D2737 | D2752 | D2767 | D2902 | D2908 | D2914 | D2920 |
| D2723 | D2738 | D2753 | D2768 | D2903 | D2909 | D2915 | |
| D2724 | D2739 | D2754 | D2769 | D2904 | D2910 | D2916 | |
| D2725 | D2740 | D2755 | D2770 | D2905 | D2911 | D2917 | |
| D2726 | D2741 | D2756 | D2771 | | | | |
| D2727 | D2742 | D2757 | D2772 | | | | |
| D2728 | D2743 | D2758 | D2773 | | | | |
| D2729 | D2744 | D2759 | D2774 | | | | |
| D2730 | D2745 | D2760 | D2775 | | | | |
| D2731 | D2746 | D2761 | D2776 | | | | |
| D2732 | D2747 | D2762 | D2777 | | | | |
| D2733 | D2748 | D2763 | D2778 | | | | |
| D2734 | D2749 | D2764 | D2779 | | | | |

## 0-4-0      Shunter

*Introduced:* 1960.
*Locomotive manufacturer:* Yorkshire Engine Co.
*Total b.h.p.:* 170
*Engine:* Rolls-Royce type C6NFL of 179 h.p. at 1,800 r.p.m.
*Transmission:* **Hydraulic.** Rolls-Royce 3-stage torque converter, Series 10,000. Yorkshire Engine Co. axle-hung double-reduction final drive with reversing mechanism.
*Weight:* 28 tons.
*Driving Wheels:* 3' 6".
*Maximum tractive effort:* 15,000 lb.

| | | | |
|---|---|---|---|
| D2850 | D2855 | D2860 | D2865 |
| D2851 | D2856 | D2861 | D2866 |
| D2852 | D2857 | D2862 | D2867 |
| D2853 | D2858 | D2863 | D2868 |
| D2854 | D2859 | D2864 | D2869 |

## 0-4-0      Shunter

*Introduced:* 1958.
*Locomotive manufacturer:* North British Locomotive Co.
*Total b.h.p.:* 330.
*Engine:* North British/M.A.N. type W6V 17.5/22 AS, super-charged.
*Transmission* **Hydraulic.** Voith-North British hydraulic torque converter type L24V. North British spiral bevel gears, reversing and reduction gears to jackshaft.
*Weight:* 36 tons.
*Driving Wheels:* 3' 9".
*Maximum tractive effort:* 24,100 lb.

## 0-4-0      Shunter

*Introduced:* 1955.
*Locomotive manufacturer:* Hunslet.
*Total b.h.p.:* 153.
*Engine:* Gardner type 6L3 of 153 b.h.p. at 1,200 r.p.m.
*Transmission.:* **Mechanical.** Hunslet patent friction clutch and four-speed gearbox incorporating reverse and final drive gears.
*Weight:* 22 tons 9 cwt.
*Driving Wheels:* 3' 4".
*Maximum tractive effort:* 10,800 lb.

**(Original numbers in brackets)**

| | |
|---|---|
| D2950 (11500) | D2952 (11502) |
| D2951 (11501) | |

## 0-4-0      Shunter

*Introduced:* 1956.
*Locomotive manufacturer:* Barclay.
*Total b.h.p.:* 153.
*Engine:* Gardner type 6L3 of 153 b.h.p. at 1,200 r.p.m.
*Transmission:* **Mechanical.** Vulcan-Sinclair rigid type hydraulic coupling. Wilson S.E. 4 type four-speed epicyclic gearbox. Wiseman type 15 RLGB reverse and final drive unit.
*Weight:* 25 tons.
*Driving Wheels:* 3' 2".
*Maximum tractive effort:* 12,750 lb.

**(Original numbers in brackets)**

| | |
|---|---|
| D2953 (11503) | D2955 (11505) |
| D2954 (11504) | D2956 (11506) |

## 0-4-0      Shunter

*Introduced:* 1956.
*Locomotive manufacturer:* Ruston & Hornsby.
*Total b.h.p.:* 165.
*Engine:* Ruston type 6VPHL of 165 b.h.p. at 1,250 r.p.m. (1 hr. rating).
*Transmission:* **Mechanical.** Oil pressure-operated S.L.M. type friction clutches incorporated in Ruston

constant mesh type gearbox. Reverse gear and final drive unit incorporating bevel gears and dog clutches and reduction gear to final drive

*Weight:* 28 tons.
*Driving Wheels:* 3′ 4″.
*Maximum tractive effort:* 14,350 lb.

**(Original numbers in brackets)**

D2957 (11507)    D2958 (11508)


# 0-4-0    Shunter

*Introduced:* 1960.
*Locomotive manufacturer:* Brush Traction Ltd.
*Total b.h.p.:* 160.
*Engine:* Petter-McLaren six-cylinder type LE6 of 180 h.p. at 1,800 r.p.m.
*Transmission:* **Electrical.** One axle-hung nose-suspended traction motor.
*Weight:* 30 tons.
*Driving Wheels:* 3′ 6″.
*Maximum tractive effort:* 19,200 lb.

D2999


# 0-6-0    Shunter

**Engines D3000-D3336 were originally numbered 13000-13336 and are being renumbered as they are overhauled.**

*Introduced:* 1953.
*Locomotive manufacturer:* British Railways.
*Total b.h.p.:* 400.
*Engine:* English Electric 6-cyl. type 6KT of 400 b.h.p. at 630 r.p.m.
*Transmission:* **Electric.** Two English Electric nose-suspended traction motors. Double reduction gear drive.
*Weight:* 49 tons 0 cwt.
*Driving Wheels:* 4′ 6″.
*Maximum tractive effort:* 35,000 lb.
*Note:* Nos. D3000-91 and D3102-3116 fitted for vacuum brake operation.

| | | | |
|---|---|---|---|
| D3000 | D3009 | D3018 | D3027 |
| D3001 | D3010 | D3019 | D3028 |
| D3002 | D3011 | D3020 | D3029 |
| D3003 | D3012 | D3021 | D3030 |
| D3004 | D3013 | D3022 | D3031 |
| D3005 | D3014 | D3023 | D3032 |
| D3006 | D3015 | D3024 | D3033 |
| D3007 | D3016 | D3025 | D3034 |
| D3008 | D3017 | D3026 | D3035 |

| | | | |
|---|---|---|---|
| D3036 | D3057 | D3077 | D3097 |
| D3037 | D3058 | D3078 | D3098 |
| D3038 | D3059 | D3079 | D3099 |
| D3039 | D3060 | D3080 | D3100 |
| D3040 | D3061 | D3081 | D3101 |
| D3041 | D3062 | D3082 | D3102 |
| D3042 | D3063 | D3083 | D3103 |
| D3043 | D3064 | D3084 | D3104 |
| D3044 | D3065 | D3085 | D3105 |
| D3045 | D3066 | D3086 | D3106 |
| D3046 | D3067 | D3087 | D3107 |
| D3047 | D3068 | D3088 | D3108 |
| D3048 | D3069 | D3089 | D3109 |
| D3049 | D3070 | D3090 | D3110 |
| D3050 | D3071 | D3091 | D3111 |
| D3051 | D3072 | D3092 | D3112 |
| D3052 | D3073 | D3093 | D3113 |
| D3053 | D3074 | D3094 | D3114 |
| D3054 | D3075 | D3095 | D3115 |
| D3055 | D3076 | D3096 | D3116 |
| D3056 | | | |


# 0-6-0    Shunter

*Introduced:* 1955.
*Locomotive manufacturer:* British Railways.
*Total b.h.p.:* 350.
*Engine:* Crossley 6-cyl. type ESNT 6 of 350 b.h.p. at 825 r.p.m. (continuous rating).
*Transmission:* **Electric.** Two Crompton Parkinson nose-suspended traction motors. Double reduction gear drive.
*Weight:* 47 tons 10 cwt.
*Driving Wheels:* 4′ 6″.
*Maximum tractive effort:* 35,000 lb.

| | | | |
|---|---|---|---|
| D3117 | D3120 | D3123 | D3126 |
| D3118 | D3121 | D3124 | |
| D3119 | D3122 | D3125 | |


# 0-6-0    Shunter

*Introduced:* 1953.
*Locomotive manufacturer:* British Railways.
*Total b.h.p.:* 400.
*Engine:* English Electric 6-cyl. type 6KT of 400 b.h.p. at 680 r.p.m.
*Transmission:* **Electric.** Two English

Electric nose-suspended traction motors. Double reduction gear drive.
*Weight:* 48 tons 0 cwt.
*Driving Wheels:* 4′ 6″.
*Maximum tractive effort:* 35,000 lb.
Fitted for vacuum brake operation

| | | | |
|---|---|---|---|
| D3127 | D3130 | D3133 | D3136 |
| D3128 | D3131 | D3134 | |
| D3129 | D3132 | D3135 | |

## 0-6-0    Shunter

*Introduced:* 1955.
*Locomotive manufacturer:* British Railways.
*Total b.h.p.:* 370.
*Engine:* Blackstone 6-cyl. type ER6T of 370 b.h.p. at 750 r.p.m.
*Transmission:* **Electric.** Two G.E.C. nose-suspended traction motors, Double reduction gear drive.
*Weight:* 47 tons 10 cwts.
*Driving Wheels:* 4′ 6″.
*Maximum tractive effort:* 35,000 lb.
Fitted for vacuum brake operation.

| | | | |
|---|---|---|---|
| D3137 | D3141 | D3145 | D3149 |
| D3138 | D3142 | D3146 | D3150 |
| D3139 | D3143 | D3147 | D3151 |
| D3140 | D3144 | D3148 | |

## 0-6-0    Shunter

*Introduced:* 1955.
*Locomotive manufacturer:* British Railways.
*Total b.h.p.:* 370.
*Engine:* Blackstone 6-cyl. type ER6T of 370 b.h.p. at 750 r.p.m.
*Transmission:* **Electric.** Two B.T.H. nose-suspended traction motors. Double reduction gear drive.
*Weight:* 47 tons 0 cwt.
*Driving Wheels:* 4′ 6″.
*Maximum tractive effort:* 35,000 lb.

| | | | |
|---|---|---|---|
| D3152 | D3156 | D3160 | D3164 |
| D3153 | D3157 | D3161 | D3165 |
| D3154 | D3158 | D3162 | D3166 |
| D3155 | D3159 | D3163 | |

**D3167-D3438. FOR PARTICULARS SEE Nos. D3127-D3136.**

| | | | |
|---|---|---|---|
| D3167 | D3211 | D3255 | D3299 |
| D3168 | D3212 | D3256 | D3300 |
| D3169 | D3213 | D3257 | D3301 |
| D3170 | D3214 | D3258 | D3302 |
| D3171 | D3215 | D3259 | D3303 |
| D3172 | D3216 | D3260 | D3304 |
| D3173 | D3217 | D3261 | D3305 |
| D3174 | D3218 | D3262 | D3306 |
| D3175 | D3219 | D3263 | D3307 |
| D3176 | D3220 | D3264 | D3308 |
| D3177 | D3221 | D3265 | D3309 |
| D3178 | D3222 | D3266 | D3310 |
| D3179 | D3223 | D3267 | D3311 |
| D3180 | D3224 | D3268 | D3312 |
| D3181 | D3225 | D3269 | D3313 |
| D3182 | D3226 | D3270 | D3314 |
| D3183 | D3227 | D3271 | D3315 |
| D3184 | D3228 | D3272 | D3316 |
| D3185 | D3229 | D3273 | D3317 |
| D3186 | D3230 | D3274 | D3318 |
| D3187 | D3231 | D3275 | D3319 |
| D3188 | D3232 | D3276 | D3320 |
| D3189 | D3233 | D3277 | D3321 |
| D3190 | D3234 | D3278 | D3322 |
| D3191 | D3235 | D3279 | D3323 |
| D3192 | D3236 | D3280 | D3324 |
| D3193 | D3237 | D3281 | D3325 |
| D3194 | D3238 | D3282 | D3326 |
| D3195 | D3239 | D3283 | D3327 |
| D3196 | D3240 | D3284 | D3328 |
| D3197 | D3241 | D3285 | D3329 |
| D3198 | D3242 | D3286 | D3330 |
| D3199 | D3243 | D3287 | D3331 |
| D3200 | D3244 | D3288 | D3332 |
| D3201 | D3245 | D3289 | D3333 |
| D3202 | D3246 | D3290 | D3334 |
| D3203 | D3247 | D3291 | D3335 |
| D3204 | D3248 | D3292 | D3336 |
| D3205 | D3249 | D3293 | D3337 |
| D3206 | D3250 | D3294 | D3338 |
| D3207 | D3251 | D3295 | D3339 |
| D3208 | D3252 | D3296 | D3340 |
| D3209 | D3253 | D3297 | D3341 |
| D3210 | D3254 | D3298 | D3342 |

| | | | |
|---|---|---|---|
| D3343 | D3367 | D3391 | D3415 |
| D3344 | D3368 | D3392 | D3416 |
| D3345 | D3369 | D3393 | D3417 |
| D3346 | D3370 | D3394 | D3418 |
| D3347 | D3371 | D3395 | D3419 |
| D3348 | D3372 | D3396 | D3420 |
| D3349 | D3373 | D3397 | D3421 |
| D3350 | D3374 | D3398 | D3422 |
| D3351 | D3375 | D3399 | D3423 |
| D3352 | D3376 | D3400 | D3424 |
| D3353 | D3377 | D3401 | D3425 |
| D3354 | D3378 | D3402 | D3426 |
| D3355 | D3379 | D3403 | D3427 |
| D3356 | D3380 | D3404 | D3428 |
| D3357 | D3381 | D3405 | D3429 |
| D3358 | D3382 | D3406 | D3430 |
| D3359 | D3383 | D3407 | D3431 |
| D3360 | D3384 | D3408 | D3432 |
| D3361 | D3385 | D3409 | D3433 |
| D3362 | D3386 | D3410 | D3434 |
| D3363 | D3387 | D3411 | D3435 |
| D3364 | D3388 | D3412 | D3436 |
| D3365 | D3389 | D3413 | D3437 |
| D3366 | D3390 | D3414 | D3438 |

**D3439-D3453. FOR PARTICULARS SEE D3137-D3151.**

| | | | |
|---|---|---|---|
| D3439 | D3443 | D3447 | D3451 |
| D3440 | D3444 | D3448 | D3452 |
| D3441 | D3445 | D3449 | D3453 |
| D3442 | D3446 | D3450 | |

**D3454-D3472. FOR PARTICULARS SEE D3127-D3136.**

| | | | |
|---|---|---|---|
| D3454 | D3459 | D3464 | D3469 |
| D3455 | D3460 | D3465 | D3470 |
| D3456 | D3461 | D3466 | D3471 |
| D3457 | D3462 | D3467 | D3472 |
| D3458 | D3463 | D3468 | |

**D3473-D3502. FOR PARTICULARS SEE D3137-D3151.**

| | | | |
|---|---|---|---|
| D3473 | D3479 | D3485 | D3491 |
| D3474 | D3480 | D3486 | D3492 |
| D3475 | D3481 | D3487 | D3493 |
| D3476 | D3482 | D3488 | D3494 |
| D3477 | D3483 | D3489 | D3495 |
| D3478 | D3484 | D3490 | D3496 |

| | | | |
|---|---|---|---|
| D3497 | D3499 | D3501 | D3502 |
| D3498 | D3500 | | |

**D3503-D3611. FOR PARTICULARS SEE D3127-D3136.**

| | | | |
|---|---|---|---|
| D3503 | D3531 | D3558 | D3585 |
| D3504 | D3532 | D3559 | D3586 |
| D3505 | D3533 | D3560 | D3587 |
| D3506 | D3534 | D3561 | D3588 |
| D3507 | D3535 | D3562 | D3589 |
| D3508 | D3536 | D3563 | D3590 |
| D3509 | D3537 | D3564 | D3591 |
| D3510 | D3538 | D3565 | D3592 |
| D3511 | D3539 | D3566 | D3593 |
| D3512 | D3540 | D3567 | D3594 |
| D3513 | D3541 | D3568 | D3595 |
| D3514 | D3542 | D3569 | D3596 |
| D3515 | D3543 | D3570 | D3597 |
| D3516 | D3544 | D3571 | D3598 |
| D3517 | D3545 | D3572 | D3599 |
| D3518 | D3546 | D3573 | D3600 |
| D3519 | D3547 | D3574 | D3601 |
| D3520 | D3548 | D3575 | D3602 |
| D3521 | D3549 | D3576 | D3603 |
| D3522 | D3550 | D3577 | D3604 |
| D3523 | D3551 | D3578 | D3605 |
| D3524 | D3552 | D3579 | D3606 |
| D3525 | D3553 | D3580 | D3607 |
| D3526 | D3554 | D3581 | D3608 |
| D3527 | D3555 | D3582 | D3609 |
| D3528 | D3556 | D3583 | D3610 |
| D3529 | D3557 | D3584 | D3611 |
| D3530 | | | |

**D3612-D3651. FOR PARTICULARS SEE D3137-D3151.**

| | | | |
|---|---|---|---|
| D3612 | D3622 | D3632 | D3642 |
| D3613 | D3623 | D3633 | D3643 |
| D3614 | D3624 | D3634 | D3644 |
| D3615 | D3625 | D3635 | D3645 |
| D3616 | D3626 | D3636 | D3646 |
| D3617 | D3627 | D3637 | D3647 |
| D3618 | D3628 | D3638 | D3648 |
| D3619 | D3629 | D3639 | D3649 |
| D3620 | D3630 | D3640 | D3650 |
| D3621 | D3631 | D3641 | D3651 |

**D3652-D4094. FOR PARTICULARS SEE D3127-D3136.**

| | | | | | | | |
|---|---|---|---|---|---|---|---|
| D3652 | D3696 | D3740 | D3784 | D3828 | D3874 | D3920 | D3966 |
| D3653 | D3697 | D3741 | D3785 | D3829 | D3875 | D3921 | D3967 |
| D3654 | D3698 | D3742 | D3786 | D3830 | D3876 | D3922 | D3968 |
| D3655 | D3699 | D3743 | D3787 | D3831 | D3877 | D3923 | D3969 |
| D3656 | D3700 | D3744 | D3788 | D3832 | D3878 | D3924 | D3970 |
| D3657 | D3701 | D3745 | D3789 | D3833 | D3879 | D3925 | D3971 |
| D3658 | D3702 | D3746 | D3790 | D3834 | D3880 | D3926 | D3972 |
| D3659 | D3703 | D3747 | D3791 | D3835 | D3881 | D3927 | D3973 |
| D3660 | D3704 | D3748 | D3792 | D3836 | D3882 | D3928 | D3974 |
| D3661 | D3705 | D3749 | D3793 | D3837 | D3883 | D3929 | D3975 |
| D3662 | D3706 | D3750 | D3794 | D3838 | D3884 | D3930 | D3976 |
| D3663 | D3707 | D3751 | D3795 | D3839 | D3885 | D3931 | D3977 |
| D3664 | D3708 | D3752 | D3796 | D3840 | D3886 | D3932 | D3978 |
| D3665 | D3709 | D3753 | D3797 | D3841 | D3887 | D3933 | D3979 |
| D3666 | D3710 | D3754 | D3798 | D3842 | D3888 | D3934 | D3980 |
| D3667 | D3711 | D3755 | D3799 | D3843 | D3889 | D3935 | D3981 |
| D3668 | D3712 | D3756 | D3800 | D3844 | D3890 | D3936 | D3982 |
| D3669 | D3713 | D3757 | D3801 | D3845 | D3891 | D3937 | D3983 |
| D3670 | D3714 | D3758 | D3802 | D3846 | D3892 | D3938 | D3984 |
| D3671 | D3715 | D3759 | D3803 | D3847 | D3893 | D3939 | D3985 |
| D3672 | D3716 | D3760 | D3804 | D3848 | D3894 | D3940 | D3986 |
| D3673 | D3717 | D3761 | D3805 | D3849 | D3895 | D3941 | D3987 |
| D3674 | D3718 | D3762 | D3806 | D3850 | D3896 | D3942 | D3988 |
| D3675 | D3719 | D3763 | D3807 | D3851 | D3897 | D3943 | D3989 |
| D3676 | D3720 | D3764 | D3808 | D3852 | D3898 | D3944 | D3990 |
| D3677 | D3721 | D3765 | D3809 | D3853 | D3899 | D3945 | D3991 |
| D3678 | D3722 | D3766 | D3810 | D3854 | D3900 | D3946 | D3992 |
| D3679 | D3723 | D3767 | D3811 | D3855 | D3901 | D3947 | D3993 |
| D3680 | D3724 | D3768 | D3812 | D3856 | D3902 | D3948 | D3994 |
| D3681 | D3725 | D3769 | D3813 | D3857 | D3903 | D3949 | D3995 |
| D3682 | D3726 | D3770 | D3814 | D3858 | D3904 | D3950 | D3996 |
| D3683 | D3727 | D3771 | D3815 | D3859 | D3905 | D3951 | D3997 |
| D3684 | D3728 | D3772 | D3816 | D3860 | D3906 | D9352 | D3998 |
| D3685 | D3729 | D3773 | D3817 | D3861 | D3907 | D3953 | D3999 |
| D3686 | D3730 | D3774 | D3818 | D3862 | D3908 | D3954 | D4000 |
| D3687 | D3731 | D3775 | D3819 | D3863 | D3909 | D3955 | D4001 |
| D3688 | D3732 | D3776 | D3820 | D3864 | D3910 | D3956 | D4002 |
| D3689 | D3733 | D3777 | D3821 | D3865 | D3911 | D3957 | D4003 |
| D3690 | D3734 | D3778 | D3822 | D3866 | D3912 | D3958 | D4004 |
| D3691 | D3735 | D3779 | D3823 | D3867 | D3913 | D3959 | D4005 |
| D3692 | D3736 | D3780 | D3824 | D3868 | D3914 | D3960 | D4006 |
| D3693 | D3737 | D3781 | D3825 | D3869 | D3915 | D3961 | D4007 |
| D3694 | D3738 | D3782 | D3826 | D3870 | D3916 | D3962 | D4008 |
| D3695 | D3739 | D3783 | D3827 | D3871 | D3917 | D3963 | D4009 |
| | | | | D3872 | D3918 | D3964 | D4010 |
| | | | | D3873 | D3919 | D3965 | D4011 |

| | | | |
|---|---|---|---|
| D4012 | D4033 | D4054 | D4075 |
| D4013 | D4034 | D4055 | D4076 |
| D4014 | D4035 | D4056 | D4077 |
| D4015 | D4036 | D4057 | D4078 |
| D4016 | D4037 | D4058 | D4079 |
| D4017 | D4038 | D4059 | D4080 |
| D4018 | D4039 | D4060 | D4081 |
| D4019 | D4040 | D4061 | D4082 |
| D4020 | D4041 | D4062 | D4083 |
| D4021 | D4042 | D4063 | D4084 |
| D4022 | D4043 | D4064 | D4085 |
| D4023 | D4044 | D4065 | D4086 |
| D4024 | D4045 | D4066 | D4087 |
| D4025 | D4046 | D4067 | D4088 |
| D4026 | D4047 | D4068 | D4089 |
| D4027 | D4048 | D4069 | D4090 |
| D4028 | D4049 | D4070 | D4091 |
| D4029 | D4050 | D4071 | D4092 |
| D4030 | D4051 | D4072 | D4093 |
| D4031 | D4052 | D4073 | D4094 |
| D4032 | D4053 | D4074 | |

## Bo-Bo 2

Introduced: 1958.
Locomotive manufacturer: B.R.
Total b.h.p.: { 1,160. / 1,160*. / 1,250†.
Engine: Sulzer 6-cyl. type 6LDA28 of 1,160 b.h.p. at 750 r.p.m.
†Sulzer 6-cyl. type 6LDA28-B of 1,250 b.h.p. at 750 r.p.m.
Transmission: **Electric.** Four B.T.H. axle-hung, nose-suspended traction motors of 213 h.p. (continuous rating).
Weight: { 75 tons. / 72 tons 17 cwt.* / 72 tons 17 cwt.†
Driving Wheels: 3′ 9″.
Maximum tractive effort: 40,000 lb.

| | | | |
|---|---|---|---|
| D5000 | D5008 | D5016 | D5024 |
| D5001 | D5009 | D5017 | D5025 |
| D5002 | D5010 | D5018 | D5026 |
| D5003 | D5011 | D5019 | D5027 |
| D5004 | D5012 | D5020 | D5028 |
| D5005 | D5013 | D5021 | D5029 |
| D5006 | D5014 | D5022 | D5030 |
| D5007 | D5015 | D5023 | D5031 |

| | | | |
|---|---|---|---|
| D5032 | D5068 | D5104* | D5140* |
| D5033 | D5069 | D5105* | D5141* |
| D5034 | D5070 | D5106* | D5142* |
| D5035 | D5071 | D5107* | D5143* |
| D5036 | D5072 | D5108* | D5144* |
| D5037 | D5073 | D5109* | D5145* |
| D5038 | D5074 | D5110* | D5146* |
| D5039 | D5075 | D5111* | D5147* |
| D5040 | D5076 | D5112* | D5148* |
| D5041 | D5077 | D5113* | D5149* |
| D5042 | D5078 | D5114* | D5150* |
| D5043 | D5079 | D5115* | D5151† |
| D5044 | D5080 | D5116* | D5152† |
| D5045 | D5081 | D5117* | D5153† |
| D5046 | D5082 | D5118* | D5154† |
| D5047 | D5083 | D5119* | D5155† |
| D5048 | D5084 | D5120* | D5156† |
| D5049 | D5085 | D5121* | D5157† |
| D5050 | D5086 | D5122* | D5158† |
| D5051 | D5087 | D5123* | D5159† |
| D5052 | D5088 | D5124* | D5160† |
| D5053 | D5089 | D5125* | D5161† |
| D5054 | D5090 | D5126* | D5162† |
| D5055 | D5091 | D5127* | D5163† |
| D5056 | D5092 | D5128* | D5164† |
| D5057 | D5093 | D5129* | D5165† |
| D5058 | D5094* | D5130* | D5166† |
| D5059 | D5095* | D5131* | D5167† |
| D5060 | D5096* | D5132* | D5168† |
| D5061 | D5097* | D5133* | D5169† |
| D5062 | D5098* | D5134* | D5170† |
| D5063 | D5099* | D5135* | D5171† |
| D5064 | D5100* | D5136* | D5172† |
| D5065 | D5101* | D5137* | D5173† |
| D5066 | D5102* | D5138* | D5174† |
| D5067 | D5103* | D5139* | D5175† |

## Bo-Bo 2

Introduced: 1958.
Locomotive manufacturer: Birmingham R.C. & W. Co.
Total b.h.p.: { 1,160. / 1,160*. / 1,250†.
Engine: Sulzer 6-cyl. type 6LDA28 of 1,160 b.h.p. at 750 r.p.m.
†Sulzer 6-cyl. type 6LDA28-B of 1,250 b.h.p. at 750 r.p.m.

Transmission: **Electric.** Four Crompton Parkinson axle-hung, nose-suspended traction motors.
†**Electric.** Four G.E.C. axle-hung, nose-suspended traction.
Weight: { 74 tons. / 77 tons 10 cwt.*. / 74 tons†.
Driving Wheels: 3' 7".
Maximum tractive effort: 42,000 lb.

cyl. JVS12T of 1,250*, 1,365 or 1,600† b.h.p. at 850*, 900 or 950† r.p.m.
Transmission: **Electric.** Four Brush 250 h.p. traction motors, single reduction gear drive.
Weight: 104 tons.
Driving Wheels: 3' 7".
Maximum tractive effort: 42,000 lb.

| | | | |
|---|---|---|---|
| D5300* | D5329 | D5358† | D5387† |
| D5301* | D5330 | D5359† | D5388† |
| D5302* | D5331 | D5360† | D5389† |
| D5303* | D5332 | D5361† | D5390† |
| D5304* | D5333 | D5362† | D5391† |
| D5305* | D5334 | D5363† | D5392† |
| D5306* | D5335 | D5364† | D5393† |
| D5307* | D5336 | D5365† | D5394† |
| D5308* | D5337 | D5366† | D5395† |
| D5309* | D5338 | D5367† | D5396† |
| D5310* | D5339 | D5368† | D5397† |
| D5311* | D5340 | D5369† | D5398† |
| D5312* | D5341 | D5370† | D5399† |
| D5313* | D5342 | D5371† | D5400† |
| D5314* | D5343 | D5372† | D5401† |
| D5315* | D5344 | D5373† | D5402† |
| D5316* | D5345 | D5374† | D5403† |
| D5317* | D5346 | D5375† | D5404† |
| D5318* | D5347† | D5376† | D5405† |
| D5319* | D5348† | D5377† | D5406† |
| D5320 | D5349† | D5378† | D5407† |
| D5321 | D5350† | D5379† | D5408† |
| D5322 | D5351† | D5380† | D5409† |
| D5323 | D5352† | D5381† | D5410† |
| D5324 | D5353† | D5382† | D5411† |
| D5325 | D5354† | D5383† | D5412† |
| D5326 | D5355† | D5384† | D5413† |
| D5327 | D5356† | D5385† | D5414† |
| D5328 | D5357† | D5386† | D5415† |

# AIA-AIA                 2 & 3†

Introduced: 1957.
Locomotive manufacturer: Brush Traction Ltd.

Total b.h.p.: { 1,250* / 1,365. / 1,600†
Engine: Mirrlees, Bickerton & Day 12-

| | | | |
|---|---|---|---|
| D5500* | D5539 | D5578 | D5617 |
| D5501* | D5540 | D5579 | D5618 |
| D5502* | D5541 | D5580 | D5619 |
| D5503* | D5542 | D5581 | D5620 |
| D5504* | D5543 | D5582 | D5621 |
| D5505* | D5544 | D5583 | D5622 |
| D5506* | D5545† | D5584 | D5623 |
| D5507* | D5546 | D5585 | D5624 |
| D5508* | D5547 | D5586 | D5625 |
| D5509* | D5548 | D5587 | D5626 |
| D5510* | D5549 | D5588 | D5627 |
| D5511* | D5550 | D5589 | D5628 |
| D5512* | D5551 | D5590 | D5629 |
| D5513* | D5552 | D5591 | D5630 |
| D5514* | D5553 | D5592 | D5631 |
| D5515* | D5554 | D5593 | D5632 |
| D5516* | D5555 | D5594 | D5633 |
| D5517* | D5556 | D5595 | D5634 |
| D5518* | D5557 | D5596 | D5635 |
| D5519* | D5558 | D5597 | D5636 |
| D5520 | D5559 | D5598 | D5637 |
| D5521 | D5560 | D5599 | D5638 |
| D5522 | D5561 | D5600 | D5639 |
| D5523 | D5562 | D5601 | D5640 |
| D5524 | D5563 | D5602 | D5641 |
| D5525 | D5564 | D5603 | D5642 |
| D5526 | D5565 | D5604 | D5643 |
| D5527 | D5566 | D5605 | D5644 |
| D5528 | D5567 | D5606 | D5645 |
| D5529 | D5568 | D5607 | D5646 |
| D5530 | D5569 | D5608 | D5647 |
| D5531 | D5570 | D5609 | D5648 |
| D5532 | D5571 | D5610 | D5649 |
| D5533 | D5572 | D5611 | D5650 |
| D5534 | D5573 | D5612 | D5651 |
| D5535 | D5574 | D5613 | D5652 |
| D5536 | D5575 | D5614 | D5653 |
| D5537 | D5576 | D5615 | D5654 |
| D5538 | D5577 | D5616 | D5655† |

| | | | |
|---|---|---|---|
| D5656† | D5667† | D5678 | D5689 |
| D5657† | D5668† | D5679 | D5690 |
| D5658† | D5669† | D5680 | D5691 |
| D5659† | D5670† | D5681 | D5692 |
| D5660† | D5671 | D5682 | D5693 |
| D5661† | D5672 | D5683 | D5694 |
| D5662† | D5673 | D5684 | D5695 |
| D5663† | D5674 | D5685 | D5696 |
| D5664† | D5675 | D5686 | D5697 |
| D5665† | D5676 | D5687 | D5698 |
| D5666† | D5677 | D5688 | D5699 |

## Co-Bo 2

Introduced: 1958.
Locomotive manufacturer: Metropolitan Vickers.
Total b.h.p.: 1,200.
Engine: Crossley 8-cyl. HST Vee 8 of 1,200 b.h.p. at 625 r.p.m. (continuous).
Transmission: **Electric.** Five Metropolitan-Vickers 180 h.p. axle-hung nose-suspended traction motors.
Weight: 97 tons.
Driving Wheels: 3' 3½".
Maximum tractive effort: 50,000 lb.

| | | | |
|---|---|---|---|
| D5700 | D5705 | D5710 | D5715 |
| D5701 | D5706 | D5711 | D5716 |
| D5702 | D5707 | D5712 | D5717 |
| D5703 | D5708 | D5713 | D5718 |
| D5704 | D5709 | D5714 | D5719 |

## AIA-AIA 2

**D5800-25 for particulars see Nos. D5500-5699.**

| | | | |
|---|---|---|---|
| D5800 | D5807 | D5814 | D5821 |
| D5801 | D5808 | D5815 | D5822 |
| D5802 | D5809 | D5816 | D5823 |
| D5803 | D5810 | D5817 | D5824 |
| D5804 | D5811 | D5818 | D5825 |
| D5805 | D5812 | D5819 | |
| D5806 | D5813 | D5820 | |

## Bo-Bo 2

Introduced: 1959.
Locomotive manufacturer: English Electric.
Total b.h.p.: 1,100.
Engine: Napier " Deltic " T9-29 9 cyl., two-stroke pressure charged type of 1,100 b.h.p. at 1,600 r.p.m.
Transmission: **Electric.** Four English Electric axle-hung nose-suspended traction motors.
Weight: 73 tons 17 cwt.
Driving Wheels: 3' 7".
Maximum tractive effort.: 47,000 lb.

| | | | |
|---|---|---|---|
| D5900 | D5903 | D5906 | D5909 |
| D5901 | D5904 | D5907 | |
| D5902 | D5905 | D5908 | |

## Bo-Bo 2

Introduced: 1959.
Locomotive manufacturer: North British Locomotive Co.
Total b.h.p.: $\begin{cases} 1,000^* \\ 1,100. \end{cases}$
Engine: N.B.L./M.A.N. 12-cyl. pressure charged L12V/18/21S of (1,000*) 1,100 b.h.p.
Transmission: **Electric.** Four G.E.C. nose-suspended traction motors.
Weight: 72 tons 10 cwt.
Driving Wheels: 3' 7".
Maximum tractive effort: 45,000 lb.

| | | | |
|---|---|---|---|
| D6100* | D6115 | D6130 | D6145 |
| D6101* | D6116 | D6131 | D6146 |
| D6102* | D6117 | D6132 | D6147 |
| D6103* | D6118 | D6133 | D6148 |
| D6104* | D6119 | D6134 | D6149 |
| D6105* | D6120 | D6135 | D6150 |
| D6106* | D6121 | D6136 | D6151 |
| D6107 | D6122 | D6137 | D6152 |
| D6108* | D6123 | D6138 | D6153 |
| D6109* | D6124 | D6139 | D6154 |
| D6110 | D6125 | D6140 | D6155 |
| D6111 | D6126 | D6141 | D6156 |
| D6112 | D6127 | D6142 | D6157 |
| D6113 | D6128 | D6143 | |
| D6114 | D6129 | D6144 | |

## B-B 2

Introduced: 1959.
Locomotive manufacturer: North British Locomotive Co.
Total b.h.p.: $\begin{cases} 1000.^* \\ 1,100. \end{cases}$
Engine: N. B. L. / M. A. N. 12-cyl. L12V18/21M of 1,000 b.h.p.* or 1,100 b.h.p.

*Transmission:* **Hydraulic.** Voith—N.B.L. L.T.306r hydraulic transmission and cardan shafts to primary gear-boxes on the inner axles and secondary gear-boxes on the outer axles.

*Weight:* { 68 tons.* / 65 tons.
*Driving Wheels:* 3′ 7″.
*Maximum tractive effort:* 40,000 lbs.

| | | | |
|---|---|---|---|
| D6300* | D6315 | D6330 | D6345 |
| D6301* | D6316 | D6331 | D6346 |
| D6302* | D6317 | D6332 | D6347 |
| D6303* | D6318 | D6333 | D6348 |
| D6304* | D6319 | D6334 | D6349 |
| D6305* | D6320 | D6335 | D6350 |
| D6306 | D6321 | D6336 | D6351 |
| D6307 | D6322 | D6337 | D6352 |
| D6308 | D6323 | D6338 | D6353 |
| D6309 | D6324 | D6339 | D6354 |
| D6310 | D6325 | D6340 | D6355 |
| D6311 | D6326 | D6341 | D6356 |
| D6312 | D6327 | D6342 | D6357 |
| D6313 | D6328 | D6343 | |
| D6314 | D6329 | D6344 | |

## Bo-Bo 3

*Introduced:* 1960.
*Locomotive manufacturer:* Birmingham R.C. & W. Co.
*Total b.h.p.:* 1,550.
*Engines:* Sulzer 8LDA28 pressure-charged 8-cyl of 1,550 b.h.p. at 750 r.p.m. (continuous).
*Transmission:* **Electric.** Four Crompton Parkinson 305 h.p. axle-hung nose-suspended traction motors.
*Weight:* 73 tons 8 cwt.
*Driving Wheels:* 3′ 7″.
*Maximum tractive effort:* 45,000 lb.

| | | | |
|---|---|---|---|
| D6500 | D6510 | D6520 | D6530 |
| D6501 | D6511 | D6521 | D6531 |
| D6502 | D6512 | D6522 | D6532 |
| D6503 | D6513 | D6523 | D6533 |
| D6504 | D6514 | D6524 | D6534 |
| D6505 | D6515 | D6525 | D6535 |
| D6506 | D6516 | D6526 | D6536 |
| D6507 | D6517 | D6527 | D6537 |
| D6508 | D6518 | D6528 | D6538 |
| D6509 | D6519 | D6529 | D6539 |

| | | | |
|---|---|---|---|
| D6540 | D6555 | D6570 | D6585 |
| D6541 | D6556 | D6571 | D6586 |
| D6542 | D6557 | D6572 | D6587 |
| D6543 | D6558 | D6573 | D6588 |
| D6544 | D6559 | D6574 | D6589 |
| D6545 | D6560 | D6575 | D6590 |
| D6546 | D6561 | D6576 | D6591 |
| D6547 | D6562 | D6577 | D6592 |
| D6548 | D6563 | D6578 | D6593 |
| D6549 | D6564 | D6579 | D6594 |
| D6550 | D6565 | D6580 | D6595 |
| D6551 | D6566 | D6581 | D6596 |
| D6552 | D6567 | D6582 | D6597 |
| D6553 | D6568 | D6583 | |
| D6554 | D6569 | D6584 | |

## Co-Co 3

*Introduced:* 1961
*Locomotive manufacturer:* English Electric.
*Total b.h.p.:* 1,750.
*Engine:* English Electric 12CSVT. 12-cyl type of 1,750 b.h.p. at 850 r.p.m.
*Transmission:* **Electric.** Four English Electric 208 h.p. axle-hung nose-suspended traction motors.
*Weight:* 108 tons.
*Driving Wheels:* 3′ 7″.
*Maximum tractive effort:* 55,500 lbs.

| | | | |
|---|---|---|---|
| D6700 | D6718 | D6736 | D6754 |
| D6701 | D6719 | D6737 | D6755 |
| D6702 | D6720 | D6738 | D6756 |
| D6703 | D6721 | D6739 | D6757 |
| D6704 | D6722 | D6740 | D6758 |
| D6705 | D6723 | D6741 | D6759 |
| D6706 | D6724 | D6742 | D6760 |
| D6707 | D6725 | D6743 | D6761 |
| D6708 | D6726 | D6744 | D6762 |
| D6709 | D6727 | D6745 | D6763 |
| D6710 | D6728 | D6746 | D6764 |
| D6711 | D6729 | D6747 | D6765 |
| D6712 | D6730 | D6748 | D6766 |
| D6713 | D6731 | D6749 | D6767 |
| D6714 | D6732 | D6750 | D6768 |
| D6715 | D6733 | D6751 | D6769 |
| D6716 | D6734 | D6752 | D6770 |
| D6717 | D6735 | D6753 | D6771 |

| D6772 | D6774 | D6776 | D6778 |
| D6773 | D6775 | D6777 | |

## B-B 3

*To be introduced:*
*Locomotive manufacturer:* Beyer-Peacock (Hymek).
*Total b.h.p.:* 1,700.
*Engine:* Bristol-Siddeley/Maybach type MD870 of 1,700 b.h.p.
*Transmission:* **Hydraulic.** Stone-Maybach "Mekydro" type 6184U.
*Weight:* 74 tons.
*Driving Wheels:* 3' 9".
*Maximum tractive effort:* 49,700 lb.

| D7000 | D7024 | D7048 | D7072 |
| D7001 | D7025 | D7049 | D7073 |
| D7002 | D7026 | D7050 | D7074 |
| D7003 | D7027 | D7051 | D7075 |
| D7004 | D7028 | D7052 | D7076 |
| D7005 | D7029 | D7053 | D7077 |
| D7006 | D7030 | D7054 | D7078 |
| D7007 | D7031 | D7055 | D7079 |
| D7008 | D7032 | D7056 | D7080 |
| D7009 | D7033 | D7057 | D7081 |
| D7010 | D7034 | D7058 | D7082 |
| D7011 | D7035 | D7059 | D7083 |
| D7012 | D7036 | D7060 | D7084 |
| D7013 | D7037 | D7061 | D7085 |
| D7014 | D7038 | D7062 | D7086 |
| D7015 | D7039 | D7063 | D7087 |
| D7016 | D7040 | D7064 | D7088 |
| D7017 | D7041 | D7065 | D7089 |
| D7018 | D7042 | D7066 | D7090 |
| D7019 | D7043 | D7067 | D7091 |
| D7020 | D7044 | D7068 | D7092 |
| D7021 | D7045 | D7069 | D7093 |
| D7022 | D7046 | D7070 | D7094 |
| D7023 | D7047 | D7071 | |

## Bo-Bo 1

*Introduced:* 1957.
*Locomotive manufacturer:* English Electric Co./Vulcan Foundry Ltd.
*Total b.h.p.:* 1,000.
*Engine:* English Electric 8 SVT Mk. II of 1,000 b.h.p. at 850 r.p.m. (continuous).
*Transmission:* **Electric.** Four axlehung, nose-suspended d.c. traction motors.

*Weight:* 72 tons.
*Driving Wheels:* 3' 7".
*Maximum tractive effort:* 42,000 lb.
Classified **D10/3** by the E.R.

| D8000 | D8032 | D8064 | D8096 |
| D8001 | D8033 | D8065 | D8097 |
| D8002 | D8034 | D8066 | D8098 |
| D8003 | D8035 | D8067 | D8099 |
| D8004 | D8036 | D8068 | D8100 |
| D8005 | D8037 | D8069 | D8101 |
| D8006 | D8038 | D8070 | D8102 |
| D8007 | D8039 | D8071 | D8103 |
| D8008 | D8040 | D8072 | D8104 |
| D8009 | D8041 | D8073 | D8105 |
| D8010 | D8042 | D8074 | D8106 |
| D8011 | D8043 | D8075 | D8107 |
| D8012 | D8044 | D8076 | D8108 |
| D8013 | D8045 | D8077 | D8109 |
| D8014 | D8046 | D8078 | D8110 |
| D8015 | D8047 | D8079 | D8111 |
| D8016 | D8048 | D8080 | D8112 |
| D8017 | D8049 | D8081 | D8113 |
| D8018 | D8050 | D8082 | D8114 |
| D8019 | D8051 | D8083 | D8115 |
| D8020 | D8052 | D8084 | D8116 |
| D8021 | D8053 | D8085 | D8117 |
| D8022 | D8054 | D8086 | D8118 |
| D8023 | D8055 | D8087 | D8119 |
| D8024 | D8056 | D8088 | D8120 |
| D8025 | D8057 | D8089 | D8121 |
| D8026 | D8058 | D8090 | D8122 |
| D8027 | D8059 | D8091 | D8123 |
| D8028 | D8060 | D8092 | D8124 |
| D8029 | D8061 | D8093 | D8125 |
| D8030 | D8062 | D8094 | D8126 |
| D8031 | D8063 | D8095 | D8127 |

## Bo-Bo 1

*Introduced:* 1957.
*Locomotive manufacturer:* British Thomson-Houston Co.
*Total b.h.p.:* 800.
*Engine:* Paxman 16-cyl. YHXL " V "-type pressure charged by two Napier exhaust gas-driven turbo chargers. 800 b.h.p. at 1,250 r.p.m.
*Transmission:* **Electric.** Four B.T.H. nose-suspended traction motors with single reduction gear drive.
*Weight:* 68 tons.

Class V2 2-6-2 No. 60936                                      *[G. Wheeler*

Class V2 2-6-2 No. 60806 (with modified front end)         *[C. Kempson*

Class B1 4-6-0 No. 61258                                   *[P. H. Groom*

Class B12 4-6-0 No. 61572      [*G. M. Kichenside*

Class B16/1 4-6-0 No. 61425      [*P. J. Hughes*

Class B16 3 4-6-0 No. 61420      [*P. H. Wells*

Class D49/2 4-4-0 No. 62763 *The Fitzwilliam* (fitted with Reidinger rotary valve gear)
[*P. H. Groom*

Class D11 4-4-0 No. 62687 *Lord James of Douglas*                    [*G. G. Cameron*

Class K3/2 2-6-0 No. 61809                    [*K. R. Pirt*

Class K1 2-6-0 No. 62009                                    [P. H. Groom

Class K2 2-6-0 No. 61766                                    [J. B. Bucknall

Class K4 2-6-0 No. 61998 *Macleod of Macleod*              [J. C. Haydon

Class O2/3 2-8-0 No. 63972 [K. R. Pirt

Class O2 2 2-8-0 No. 63944 [K. R. Pirt

Class O1 2-8-0 No. 63755 (fitted with air pumps for working Tyne Dock–Consett ore train wagon doors) [I. Strachan

Class J25 0-6-0 No. 65726                                          [D. J. Dipple

Class J26 0-6-0 No. 65741                                          [Brian E. Morrison

Class J27 0-6-0 No. 65817                                          [J. Davenport

Class J11 0-6-0 No. 64308                                              [J. C. Haydon

Class J11 3 0-6-0 No. 64442                                       [J. C. Haydon

Class J6 0-6-0 No. 64223                                            [R. C. Riley

*Above:*
Class J20 0-6-0
No. 64689
(since withdrawn)
　　　　[R. A. Panting

*Right:*
Class J69/1 0-6-0T
No. 68550 (with original
low cab roof)
　　　　[A. R. Carpenter

*Below:*
Class J69/1 0-6-0T
No. 68508
(since withdrawn)
　　　　[P. H. Wells

Class J94 0-6-0ST No. 68047              [P. H. Wells

Class J50/3 0-6-0T No. 68963              [J. Davenpor

Class J52/2 0-6-0ST departmental No. 2           [D. Murdoch

*Right :*
**Class Y9 0-4-0ST
No. 68095**
[*P. J. Lynch*

*Centre :*
**Class L1 2-6-4T
No. 67739**
[*R. A. Panting*

*Bottom :*
**Class V3 2-6-2T
No. 67690**
[*Brian E. Morrison*

Class N10 0-6-2T No. 69109            [R. K. Evans

Class N2/4 0-6-2T No. 69583 (with condensing equipment and small chimney)
[J. C. Haydon

Class N7/3 0-6-2T No. 69723            [F. W. Day

*Above :*
Class N15 0-6-2T
No. 69211

[*K. L. Cook*

*Left :*
Class J88 0-6-0T
No. 68345

[*D. Penney*

*Below :*
Class J83 0-6-0T
No. 68470

[*Hamish Stevenson*

Derby-Sulzer Type 2  1,160 b.h.p  diesel-electric Bo-Bo No. D5129
*[J. B. Bucknall*

Derby-Sulzer Type 4  2,500 b.h.p. diesel-electric 1Co-Co1 No. D2 *Helvellyn*
*[R. A. Panting*

Birmingham R.C.W./Sulzer Type 2  1,160 b.h.p. diesel-electric Bo-Bo
No. D5305
*[P. J. Sharpe*

Brush Type 2  1.365 b.h p. diesel-electric A1A-A1A No. D5546          [R. J. Buckley]

Metropolitan-Vickers (A.E.I.) Type 2  1,200 b.h.p. diesel-electric Co-Bo No. D5710
                                                              [J. B. Bucknall

English Electric Type 2  1,100 b.h.p  diesel-electric Bo-Bo No. D5906          [P. H. Wells

English Electric/Vulcan Type I 1,000 b.h.p. diesel-electric Bo-Bos Nos. D8002 and D8001
[*J. B. Bucknall*

B.T.H. Type I 800 b.h.p. diesel-electric Bo-Bo No. D8218 [*L. Harper*

North British Type I 800 b.h.p. diesel-electric Bo-Bo No. D8400 [*C. P. Boocock*

Later Ashford/English Electric 350 b.h.p. diesel-electric 0-6-0 shunter No. 15228. Built 1949
[P. H. Groom

Hunslet 204 b.h.p. diesel-mechanical 0-6-0 shunter No. D2600. Introduced 1955
[P. H. Groom

*Driving Wheels:* 3′ 3½″.
*Maximum tractive effort:* 37,500 lb.

| D8200 | D8211 | D8222 | D8233 |
|-------|-------|-------|-------|
| D8201 | D8212 | D8223 | D8234 |
| D8202 | D8213 | D8224 | D8235 |
| D8203 | D8214 | D8225 | D8236 |
| D8204 | D8215 | D8226 | D8237 |
| D8205 | D8216 | D8227 | D8238 |
| D8206 | D8217 | D8228 | D8239 |
| D8207 | D8218 | D8229 | D8240 |
| D8208 | D8219 | D8230 | D8241 |
| D8209 | D8220 | D8231 | D8242 |
| D8210 | D8221 | D8232 | D8243 |

## Bo-Bo                           1

*Introduced:* 1958.
*Locomotive manufacturer:* North British
   Locomotive Co.
*Total b.h.p.:* 800.
*Engine:* Paxman 16-cyl. type 16YHXL
   of 800 b.h.p. at 1,250 r.p.m.
*Transmission:* **Electric.** Four G.E.C.
   axle-hung nose-suspended traction
   motors.
*Weight:* 68 tons.
*Driving Wheels:* 3′ 7″.
*Maximum tractive effort:* 42,000 lb.

| D8400 | D8403 | D8406 | D8408 |
|-------|-------|-------|-------|
| D8401 | D8404 | D8407 | D8409 |
| D8402 | D8405 |       |       |

## Co-Co      Deltic      5

*Introduced:* 1961.
*Locomotive manufacturer:* English Electric
*Total b.h.p.:* 3,300.
*Engines:* Two Napier " Deltic " 18-cyl.
   type 18·25 of 1,650 b.h.p. at 1,500
   r.p.m.
*Transmission:* **Electric.** Six English
   Electric type EE750/25G axle-hung
   nose-suspended traction motors.
*Weight:* 108 tons.
*Driving Wheels:* 3′ 7″.
*Maximum tractive effort:* 50,000 lb.

| D9000 | D9006 | D9012 | D9018 |
|-------|-------|-------|-------|
| D9001 | D9007 | D9013 | D9019 |
| D9002 | D9008 | D9014 | D9020 |
| D9003 | D9009 | D9015 | D9021 |
| D9004 | D9010 | D9016 |       |
| D9005 | D9011 | D9017 |       |

**NOTE: British Railways are pro-
viding facilities for road tests of
the prototype " Deltic " locomotive, which remains the property of
the manufacturer, and is not included in B.R. stock. It carries
no running number.**

*Introduced:* 1955.
*Locomotive manufacturer:* English Electric
*Total b.h.p.:* 3,300.
*Engines:* Two Napier "Deltic" 18-cyl.
   engines of 1,650 b.h.p.
*Transmission:* **Electric.** Six axle-hung
   nose-suspended traction motors.
*Weight:* 106 tons.
*Driving Wheels:* 3′ 7″
*Maximum tractive effort:* 60,000 lb.

## Co-Co      5P/5F

*Introduced:* 1947.
*Locomotive manufacturer:* Derby Works,
   L.M.S.
*Total b.h.p.:* 1,600.
*Engine :* English Electric 16-cyl. of
   1,600 b.h.p. at 750 r.p.m. (continuous
   rating).
*Transmission:* **Electric.** Six nose-
   suspended motors, single reduction
   gear drive.
*Weight:* 127 tons 13 cwt.
*Driving Wheels:* 3′ 6″.
*Maximum tractive effort:* 41,400 lb.

| 10000 | 10001 | **Total 2** |
|-------|-------|-------------|

## 1Co-Co1   { 10201/2 5P/5F
                10203   6P/6F }

*Introduced:* { 1951
                1954* }
*Locomotive manufacturer:*      Ashford
   Works, B.R.
*Total b.h.p.:* { 1,750
                  2,000* }
*Engine:* English Electric Co. **16-cyl**
   1,750 b.h.p. (2,000 b.h.p.*)
*Transmission:* **Electric.** six nose-
   suspended, axle-hung motors of
   260 h.p. (1-hour rating).
*Weight:* { 135 tons.
             132 tons* }
*Driving Wheels:* 3′ 7″.
*Maximum tractive effort:* { 48,000 lb.
                             50,000 lb.* }

| 10201 | 10202 | *10203 |
|-------|-------|--------|
|       |       | **Total 3** |

## 0-6-0     Shunter

*Introduced:* 1936.
*Locomotive manufacturer:* English Electric for L.M.S.
*Total b.h.p.:* 350.
*Engine:* English Electric 6-cyl. 350 b.h.p.
*Transmission:* **Electric.** Two nose-suspended motors, single reduction gear drive.
*Weight:* 51 tons.
*Driving Wheels:* 4′ 0½″.
*Maximum tractive effort:* 30,000 lb.

| 12000 | 12001 | **Total 2** |
|---|---|---|

## 0-6-0     Shunter

*Introduced:* 1939.
*Locomotive manufacturer:* Derby Works, L.M.S.
*Total b.h.p.:* 350.
*Engine:* English Electric, 6-cyl. 350 b.h.p.
*Transmission:* **Electric.** Single motor; jackshaft drive.
*Weight:* 54 tons 16 cwt.
*Driving Wheels:* 4′ 3″.
*Maximum tractive effort:* 33,000 lb.

| 12003 | 12011 | 12019 | 12027 |
|---|---|---|---|
| 12004 | 12012 | 12020 | 12028 |
| 12005 | 12013 | 12021 | 12029 |
| 12006 | 12014 | 12022 | 12030 |
| 12007 | 12015 | 12023 | 12031 |
| 12008 | 12016 | 12024 | 12032 |
| 12009 | 12017 | 12025 | |
| 12010 | 12018 | 12026 | |

**Total 30**

## 0-6-0     Shunter

*Introduced:* 1945.
*Locomotive manufacturer:* L.M.S. and B.R.
*Total b.h.p.:* 350.
*Engine:* English Electric, 6-cyl. 350 b.h.p.
*Transmission:* **Electric.** Two 135 h.p., nose-suspended motors, double reduction gear drive.
*Weight:* 47 tons 5 cwt.
*Driving Wheels:* 4′ 0½″.
*Maximum tractive effort:* 35,000 lb.

| 12033 | 12060 | 12087 | 12114 |
|---|---|---|---|
| 12034 | 12061 | 12088 | 12115 |
| 12035 | 12062 | 12089 | 12116 |
| 12036 | 12063 | 12090 | 12117 |
| 12037 | 12064 | 12091 | 12118 |
| 12038 | 12065 | 12092 | 12119 |
| 12039 | 12066 | 12093 | 12120 |
| 12040 | 12067 | 12094 | 12121 |
| 12041 | 12068 | 12095 | 12122 |
| 12042 | 12069 | 12096 | 12123 |
| 12043 | 12070 | 12097 | 12124 |
| 12044 | 12071 | 12098 | 12125 |
| 12045 | 12072 | 12099 | 12126 |
| 12046 | 12073 | 12100 | 12127 |
| 12047 | 12074 | 12101 | 12128 |
| 12048 | 12075 | 12102 | 12129 |
| 12049 | 12076 | 12103 | 12130 |
| 12050 | 12077 | 12104 | 12131 |
| 12051 | 12078 | 12105 | 12132 |
| 12052 | 12079 | 12106 | 12133 |
| 12053 | 12080 | 12107 | 12134 |
| 12054 | 12081 | 12108 | 12135 |
| 12055 | 12082 | 12109 | 12136 |
| 12056 | 12083 | 12110 | 12137 |
| 12057 | 12084 | 12111 | 12138 |
| 12058 | 12085 | 12112 | |
| 12059 | 12086 | 12113 | |

**Total 106**

## 0-6-0     Shunter

*Introduced:* 1944.
*Locomotive manufacturer:* Doncaster Works, L.N.E.R.
*Total b.h.p.:* 350.
*Engine:* English Electric, 6-cyl. 350 b.h.p.
*Transmission:* **Electric.** Two 135 h.p. nose-suspended motors, double reduction gear drive.
*Weight:* 50 tons.
*Driving Wheels:* 4′ 0″.
*Maximum tractive effort:* 32,000 lb.

| 15000 | 15001 | 15002 | 15003 |
|---|---|---|---|

**Total 4**

## 0-6-0 Shunter

*Introduced:* 1949.
*Locomotive manufacturer:* Doncaster Works, B.R.
*Total b.h.p.:* 360.
*Engine:* Petter SS4 4-cyl. 360 b.h.p.
*Transmission:* **Electric.** Two 135 h.p. nose-suspended traction motors double reduction gear drive.
*Weight:* 51 tons.
*Driving Wheels:* 4′ 0″.
*Maximum tractive effort:* 32,000 lb.

15004        **Total 1**

## 0-6-0 Shunter

*Introduced:* 1936.
*Locomotive manufacturer:* English Electric for G.W.R.
*Total b.h.p.:* 350.
*Engine:* English Electric, 6-cyl. 350 b.h.p.
*Transmission:* **Electric.** Two nose-suspended motors, single reduction gear drive.
*Weight:* 51 tons 10 cwt.
*Driving Wheels:* 4′ 1″.
*Maximum tractive effort:* 30,000 lb.

15100        **Total 1**

## 0-6-0 Shunter

*Introduced:* 1948.
*Locomotive manufacturer:* Swindon Works, B.R.
*Total b.h.p.:* 350.
*Engine:* English Electric, 6-cyl. 350 b.h.p.
*Transmission:* **Electric.** Two 135 h.p. nose-suspended motors, double reduction gear drive.
*Weight:* 50 tons.
*Driving Wheels:* 4′ 0½″.
*Maximum tractive effort:* 33,500 lb.

| | | |
|---|---|---|
| 15101 | 15103 | 15105 |
| 15102 | 15104 | 15106 **Total 6** |

## 0-6-0 Shunter

*Introduced:* 1937.
*Locomotive manufacturer:* Ashford Works, S.R.
*Total b.h.p.:* 350.
*Engine:* English Electric, 6-cyl. 350 b.h.p.
*Transmission:* **Electric.** Two nose-suspended motors, single reduction gear drive.
*Weight:* 55 tons 5 cwt.
*Driving Wheels:* 4′ 6″.
*Maximum tractive effort:* 30,000 lb.

15201   15202   15203 **Total 3**

## 0-6-0 Shunter

*Introduced:* 1949.
*Locomotive manufacturer:* Ashford Works, B.R.
*Total b.h.p.:* 350.
*Engine:* English Electric, 6-cyl. 350 b.h.p.
*Transmission:* **Electric.** Two 135 h.p. nose-suspended motors, double reduction gear drive.
*Weight:* 45 tons.
*Driving Wheels:* 4′ 6″.
*Maximum tractive effort:* 24,000 lb.

| | | | |
|---|---|---|---|
| 15211 | 15218 | 15225 | 15232 |
| 15212 | 15219 | 15226 | 15233 |
| 15213 | 15220 | 15227 | 15234 |
| 15214 | 15221 | 15228 | 15235 |
| 15215 | 15222 | 15229 | 15236 |
| 15216 | 15223 | 15230 | |
| 15217 | 15224 | 15231 | |

**Total 26**

**NOTE:** British Railways are providing facilities for road tests of the following three locomotives, which remain the property of the manufacturer and are not included in B.R. stock.

## 0-6-0 Shunter

*Introduced:* 1957.
*Locomotive manufacturer:* English Electric.
*Total b.h.p.:* 500.
*Engine:* English Electric 6RKT of 500 b.h.p. at 750 r.p.m.

*Transmission:* **Electric.** One English Electric traction motor coupled to double-reduction gear box final drive.
*Weight:* 48 tons.
*Driving Wheels:* 4′ 0″.
*Maximum tractive effort:* 33,000 lb.

D0226

## 0-6-0      Shunter

*Introduced:* 1957.
*Locomotive manufacturer:* English Electric.
*Total b.h.p.:* 500.
*Engine:* English Electric, 6RKT of 500 b.h.p. at 750 r.p.m.
*Transmission:* **Hydraulic.** Lysholm-Smith torque-converter and three-speed reduction gear to final drive.
*Weight:* 48 tons.

*Driving Wheels:* 4′ 0″.
*Maximum tractive effort:* 33,000 lb.

D0227

## 4-6-0    (2C)    **Gas Turbine**

*Introduced:* 1961.
*Locomotive manufacturer:* English Electric Co.
*Total b.h.p.:* 2,750.
*Engine:* English Electric gas turbine of 2,750 b.h.p. at 9,000 r.p.m.
*Transmission:* **Mechanical.** Gearbox and flexible drive to coupled axles.
*Weight:* 79 tons.
*Driving Wheels:* 4′ 0½″.
*Maximum tractive effort:* 60,000 lb.
*Weight: Locomotive:* 79 tons 16 cwt.
     „    *Tender:* 44 tons.
*Maximum tractive effort:* 38,000 lb.

GT3

# SERVICE LOCOMOTIVES

## Western Region

### 0-4-0

*Introduced:* 1957.
*Locomotive manufacturer:* Ruston & Hornsby.
*Total b.h.p.:* 88.
*Engine:* Ruston & Hornsby 4-cyl. type of 88 b.h.p.
*Transmission:* **Mechanical.** Chain driven from gearbox.
*Weight:* 17 tons.
*Wheel Diameter:* 3′ 0″.
*Maximum tractive effort:* 9,500 lb.

20

### 0-6-0

*Introduced:* 1953.
*Locomotive manufacturer:* Ruston & Hornsby.
*Total b.h.p.:* 165.
*Engine:* Ruston & Hornsby 6-cyl. type of 165 b.h.p.
*Transmission:* **Electric.** One B.T.H. nose-suspended traction motor.
*Weight:* 30 tons.
*Driving Wheels:* 3′ 2½″.
*Maximum tractive effort:* 17,000 lb.

| PWM650 | PWM652 | PWM654 |
| PWM651 | PWM653 | |

Also Petrol Locomotives 24 and 27.

## Southern Region

### 0-4-0

*Introduced:* 1947.
*Locomotive manufacturer:* John Fowler & Co.
*Total b.h.p.:* 150.
*Engine:* Fowler.
*Transmission:* **Mechanical.** Four-speed gearbox.
*Weight:* 29 tons.
*Driving Wheels:* 3′ 3″.
*Maximum tractive effort:* 15,000 lb.

DS600

### 0-4-0

*Introduced:*
*Locomotive manufacturer:* Ruston & Hornsby.
*Total b.h.p.:*
*Engine:*
*Transmission:*
*Weight:*
*Driving Wheels:*
*Maximum tractive effort:*

DS1169

## 0-6-0

Introduced: 1947.
Locomotive manufacturer: Drewry.
Total b.h.p.: 204.
Engine: Gardner 8L3 or 204 b.h.p.
Transmission: **Mechanical.** Five-
    speed gearbox.
Weight: 24 tons 15 cwt.
Driving Wheels: 3′ 3″.
Maximum tractive effort: 16,850 lb.
DS1173

# London Midland Region

## 0-4-0

Introduced: 1936.
Locomotive manufacturer: John Fowler
    & Co.
Total b.h.p.: 88.
Engine: Ruston & Hornsby 6-cyl. type
    VQ of 88 b.h.p.
Transmission: **Mechanical.** Four-speed
    constant-mesh gearbox with multiple-
    disc dry clutch manually operated.
Weight: 25 tons.
Driving Wheels: 3′ 0″.
Maximum tractive effort: 8,940 lb.
ED1

## 0-4-0

Introduced: 1936.
Locomotive manufacturer: John Fowler
    & Co.
Total b.h.p.: 150.
Engine: Fowler type 4C vertical or 150
    b.h.p. at 1,000 r.p.m. (1 hr. rating).
Transmission: **Mechanical.** Four speed
    gearbox.
Weight: 29 tons.
Driving Wheels: 3′ 3″.
Maximum tractive effort: 15,000 lb.

| ED2 | ED4 | ED6 |
| ED3 | ED5 | |

## 0-4-0

Introduced: 1955.
Locomotive manufacturer: John Fowler
    & Co.
Total b.h.p.: 150.
Engine: Fowler 4-cyl. type C of 150
    b.h.p.

Transmission: **Mechanical.** Three-lobe
    synchromesh gearbox with multiple
    disc dry clutch manually operated.
Weight: 29 tons.
Driving Wheels: 3′ 3″.
Maximum tractive effort: 15,000 lb.
ED7

## 0-4-0

Introduced: 1958.
Locomotive manufacturer: Ruston &
    Hornsby.
Total b.h.p.:
Engine: Ruston type 4YCL.
Transmission: **Mechanical.** Chain
    drive.
Weight: 8 tons 4 cwt.
Driving Wheel: 2′ 6″.
Maximum tractive effort: 4,200 lb
Gauge: 3′ 0″.
ED10

## 0-4-0

Introduced: 1958.
Locomotive manufacturer: Ruston &
    Hornsby.
Total b.h.p.: 20.
Engine:
Transmission:
Weight: 3 tons 10 cwt.
Driving Wheels:
Maximum tractive effort: 1,890 lb.
Gauge: 1′ 6″.
ZM32

# North Eastern Region
## 0-6-0       Shunter

Introduced: 1955.
Locomotive manufacturer: Hunslet.
Total b.h.p.: 204.
Engine: Gardner type 8L3 of 204 b.h.p.
    at 1,200 r.p.m.
Transmission: **Mechanical.** Hunslet
    patent friction clutch. Hunslet four-
    speed gearbox incorporating reverse
    and final drive gears.
Weight: 30 tons.
Driving Wheels: 3′ 4″.
Maximum tractive effort: 14,500 lb.
    **(Original number in brackets)**
88 (D2612)

## Eastern Region

### 0-4-0

*Introduced:* 1950.
*Locomotive manufacturer:* Hibberd & Co.
*Total b.h.p.:* 52.
*Engine:* English National 4-cyl. Gas type. DA4 of 52 b.h.p. at 1,250 r.p.m.
*Transmission:* **Mechanical.** Spur-type three-speed gearbox with roller chains.
*Weight:* 11 tons.
*Driving Wheels:*
*Maximum tractive effort.*

52 (11104)

### 0-4-0

*Introduced:* 1955.
*Locomotive manufacturer:* Ruston & Hornsby.
*Total b.h.p.:* 88.
*Engine:* Ruston & Hornsby Mark 4V vertical 4-cyl. of 88 b.h.p.
*Transmission:* **Mechanical.**
*Weight:* 17 tons.
*Driving Wheels:* 3′ 0″.
*Maximum tractive effort:* 9,500 lb.

56

### 0-4-0

*Introduced:* 1958.
*Locomotive manufacturer:* Andrew Barclay.
*Total b.h.p.:* 150.

*Engine:*
*Transmission:* **Mechanical.**
*Weight:*
*Driving Wheels:*
*Maximum tractive effort:*

81

### 0-4-0

*Introduced:* 1959.
*Locomotive manufacturer:* Ruston & Hornsby.
*Total b.h.p.:*
*Engine:*
*Transmission:*
*Weight:*
*Driving Wheels:*
*Maximum tractive effort:*

85

### 0-6-0

*Introduced:* 1958.
*Locomotive manufacturer:* Swindon Works, B.R.
*Total b.h.p.:* 200.
*Engine:* Gardner type 8L3 of 204 b.h.p. at 1,200 r.p.m.
*Transmission:* **Mechanical.** Wilson-Drewry Director air-operated epicyclic gearbox. R.F.11 Spiral Bevel reverse/final drive unit.
*Weight:* 30 tons 4 cwt.
*Driving Wheels:* 3′ 7″.
*Maximum tractive effort:* 15,000 lb.

91          92

## EASTERN REGION DIESEL LOCOMOTIVE CLASSIFICATION

| Horse-power | Description | Loco. Nos. | Code |
|---|---|---|---|
| 153 | Hunslet/Gardner ... ... ... | D2950–2 ... | D1/1 |
| 153 | Barclay/Gardner ... ... ... | D2953–6 ... | D1/2 |
| 165 | Ruston & Hornsby ... ... ... | D2957–8 ... | D1/3 |
| 170 | Yorkshire Engine Co. ... | D2850–69 ... | D1/4 |
| 200 | N.B. Loco. Co./Paxman ... | D2700–7 ... | D2/1 |
| 200 | Brush/ Petter ... ... ... | D2999 ... | D2/11 |
| 204 | B.R./Gardner ... ... ... | D2000–2176 ... | D2/2 |
| 204 | Drewry/Gardner (3′ 3″ wheel) | D2200–14 ... | D2/3 |
| 204 | Drewry/Gardner (3′ 6″ wheel) | D2215–73 ... | D2/4 |
| 204 | Drewry/Gardner (3′ 7″ wheel) | D2274–2340 ... | D2/13 |
| 204 | Barclay/Gardner (4-speed) | D2400–9 ... | D2/5 |
| 204 | Barclay/Gardner (5-speed) ... | D2410–44 ... | D2/6 |
| 204 | Hudswell-Clarke/Gardner... | D2500–19 ... | D2/7 |

| Horse-power | Description | Loco Nos. | Code |
|---|---|---|---|
| 204 | Hunslet/Gardner (3′ 4″ wheel) ... ... | D2550–73 ... ... | D2/8 |
| 204 | Hunslet/Gardner (3′ 9″ wheel) ... | D2574–D2618 ... | D2/9 |
| 225 | N.B. Loco. Co./M.A.N. ... ... | D2708–79 ... ... | D2/10 |
| 330 | N.B. Loco. Co./M.A.N. ... ... | D2900–13 ... ... | D3/1 |
| 350 | B.R./English Electric ... ... | D3000–3116/27–36/67–3438/54–72, 3503–3611/52–4048 ... | D3/2 |
| 350 | B.R./Crossley ... ... | D3117–26 ... ... | D3/3 |
| 350 | B.R./Blackstone/G.E.C. ... ... | D3137–51, 3439–53/73–3502, 3612–51/4049–94 ... | D3/4 |
| 350 | B.R./Blackstone/B.T.H. ... ... | D3152–66 ... ... | D3/5 |
| 350 | L.M.S./English Electric (4′ 0½″ wheel) ... ... ... | 12000/1 ... ... | D3/6 |
| 350 | L.M.S./English Electric (4′ 3″ wheel) ... ... ... | 12003–32 ... ... | D3/7 |
| 350 | B.R./English Electric ... ... | 12033–12138 ... | D3/8 |
| 350 | L.N.E./English Electric ... ... | 15000–3 ... ... | D3/9 |
| 350 | G.W./English Electric (4′ 1″ wheel) | 15100 ... ... | D3/10 |
| 350 | G.W./English Electric (4′ 0½″ wheel) | 15101–6 ... ... | D3/11 |
| 350 | S.R./English Electric ... ... | 15201–3 ... ... | D3/12 |
| 350 | S.R./English Electric ... ... | 15211–36 ... ... | D3/13 |
| 360 | L.N.E./Petter ... ... ... | 15004 ... ... | D3/14 |
| 800 | B.T.H./Paxman ... ... | D8200–43 ... ... | D8/1 |
| 800 | N.B. Loco. Co./Paxman ... | D8400–9 ... ... | D8/2 |
| 1,000 | N.B. Loco. Co./M.A.N./G.E.C. | D6100–6/8/9 ... | D10/1 |
| 1,000 | N.B. Loco. Co./M.A.N./Voith | D6300–5 ... ... | D10/2 |
| 1,000 | English Electric ... ... | D8000–27 ... ... | D10/3 |
| 1,100 | English Electric/Napier ... | D5900–9 ... ... | D11/1 |
| 1,100 | N.B. Loco. Co./M.A.N./G.E.C. | D6110–57 ... ... | D11/2 |
| 1,160 | B.R./Sulzer ... ... ... | D5000–5150 ... | D11/3 |
| 1,160 | Birmingham/Sulzer... ... | D5300–46 ... ... | D11/4 |
| 1,100 | N.B. Loco. Co./M.A.N./Voith | D6306–57 ... ... | D11/5 |
| 1,200 | Metro. Vickers/Crossley ... | D5700–19 ... ... | D12/1 |
| 1,250 | Brush/Mirrlees ... ... | D5500–19 ... ... | D12/2 |
| 1,250 | Birmingham/Sulzer... ... | D5347–5415 ... | D12/3 |
| 1,250 | B.R./Sulzer ... ... ... | D5151–75 ... ... | D12/4 |
| 1,365 | Brush/Mirrlees ... ... | D5520–44/6–5654/71–99, 5800–25 ... | D13/1 |
| 1,550 | Birmingham/Sulzer... ... | D6500–85 ... ... | D15/1 |
| 1,550 | Birmingham/Sulzer... ... ... | D6586–97 ... ... | D15/2 |
| 1,600 | L.M.S./English Electric ... | 10000–1 ... ... | D16/1 |
| 1,600 | S.R./English Electric ... ... | 10201–2 ... ... | D16/2 |
| 1,600 | Brush/Mirrlees ... ... | D5545, 5655–70 ... | D16/3 |
| 1,750 | English Electric ... ... | D6700–78 ... ... | D17/1 |
| 1,700 | Beyer Peacock/Maybach ... | D7000–94 ... ... | D17/2 |
| 2,000 | English Electric ... ... | D200–399 ... ... | D20/1 |
| 2,000 | N.B. Loco. Co./M.A.N./Voith | D600–4 ... ... | D20/2 |
| 2,000 | S.R./English Electric ... ... | 10203 ... ... | D20/3 |
| 2,200 | Maybach/Mekydro ... ... | D800–32/66–70 ... | D22/1 |
| 2,200 | N.B. Loco. Co. ... ... | D833–65 ... ... | D22/2 |
| 2,300 | B.R./Sulzer ... ... ... | D1–10 ... ... | D23/1 |
| 2,500 | B.R./Sulzer ... ... ... | D11–199, 1500–13 ... | D25/1 |
| 2,700 | B.R./Maybach/Voith ... ... | D1000–73 ... ... | D27/1 |
| 3,300 | English Electric/Napier Deltic ... | D9000–21 ... ... | D33/1 |

# NUMERICAL LIST OF
# ELECTRIC LOCOMOTIVES

## AIA-AIA

*Introduced:* 1958.
*Locomotive manufacturer:* Metropolitan-Vickers.
*Total h.p.:* 2,500.
*Equipment:* Four 625 h.p. Metropolitan-Vickers nose-suspended traction motors.
*Weight:* 109 tons.
*Driving Wheels:* 3' 8".
*Maximum tractive effort:* 40,000 lb.
*System:* 25 kV. a.c. Overhead.
(Rebuilt from former Gas Turbine Loco. No. 18100.)

E2001 (formerly E1000)

## Bo-Bo     "A"

*Introduced:* 1959.
*Locomotive manufacturer:* A.E.I. (British Thomson-Houston.)
*Total h.p.:* 3,300.
*Equipment:* Four A.E.I. (B.T.H.) spring-borne d.c. traction motors of 847 h.p. (continuous) driving through Alsthom quill drive.
*Weight:* 79 tons 12 cwt.
*Driving Wheels:* 4' 0".
*Maximum tractive effort:* 48,000 lb.
*System:* 25 kV. a.c. overhead.

| E3001 | E3007 | E3013 | E3019 |
|-------|-------|-------|-------|
| E3002 | E3008 | E3014 | E3020 |
| E3003 | E3009 | E3015 | E3021 |
| E3004 | E3010 | E3016 | E3022 |
| E3005 | E3011 | E3017 | E3023 |
| E3006 | E3012 | E3018 |       |

## Bo-Bo     "A"

*Introduced:* 1960.
*Locomotive manufacturer:* English Electric.
*Total h.p.:* 3,300.
*Equipment:* Four English Electric spring-borne d.c. traction motors of 740 h.p. (continuous) driving through S.L.M. resilient drive.
*Weight:* 73 tons.
*Driving Wheels:* 4' 0".
*Maximum tractive effort:* 40,000 lb.
*System:* 25 kV. a.c. overhead.

| E3024 | E3027 | E3030 | E3033 |
|-------|-------|-------|-------|
| E3025 | E3028 | E3031 | E3034 |
| E3026 | E3029 | E3032 | E3035 |

## Bo-Bo     "A"

*Introduced:* 1960.
*Locomotive manufacturer:* General Electric.
*Total h.p.:* 3,300.
*Equipment:* Four G.E.C. spring-borne d.c. traction motors of 750 h.p. (continuous), driving through Brown-Boveri spring drives.
*Weight:* 76 tons 10 cwt.
*Driving Wheels:* 4' 0".
*Maximum tractive effort:* 50,000 lb.
*System:* 25 kV. a.c. overhead.

| E3036 | E3039 | E3042 | E3044 |
|-------|-------|-------|-------|
| E3037 | E3040 | E3043 | E3045 |
| E3038 | E3041 |       |       |

## Bo-Bo     "A"

*Introduced:* 1960.
*Locomotive manufacturer:* A.E.I. (Metropolitan-Vickers).
*Total h.p.:* 3,300.
*Equipment:* Four A.E.I. (M.V.) d.c. traction motors of 847 h.p. (continuous) driving through Alsthom quill drive.
*Weight:* 78 tons 8 cwt.
*Driving Wheels:* 4' 0".
*Maximum tractive effort:* 48,000 lb.
*System:* 25 kV. a.c. overhead.

| E3046 | E3049 | E3052 | E3054 |
|-------|-------|-------|-------|
| E3047 | E3050 | E3053 | E3055 |
| E3048 | E3051 |       |       |

## Bo-Bo     "A"

*Introduced:* 1960.
*Locomotive manufacturer:* B.R., Doncaster.
*Total h.p.:* 3,300
*Equipment:* Four A.E.I. (BTH) d.c. traction motors of 847 h.p. (continuous) driving through Alsthom quill drive.
*Weight:* 79 tons
*Driving Wheels:* 4' 0".
*Maximum tractive effort:* 48,000 lb.
*System:* 25 kV. a.c. overhead.

| E3056 | E3061 | E3066 | E3071 |
|-------|-------|-------|-------|
| E3057 | E3062 | E3067 | E3072 |
| E3058 | E3063 | E3068 | E3073 |
| E3059 | E3064 | E3069 | E3074 |
| E3060 | E3065 | E3070 | E3075 |

## Bo-Bo     "A"

*To be introduced:*
*Locomotive manufacturer:* B.R., Crewe.
*Total h.p.:* 3,300.
*Equipment:* B.T.H.
*Weight:*
*Driving Wheels:*
*Maximum tractive effort:*
*System:* 25 kV. a.c. overhead.

| | | | |
|---|---|---|---|
| E3076 | E3081 | E3086 | E3091 |
| E3077 | E3082 | E3087 | E3092 |
| E3078 | E3083 | E3088 | E3093 |
| E3079 | E3084 | E3089 | E3094 |
| E3080 | E3085 | E3090 | E3095 |

## Bo-Bo     "B"

*To be introduced:*
*Locomotive manufacturer:* A.E.I. (British Thomson-Houston).
*Total h.p.:* 3,300.
*Equipment:* Four A.E.I. (B.T.H.) spring-borne d.c. traction motors of 847 h.p. (continuous) driving through Alsthom quill drive.
*Weight:* 80 tons.
*Driving Wheels:* 4' 0"
*Maximum tractive effort:* 60,000 lb.
*System:* 25 kV. a.c. overhead.

| | |
|---|---|
| E3301 | E3302 |

## Bo-Bo     "B"

*To be introduced:*
*Locomotive manufacturer:* English Electric.
*Total h.p.:* 3,300
*Equipment:*
*Weight:*
*Driving Wheels:*
*Maximum tractive effort:*
*System:* 25 kV. a.c. overhead.

| | | |
|---|---|---|
| E3303 | E3304 | E3305 |

## Bo-Bo

*Introduced:* 1958.
*Locomotive manufacturer:* B.R., Doncaster.
*Total h.p.:* 2,552.
*Equipment:* Motor generator booster set and four 638 h.p. English Electric spring-borne traction motors driving through S.L.M. flexible drive.
*Weight:* 77 tons.
*Driving Wheels:* 4' 0".
*Maximum tractive effort:* 43,000 lb.
*System:* 750 V. d.c. 3rd rail and overhead.

| | | | |
|---|---|---|---|
| E5000 | E5006 | E5012 | E5018 |
| E5001 | E5007 | E5013 | E5019 |
| E5002 | E5008 | E5014 | E5020 |
| E5003 | E5009 | E5015 | E5021 |
| E5004 | E5010 | E5016 | E5022 |
| E5005 | E5011 | E5017 | E5023 |

## Co-Co     Class CC

*Introduced:* $\begin{cases} 1941. \\ 1948.* \end{cases}$
*Locomotive manufacturer:* S.R., Ashford.
*Total h.p.:* 1,470.
*Equipment:* Motor generator booster set and six 245 h.p. English Electric nose-suspended traction motors.
*Weight:* $\begin{cases} 99 \text{ tons } 14 \text{ cwt.} \\ 104 \text{ tons } 14 \text{ cwt.*} \end{cases}$
*Driving Wheels:* 3' 6".
*Maximum tractive effort:* $\begin{cases} 40,000 \text{ lb.} \\ 45,000 \text{ lb.*} \end{cases}$
*System:* 750 V. d.c. 3rd rail and overhead.

| | | |
|---|---|---|
| 20001 | 20002 | 20003* |

## Bo-Bo     Class EM1

*Introduced:* $\begin{cases} 1941.* \\ 1950. \end{cases}$
*Locomotive manufacturer:* B.R., Doncaster.
*Total h.p.:* 1,868.
*Equipment:* Four 467 h.p. Metropolitan-Vickers nose-suspended traction motors.
*Weight:* 87 tons 18 cwt.
*Driving Wheels:* 4' 2".
*Maximum tractive effort:* 45,000 lb.
*System:* 1,500 V. d.c. overhead.

26000* Tommy

| | | | |
|---|---|---|---|
| 26001 | 26013 | 26024 | 26035 |
| 26002 | 26014 | 26025 | 26036 |
| 26003 | 26015 | 26026 | 26037 |
| 26004 | 26016 | 26027 | 26038 |
| 26005 | 26017 | 26028 | 26039 |
| 26006 | 26018 | 26029 | 26040 |
| 26007 | 26019 | 26030 | 26041 |
| 26008 | 26020 | 26031 | 26042 |
| 26009 | 26021 | 26032 | 26043 |
| 26010 | 26022 | 26033 | 26044 |
| 26011 | 26023 | 26034 | 26045 |
| 26012 | | | |

| 26046 | Archimedes |
| 26047 | Diomedes |
| 26048 | Hector |
| 26049 | Jason |
| 26050 | Stentor |
| 26051 | Mentor |
| 26052 | Nestor |
| 26053 | Perseus |
| 26054 | Pluto |
| 26055 | Prometheus |
| 26056 | Triton |
| 26057 | Ulysses |

## Bo-Bo     Class ESI

*Introduced:* 1902.
*Locomotive manufacturer:* Brush Traction.
*Total h.p.:*
*Equipment:* Four B.T.H. nose-suspended traction motors.
*Weight:* 46 tons.
*Driving Wheels:*
*Maximum tractive effort:* 25,000 lb.
*System:* 630 V. d.c. overhead and 3rd rail.

| 26500 | 26501 |

## Co-Co     Class EM2

*Introduced:* 1954.
*Locomotive manufacturer:* B.R., Gorton.
*Total h.p.:* 2,490.
*Equipment:* Six 415 h.p. Metropolitan-Vickers nose-suspended traction motors.
*Weight:* 102 tons.
*Driving Wheels:* 4' 2".
*Maximum tractive effort:* 45,000 lb.
*System:* 1,500 V.d.c. overhead.

| 27000 | Electra |
| 27001 | Ariadne |
| 27002 | Aurora |
| 27003 | Diana |
| 27004 | Juno |
| 27005 | Minerva |
| 27006 | Pandora |

## Service Locomotives
## Eastern Region
## Bo-Bo     Class EBI

*Introduced:* 1946.
*Locomotive manufacturer:*
*Total h.p.:*
*Equipment:*
*Weight:* 74 tons 8 cwt.
*Driving Wheels:* 4' 0".
*Maximum tractive effort:* 37,600 lb.
*System:* 1,500 V. d.c. overhead.
100

## Southern Region
DS 74        DS 75

# NUMERICAL LIST OF
# DIESEL MULTIPLE UNITS

**The numbers of diesel cars have been checked to December 31st, 1960**

*Unless otherwise stated, all multiple-unit trains are gangwayed within each set, with guard's and luggage compartment at the inner end of motor brake coaches and seating is in open saloons with centre and/or end doors. The letter L in the headings indicates an open vehicle fitted with toilet facilities : K indicates a side corridor vehicle with toilet. Two standard lengths of underframe are in use, namely 56 ft. 11 in. and 63 ft. 5 in. but the actual body lengths vary by a few inches for the same type of underframe. The dimensions shown are the length over body and the overall width.*

*Several of the types listed are sub-divided by reason of detail or mechanical differences. For example, a certain number of cars in a class may have a different seating arrangement or a different make of engine but are otherwise similar to the main batch. Such differences are noted in the heading to the class and given a reference mark by which the relevant dimensions or details and the cars concerned can be identified. The type of set in which each class is formed on delivery is shown at the head of the details for that class, although it should be noted that changes may occur owing to varying operating conditions, even to the extent of coupling different makes of car in the same set or running power cars without intermediate trailers.*

# COUPLING OF DIESEL MULTIPLE UNITS

*Although several multiple-unit diesel sets can be coupled together and driven by one man in the leading cab, for various reasons it is not possible for all types of diesel unit to work together. In order to distinguish cars that can run together, all have painted under the left and right headlights a colour code symbol. This is repeated at the inner end of the car in similar positions and a miniature symbol also appears on the plug socket covers. Only units bearing the same symbol can be coupled together.*

- ▲ **RED TRIANGLE**
- ◆ **YELLOW DIAMOND**
- ● **WHITE CIRCLE**
- ■ **BLUE SQUARE**
- ★ **ORANGE STAR**

## Motor Brake Second
### (TWIN UNITS)

Built by: **Derby Works, B.R.**

Engines: Two B.U.T. (Leyland) 6-cyl. horizontal type of 238 b.h.p.
*Two Rolls Royce 8-cyl. horizontal type of 238 b.h.p.
†Two B.U.T. (Leyland) 6-cyl. horizontal type of 230 b.h.p.

Transmission: **Mechanical.** Cardan shaft and freewheel to four-speed epicyclic gearbox and further cardan shaft to final drive.
*Hydraulic. Twin-disc Torque converter
†Mechanical. Cardan shaft and free wheel to Self Changing Gears Ltd. automatic four-speed gearbox and further cardan shaft to final drive.

Body: 64′ 6″ × 9′ 3″.

Weight: { 35 tons 10 cwt.
{ 37 tons 10 cwt.†

Seats 2nd: 62.

| | | |
|---|---|---|
| E50000* | E50017 | E50034 |
| E50001 | E50018 | E50035 |
| E50002 | E50019 | E50036 |
| E50003 | E50020 | E50037 |
| E50004 | E50021 | E50038 |
| E50005 | E50022 | E50039 |
| E50006 | E50023 | E50040 |
| E50007 | E50024 | E50041 |
| E50008 | E50025 | E50042 |
| E50009 | E50026 | E50043 |
| E50010 | E50027 | E50044 |
| E50011 | E50028 | E50045 |
| E50012 | E50029 | E50046 |
| E50013 | E50030 | E50047 |
| E50014 | E50031 | E50048 |
| E50015 | E50032 | E50049† |
| E50016 | E50033 | |

## Motor Brake Second
### (THREE-CAR SUBURBAN)

Built by: **Derby Works, B.R.**

Engines: Two B.U.T. (Leyland) 6-cyl. horizontal type of 150 b.h.p.

Transmission: **Mechanical.** Cardan shaft and freewheel to four-speed epicyclic gearbox and further cardan shaft to final drive.

Body: 64′ 0″ × 9′ 3″. Non-gangwayed, side doors to each seating bay.

Weight: 35 tons 10 cwt.

Seats 2nd: 65.

| | | |
|---|---|---|
| W50050 | W50064 | W50078 |
| W50051 | W50065 | W50079 |
| W50052 | W50066 | W50080 |
| W50053 | W50067 | W50081 |
| W50054 | W50068 | W50082 |
| W50055 | W50069 | W50083 |
| W50056 | W50070 | W50084 |
| W50057 | W50071 | W50085 |
| W50058 | W50072 | W50086 |
| W50059 | W50073 | W50087 |
| W50060 | W50074 | W50088 |
| W50061 | W50075 | W50089 |
| W50062 | W50076 | W50090 |
| W50063 | W50077 | W50091 |

## Motor Second
### (THREE-CAR SUBURBAN)

Built by: **Derby Works, B.R.**

Engines: Two B.U.T. (Leyland) 6-cyl. horizontal type of 150 b.h.p.

Transmission: **Mechanical.** Cardan shaft and freewheel to four-speed epicyclic gearbox and further cardan shaft to final drive.

Body: 64′0″×9′3″. Non-gangwayed, side doors to each seating bay.

Weight: 35 tons 10 cwt.

Seats 2nd: 95.

| | | |
|---|---|---|
| W50092 | W50106 | W50120 |
| W50093 | W50107 | W50121 |
| W50094 | W50108 | W50122 |
| W50095 | W50109 | W50123 |
| W50096 | W50110 | W50124 |
| W50097 | W50111 | W50125 |
| W50098 | W50112 | W50126 |
| W50099 | W50113 | W50127 |
| W50100 | W50114 | W50128 |
| W50101 | W50115 | W50129 |
| W50102 | W50116 | W50130 |
| W50103 | W50117 | W50131 |
| W50104 | W50118 | W50132 |
| W50105 | W50119 | W50133 |

## Motor Brake Second ■
### (TWIN UNITS)

*Built by:* **Metropolitan Cammell.**
*Engines:* Two Rolls Royce 6-cyl. horizontal type of 180 b.h.p.
*Two Rolls Royce 6-cyl. type supercharged to 230 b.h.p.
*Transmission:* **Mechanical.** Cardan shaft and freewheel to four-speed epicyclic gearbox and further cardan shaft to final drive.
*Body:* 57′ 0″ × 9′ 3″.
*Weight:* 33 tons.
*Seats* 2nd: 52.

| | | |
|---|---|---|
| M50134 | M50136 *| M50137 |
| M50135 | | |

## Motor Composite (L) ■
### (FOUR-CAR UNITS)

*Built by:* **Metropolitan Cammell.**
*Engines:* Two B.U.T. (A.E.C.) 6-cyl. horizontal type of 150 b.h.p.
*Transmission:* **Mechanical.** Cardan shaft and freewheel to four-speed epicyclic gearbox and further cardan shaft to final drive.
*Body:* 57′ 0″ × 9′ 3″.
*Weight:* 32 tons.
*Seats* 1st: 12.
2nd: 45.

| | | |
|---|---|---|
| E50138 | E50143 | E50148 |
| E50139 | E50144 | E50149 |
| E50140 | E50145 | E50150 |
| E50141 | E50146 | E50151 |
| E50142 | E50147 | |

## Motor Brake Second ■
### (TWIN UNITS)

*Built by:* **Metropolitan Cammell.**
*Engines:* Two B.U.T. (A.E.C.) 6-cyl. horizontal type of 150 b.h.p.
*Transmission:* **Mechanical.** Cardan shaft and freewheel to four-speed epicyclic gearbox and further cardan shaft to final drive.
*Body:* 57′ 0″ × 9′ 3″.
*Weight:* 32 tons.
*Seats:* 2nd: 52.

| | | |
|---|---|---|
| E50152 | E50154 | E50156 |
| E50153 | E50155 | E50157 |

## Motor Composite (L) ■
### (TWIN UNITS)

*Built by:* **Metropolitan Cammell.**
*Engines:* Two B.U.T. (A.E.C.) 6-cyl. horizontal type of 150 b.h.p.
*Transmission:* **Mechanical.** Cardan shaft and freewheel to four-speed epicyclic gearbox and further cardan shaft to final drive.
*Body:* 57′ 0″ × 9′ 3″.
*Weight:* 32 tons.
*Seats:* 1st: 12.
2nd: 53.

| | | |
|---|---|---|
| E50158 | E50160 | E50162 |
| E50159 | E50161 | E50163 |

## Motor Brake Second ■
### (TWIN UNITS)
**For details see E50152-7**

| | | |
|---|---|---|
| E50164 | E50166 | E50167 |
| E50165 | | |

## Motor Composite (L) ■
### (TWIN UNITS)
**For details see E50158-63**

| | | |
|---|---|---|
| E50168 | E50170 | E50171 |
| E50169 | | |

## Motor Composite (L) ■
### (FOUR-CAR UNITS)

*Built by:* **Metropolitan Cammell.**
*Engines:* B.U.T. (A.E.C.), 6-cyl. horizontal type of 150 b.h.p.
*Transmission:* **Mechanical.** Cardan shaft and freewheel to four-speed epicyclic gearbox and further cardan shaft to final drive.
*Body:* 57′ 0″ × 9′ 3″.
*Weight:* 32 tons.
*Seats* 1st: 12.
2nd: 53.

| | | |
|---|---|---|
| E50172 | E50182 | E50191 |
| E50174 | E50183 | E50192 |
| E50175 | E50184 | E50193 |
| E50176 | E50185 | E50194 |
| E50177 | E50186 | E50195 |
| E50178 | E50187 | E50196 |
| E50179 | E50188 | E50197 |
| E50180 | E50189 | |
| E50181 | E50190 | |

## Motor Brake Second ■
### (TWIN UNITS)

*Built by:* **Metropolitan Cammell.**
*Engines:* Two B.U.T. (A.E.C.) 6-cy!.
horizontal type of 150 b.h.p.
*Transmission:* **Mechanical.** Cardan
shaft and freewheel to four-speed
epicyclic gearbox and further cardan
shaft to final drive.
*Body:* 57′ 0″ × 9′ 3″.
*Weight:* 32 tons.
*Seats 2nd:* 52.

| E50198 | E50210 | E50222 |
|--------|--------|--------|
| E50199 | E50211 | E50223 |
| E50200 | E50212 | E50224 |
| E50201 | E50213 | E50225 |
| E50202 | E50214 | E50226 |
| E50203 | E50215 | E50227 |
| E50204 | E50216 | E50228 |
| E50205 | E50217 | E50229 |
| E50206 | E50218 | E50230 |
| E50207 | E50219 | E50231 |
| E50208 | E50220 | E50232 |
| E50209 | E50221 | E50233 |

## Motor Composite (L) ■
### (FOUR-CAR UNITS)
For details see E50I38-51

| E50234 | E50238 | E50242 |
|--------|--------|--------|
| E50235 | E50239 | E50243 |
| E50236 | E50240 | E50244 |
| E50237 | E50241 | E50245 |

## Motor Brake Second ■
### (TWIN UNITS)

*Built by:* **Metropolitan Cammell.**
*Engines:* Two B.U.T. (A.E.C.) 6-cyl.
horizontal type of 150 b.h.p.
*Transmission:* **Mechanical.** Cardan
shaft and freewheel to four-speed
epicyclic gearbox and further cardan
shaft to final drive.
*Body:* 57′ 0″ × 9′ 3″.
*Weight:* 32 tons.
*Seats 2nd:* 44.

| E50246 | E50247 | E50248 |
|--------|--------|--------|

## Motor Brake Second ■
### (FOUR-CAR UNITS)

*Built by:* **Cravens.**
*Engines:* Two B.U.T. (A.E.C.) 6cyl.
horizontal type of 150 b.h.p.
*Transmission:* **Mechanical.** Cardan
shaft and freewheel to four-speed
epicyclic gearbox and further cardan
shaft to final drive.
*Body:* 57′ 6″ × 9′ 2″.
*Weight:* 30 tons 10 cwt.
*Seats 2nd:* 52.

| E50249 |
|--------|

## Motor Brake Second ■
### (TWIN UNITS)

*Built by:* **Metropolitan Cammell.**
*Engines:* Two B.U.T. (A.E.C.) 6-cyl.
horizontal type of 150 b.h.p.
*Transmission:* **Mechanical.** Cardan
shaft and freewheel to four-speed
epicyclic gearbox and further cardan
shaft to final drive.
*Body:* 57′ 0″ × 9′ 3″.
*Weight:* 32 tons.
*Seats 2nd:* 52.

| E50250 | E50254 | E50258 |
|--------|--------|--------|
| E50251 | E50255 | E50259 |
| E50252 | E50256 |        |
| E50253 | E50257 |        |

## Motor Composite (L) ■
### (TWIN UNITS)

*Built by:* **Metropolitan Cammell.**
*Engines:* Two B.U.T. (A.E.C.) 6-cyl.
horizontal type of 150 b.h.p.
*Transmission:* **Mechanical.** Cardan
shaft and freewheel to four-speed
epicyclic gearbox and further cardan
shaft to final drive.
*Body:* 57′ 0″ × 9′ 3″.
*Weight:* 32 tons.
*Seats 1st:* 12.
*        2nd:* 53.

| E50260 | E50264 | E50268 |
|--------|--------|--------|
| E50261 | E50265 | E50269 |
| E50262 | E50266 |        |
| E50263 | E50267 |        |

## Motor Composite (L) ■
### (THREE-CAR UNITS)

*Built by:* **Metropolitan Cammell.**
*Engines:* Two Rolls Royce 6-cyl. horizontal type of 180 b.h.p.
*Transmission:* **Mechanical.** Cardan shaft and freewheel to four-speed epicyclic gearbox and further cardan shaft to final drive.
*Body:* 57′ 0″ × 9′ 3″.
*Weight:* 33 tons.
*Seats* 1st: 12.
2nd: 53.

| | | |
|---|---|---|
| E50270 | E50274 | E50278 |
| E50271 | E50275 | E50279 |
| E50272 | E50276 | |
| E50273 | E50277 | |

## Motor Brake Second ■
### (THREE-CAR UNITS)

*Built by:* **Metropolitan Cammell.**
*Engine:* Two Rolls Royce 6-cyl. horizontal type of 180 b.h.p.
*Transmission:* **Mechanical.** Cardan shaft and freewheel to four-speed epicyclic gearbox and further cardan shaft to final drive.
*Body:* 57′ 0″ × 9′ 3″.
*Weight:* 33 tons.
*Seats* 2nd: 52.

| | | |
|---|---|---|
| E50280 | E50285 | E50290 |
| E50281 | E50286 | E50291 |
| E50282 | E50287 | E50292 |
| E50283 | E50288 | |
| E50284 | E50289 | |

## Motor Brake Second ■
### (TWIN UNITS)

*Built by:* **Metropolitan Cammell.**
*Engines:* Two B.U.T. (A.E.C.) 6-cyl. horizontal type of 150 b.h.p.
*Transmission:* **Mechanical.** Cardan shaft and freewheel to four-speed epicyclic gearbox and further cardan shaft to final drive.
*Body:* 57′ 0″ × 9′ 3″.
*Weight:* 32 tons.
*Seats* 2nd: 52.

| | | |
|---|---|---|
| E50293 | E50295 | E50296 |
| E50294 | | |

## Motor Brake Second ■
### (THREE-CAR UNITS)

*Built by:* **Metropolitan Cammell.**
*Engines:* Two B.U.T. 6-cyl. horizontal type of 150 b.h.p.
*Transmission:* **Mechanical.** Cardan shaft and freewheel to four-speed epicyclic gearbox and further cardan shaft to final drive.
*Body:* 57′ 0″ × 9′ 3″.
*Weight:* 31 tons 10 cwt.
*Seats* 2nd: 52.

| | | |
|---|---|---|
| M50303 | M50309 | M50315 |
| M50304 | M50310 | M50316 |
| M50305 | M50311 | M50317 |
| M50306 | M50312 | M50318 |
| M50307 | M50313 | M50319 |
| M50308 | M50314 | M50320 |

## Motor Composite (L) ■
### (THREE-CAR UNITS)

*Built by:* **Metropolitan Cammell.**
*Engines:* Two B.U.T. 6-cyl. horizontal type of 150 b.h.p.
*Transmission:* **Mechanical.** Cardan shaft and freewheel to four-speed epicyclic gearbox and further cardan shaft to final drive.
*Body:* 57′ 0″ × 9′ 3″.
*Weight:* 32 tons.
*Seats* 1st: 12.
2nd: 53.

| | | |
|---|---|---|
| M50321 | M50327 | M50333 |
| M50322 | M50328 | M50334 |
| M50323 | M50329 | M50335 |
| M50324 | M50330 | M50336 |
| M50325 | M50331 | M50337 |
| M50326 | M50332 | M50338 |

## Motor Brake Second ■
### (TWIN UNITS)

*Built by:* **Gloucester R.C. & W. Co.**
*Engines:* Two B.U.T. (A.E.C.) 6-cyl. horizontal type of 150 b.h.p.
*Transmission:* **Mechanical.** Cardan shaft and freewheel to four-speed epicyclic gearbox and further cardan shaft to final drive.
*Body:* 57′ 6″ × 9′ 3″.
*Weight:* 30 tons 5 cwt.
*Seats* 2nd: 52.

| | | | | | |
|---|---|---|---|---|---|
| SC50339 | SC50346 | M50353 | M50395 | M50402 | M50409 |
| SC50340 | SC50347 | M50354 | M50396 | M50403 | M50410 |
| SC50341 | SC50348 | M50355 | M50397 | M50404 | M50411 |
| SC50342 | SC50349 | M50356 | M50398 | M50405 | M50412 |
| SC50343 | M50350 | M50357 | M50399 | M50406 | M50413 |
| SC50344 | M50351 | M50358* | M50400 | M50407 | M50414 |
| SC50345 | M50352 | | M50401 | M50408 | |

*Fitted with C.A.V. Ltd. automatic gear change equipment.

## Motor Brake Second ■
### (TWIN UNITS)

*Built by:* **Cravens.**
*Engines:* Two B.U.T. (Leyland) (A.E.C.*) 6-cyl. horizontal type of 150 b.h.p.
*Transmission:* **Mechanical.** Cardan shaft and freewheel to four-speed epicyclic gearbox and further cardan shaft to final drive.
*Body:* 57′ 6″ × 9′ 2″.
*Weight:* 29 tons.
*Seats* 2nd: 52.

| | | |
|---|---|---|
| E50359 | E50371* | E50383* |
| E50360 | E50372* | E50384* |
| E50361 | E50373* | E50385* |
| E50362 | E50374* | E50386* |
| E50363 | E50375* | E50387* |
| E50364 | E50376* | E50388* |
| E50365 | E50377* | E50389* |
| E50366 | E50378* | M50390* |
| E50367 | E50379* | M50391* |
| E50368 | E50380* | M50392* |
| E50369 | E50381* | M50393* |
| E50370 | E50382* | M50394* |

## Motor Brake Second ■
### (TWIN UNITS)

*Built by:* **Park Royal Vehicles.**
*Engines:* Two B.U.T. (A.E.C.) 6-cyl. horizontal type of 150 b.h.p.
*Transmission:* **Mechanical.** Cardan shaft and freewheel to four-speed epicyclic gearbox and further cardan shaft to final drive.
*Body:* 57′ 6″ × 9′ 3″.
*Weight:* 33 tons 8 cwt.
*Seats* 2nd: 52.

## Motor Brake Second ■
### (TWIN UNITS)

*Built by:* **D. Wickham & Co. Ltd.**
*Engines:* Two B.U.T. (Leyland) 6-cyl. horizontal type of 150 b.h.p.
*Transmission:* **Mechanical.** Cardan shaft and freewheel to four-speed epicyclic gearbox and further cardan shaft to final drive.
*Body:* 57′ 0″ × 9′ 3″.
*Weight:* 27 tons 10 cwt.
*Seats* 2nd: 59.

| | | |
|---|---|---|
| E50415 | E50417 | E50419 |
| E50416 | E50418 | |

## Motor Brake Second ▨
### (L.M. THREE-CAR UNITS)

*Built by:* **Birmingham R.C. & W. Co.**
*Engines:* Two B.U.T. (Leyland) 6-cyl. horizontal type of 150 b.h.p.
*Transmission:* **Mechanical.** Cardan shaft and freewheel to four-speed epicyclic gearbox and further cardan shaft to final drive.
*Body:* 57′ 6″ × 9′ 3″.
*Weight:* 31 tons.
*Seats* 2nd: 52.

| | | |
|---|---|---|
| M50420 | M50422 | M50423 |
| M50421 | | |

## Motor Composite (L) ▨
### (THREE-CAR UNITS)

*Built by:* **Birmingham R. C. & W. Co.**
*Engines:* Two B.U.T. (Leyland) 6-cyl. horizontal type of 150 b.h.p.
*Transmission:* **Mechanical.** Cardan shaft and freewheel to four-speed epicyclic gearbox and further cardan shaft to final drive.
*Body:* 57′ 6″ × 9′ 3″.
*Weight:* 31 tons.
*Seats* 1st: 12.
2nd: 54.

| | | |
|---|---|---|
| M50424 | M50426 | M50427 |
| M50425 | | |

## Motor Brake Second ■
### (THREE-CAR UNITS)
**For details see M50420-3**

| | | |
|---|---|---|
| M50428 | M50446 | M50464 |
| M50429 | M50447 | M50465 |
| M50430 | M50448 | M50466 |
| M50431 | M50449 | M50467 |
| M50432 | M50450 | M50468 |
| M50433 | M50451 | M50469 |
| M50434 | M50452 | M50470 |
| M50435 | M50453 | M50471 |
| M50436 | M50454 | M50472 |
| M50437 | M50455 | M50473 |
| M50438 | M50456 | M50474 |
| M50439 | M50457 | M50475 |
| M50440 | M50458 | M50476 |
| M50441 | M50459 | M50477 |
| M50442 | M50460 | M50478 |
| M50443 | M50461 | M50479 |
| M50444 | M50462 | |
| M50445 | M50463 | |

## Motor Brake Second ■
### (TWIN UNITS)
*Built by:* **Birmingham R. C. & W. Co.**
*Engines:* Two B.U.T. (Leyland) 6-cyl. horizontal type of 150 b.h.p.
*Transmission:* **Mechanical.** Cardan shaft and freewheel to four-speed epicyclic gearbox and further cardan shaft to final drive.
*Body:* 57' 6" × 9' 3"
*Weight:* 31 tons.
*Seats 2nd:* 52.

| | | |
|---|---|---|
| M50532 | M50536 | M50540 |
| M50533 | M50537 | M50541 |
| M50534 | M50538 | |
| M50535 | M50539 | |

## Motor Composite (L) ■
### (THREE-CAR UNITS)
**For details see M50424-7.**

| | | |
|---|---|---|
| M50480 | M50498 | M50516 |
| M50481 | M50499 | M50517 |
| M50482 | M50500 | M50518 |
| M50483 | M50501 | M50519 |
| M50484 | M50502 | M50520 |
| M50485 | M50503 | M50521 |
| M50486 | M50504 | M50522 |
| M50487 | M50505 | M50523 |
| M50488 | M50506 | M50524 |
| M50489 | M50507 | M50525 |
| M50490 | M50508 | M50526 |
| M50491 | M50509 | M50527 |
| M50492 | M50510 | M50528 |
| M50493 | M50511 | M50529 |
| M50494 | M50512 | M50530 |
| M50495 | M50513 | M50531 |
| M50496 | M50514 | |
| M50497 | M50515 | |

## Motor Composite (L) ■
### (FOUR-CAR UNITS)
*Built by:* **Birmingham R. C. & W. Co.**
*Engines:* Two B.U.T. (Leyland) 6-cyl. horizontal type of 150 b.h.p.
*Transmission:* **Mechanical.** Cardan shaft and freewheel to four-speed epicyclic gearbox and further cardan shaft to final drive.
*Body:* 57' 6" × 9' 3"
*Weight:* 31 tons.
*Seats 1st:* 12.
  *2nd:* 51.

| | | |
|---|---|---|
| E50542 | E50560 | E50578 |
| E50543 | E50561 | E50579 |
| E50544 | E50562 | E50580 |
| E50545 | E50563 | E50581 |
| E50546 | E50564 | E50582 |
| E50547 | E50565 | E50583 |
| E50548 | E50566 | E50584 |
| E50549 | E50567 | E50585 |
| E50550 | E50568 | E50586 |
| E50551 | E50569 | E50587 |
| E50552 | E50570 | E50588 |
| E50553 | E50571 | E50589 |
| E50554 | E50572 | E50590 |
| E50555 | E50573 | E50591 |
| E50556 | E50574 | E50592 |
| E50557 | E50575 | E50593 |
| E50558 | E50576 | |
| E50559 | E50577 | |

## Motor Brake Second ∎
### (TWIN UNITS)
*Built by:* **Birmingham R. C. & W. Co.**
*Engines:* Two B.U.T. (Leyland) 6-cyl.
horizontal type of 150 b.h.p.
*Transmission:* **Mechanical.** Cardan
shaft and freewheel to four-speed
epicyclic gearbox and further cardan
shaft to final drive.
*body:* 57′ 6″ × 9′ 3″.
*Weight:* 31 tons.
*Seats* 2nd: 52.

| E50594 | E50596 | E50598 |
|--------|--------|--------|
| E50595 | E50597 |        |

## Motor Brake Second ∎
### (TWIN OR THREE*-CAR UNITS)
*Built by:* **Derby Works, B.R.**
*Engines:* Two B.U.T. (Leyland) 6-cyl.
horizontal type of 150 b.h.p.
*Transmission:* **Mechanical.** Cardan
shaft and freewheel to four-speed
epicyclic gearbox and further cardan
shaft to final drive.
*Body:* 57′ 6″ × 9′ 2″.
*Weight:* 28 tons 10 cwt.
*Seats* 2nd: 52.

| E50599 | E50610 | E50621* |
|--------|--------|---------|
| E50600 | E50611 | E50622* |
| E50601 | E50612 | E50623* |
| E50602 | E50613 | E50624* |
| E50603 | E50614 | M50625  |
| E50604 | E50615 | M50626  |
| E50605 | E50616 | M50627  |
| E50606 | E50617 | M50628  |
| E50607 | E50618 | M50629  |
| E50608 | E50619 |         |
| E50609 | E50620* |        |

## Motor Composite (L) ∎
### (THREE* AND FOUR-CAR UNITS)
*Built by:* **Derby Works, B.R.**
*Engines:* Two B.U.T. (Leyland) 6-cyl.
horizontal type of 150 b.h.p.
*Transmission:* **Mechanical.** Cardan
shaft and freewheel to four-speed
epicyclic gearbox and further cardan
shaft to final drive.
*Body:* 57′ 6″ × 9′ 2″.
*Weight:* 28 tons.
*Seats* 1st: 12.
2nd: 50.

| E50630 | E50636 | E50642* |
|--------|--------|---------|
| E50631 | E50637 | E50643* |
| E50632 | E50638 | E50644* |
| E50633 | E50639 | E50645* |
| E50634 | E50640 | E50646* |
| E50635 | E50641 |         |

## Motor Second (L) ∎
### (THREE-CAR CROSS-COUNTRY)
*Built by:* **Swindon Works B.R.**
*Engines:* Two B.U.T. (A.E.C.) 6-cyl.
horizontal type of 150 b.h.p.
*Transmission:* **Mechanical.** Cardan
shaft and freewheel to four-speed
epicyclic gearbox and further cardan
shaft to final drive.
*Body:* 64′ 6″ × 9′ 3″.
*Weight:* 36 tons 10 cwt.
*Seats* 2nd: 68.

| W50647 | W50664 | W50681 |
|--------|--------|--------|
| W50648 | W50665 | W50682 |
| W50649 | W50666 | W50683 |
| W50650 | W50667 | W50684 |
| W50651 | W50668 | W50685 |
| W50652 | W50669 | W50686 |
| W50653 | W50670 | W50687 |
| W50654 | W50671 | W50688 |
| W50655 | W50672 | W50689 |
| W50656 | W50673 | W50690 |
| W50657 | W50674 | W50691 |
| W50658 | W50675 | W50692 |
| W50659 | W50676 | W50693 |
| W50660 | W50677 | W50694 |
| W50661 | W50678 | W50695 |
| W50662 | W50679 |        |
| W50663 | W50680 |        |

## Motor Brake Composite ∎
### (THREE-CAR CROSS-COUNTRY)
*Built by:* **Swindon Works B.R.**
*Engines:* Two B.U.T. (A.E.C.) 6-cyl.
horizontal type of 150 b.h.p.
*Transmission:* **Mechanical.** Cardan
shaft and freewheel to four-speed
epicyclic gearbox and further cardan
shaft to final drive.
*Body:* 64′ 6″ × 9′ 3″.
*Weight:* 36 tons.
*Seats* 1st: 18.
2nd: 16.

| W50696 | W50713 | W50730 |
|--------|--------|--------|
| W50697 | W50714 | W50731 |
| W50698 | W50715 | W50732 |
| W50699 | W50716 | W50733 |
| W50700 | W50717 | W50734 |
| W50701 | W50718 | W50735 |
| W50702 | W50719 | W50736 |
| W50703 | W50720 | W50737 |
| W50704 | W50721 | W50738 |
| W50705 | W50722 | W50739 |
| W50706 | W50723 | W50740 |
| W50707 | W50724 | W50741 |
| W50708 | W50725 | W50742 |
| W50709 | W50726 | W50743 |
| W50710 | W50727 | W50744 |
| W50711 | W50728 | |
| W50712 | W50729 | |

## Motor Composite (L) ■
### (THREE-CAR UNITS)

*Built by:* **Metropolitan Cammell.**
*Engines:* Two Rolls Royce 6-cyl. horizontal type of 180 b.h.p.
*Transmission:* **Mechanical:** Cardan shaft and freewheel to four-speed epicyclic gearbox and further cardan shaft to final drive.
*Body:* 57′ 0″ × 9′ 3″.
*Weight:* 32 tons.
*Seats* 1st: 12.
    2nd: 53.

| E50745 | E50746 | E50747 |
|--------|--------|--------|

## Motor Composite (L) ■
### N.E. FOUR-CAR UNITS)

*Built by:* **Metropolitan Cammell.**
*Engines:* Two B.U.T. (A.E.C.) 6-cyl. horizontal type of 150 b.h.p.
*Transmission:* **Mechanical.** Cardan shaft and freewheel to four-speed epicyclic gearbox and further cardan shaft to final drive.
*Body:* 57′ 0″ × 9′ 3″.
*Weight:* 32 tons.
*Seats* 1st: 12.
    2nd: 53.

| E50748 | E50750 | E50751 |
|--------|--------|--------|
| E50749 | | |

## Motor Brake Second ■
### (THREE-CAR UNITS)

*Built by:* **Cravens.**
*Engines:* Two B.U.T. (Leyland) 6-cyl. horizontal type of 150 b.h.p.
*Transmission:* **Mechanical.** Cardan shaft and freewheel to four-speed epicyclic gearbox and further cardan shaft to final drive.
*Body:* 57′ 6″ × 9′ 2″.
*Weight:* 30 tons.
*Seats* 2nd: 52.

| M50752 | M50759 | M50766 |
|--------|--------|--------|
| M50753 | M50760 | M50767 |
| M50754 | M50761 | M50768 |
| M50755 | M50762 | M50769 |
| M50756 | M50763 | M50770 |
| M50757 | M50764 | |
| M50758 | M50765 | |

## Motor Brake Second ■
### (TWIN UNITS)

*Built by:* **Cravens.**
*Engines:* Two B.U.T. (A.E.C.) 6-cyl. horizontal type of 150 b.h.p.
*Transmission:* **Mechanical.** Cardan shaft and freewheel to four-speed epicyclic gearbox and further cardan shaft to final drive.
*Body:* 57′ 6″ × 9′ 2″.
*Weight:* 30 tons.
*Seats* 2nd: 52.

| M50771 | M50776 | M50781 |
|--------|--------|--------|
| M50772 | M50777 | M50782 |
| M50773 | M50778 | M50783 |
| M50774 | M50779 | M50784 |
| M50775 | M50780 | |

## Motor Composite (L) ■
### (L.M. THREE-CAR UNITS)

*Built by:* **Cravens.**
*Engines:* Two B.U.T. (Leyland) 6-cyl. horizontal type of 150 b.h.p.
*Transmission:* **Mechanical.** Cardan shaft and freewheel to four-speed epicyclic gearbox and further cardan shaft to final drive.
*Body:* 57′ 6″ × 9′ 2″
*Weight:* 30 tons.
*Seats* 1st: 12.
    2nd: 51.

| M50785 | M50792 | M50799 |
|--------|--------|--------|
| M50786 | M50793 | M50800 |
| M50787 | M50794 | M50801 |
| M50788 | M50795 | M50802 |
| M50789 | M50796 | M50803 |
| M50790 | M50797 | |
| M50791 | M50798 | |

### Motor Composite (L) ■

#### (TWIN UNITS)

*Built by:* **Cravens.**
*Engines:* Two B.U.T. (A.E.C.) 6-cyl. horizontal type of 150 b.h.p.
*Transmission:* **Mechanical.** Cardan shaft and freewheel to four-speed epicyclic gearbox and further cardan shaft to final drive.
*Body:* 57′ 6″ × 9′ 2″
*Weight:* 30 tons.
*Seats* 1st: 12.
2nd: 51.

| M50804 | M50809 | M50814 |
|--------|--------|--------|
| M50805 | M50810 | M50815 |
| M50806 | M50811 | M50816 |
| M50807 | M50812 | M50817 |
| M50808 | M50813 | |

### Motor Brake Second ■

#### (THREE-CAR SUBURBAN)
For details see W50050-91

| W50818 | W50836 | W50854 |
|--------|--------|--------|
| W50819 | W50837 | W50855 |
| W50820 | W50838 | W50856 |
| W50821 | W50839 | W50857 |
| W50822 | W50840 | W50858 |
| W50823 | W50841 | W50859 |
| W50824 | W50842 | W50860 |
| W50825 | W50843 | W50861 |
| W50826 | W50844 | W50862 |
| W50827 | W50845 | W50863 |
| W50828 | W50846 | W50864 |
| W50829 | W50847 | W50865 |
| W50830 | W50848 | W50866 |
| W50831 | W50849 | W50867 |
| W50832 | W50850 | W50868 |
| W50833 | W50851 | W50869 |
| W50834 | W50852 | W50870 |
| W50835 | W50853 | |

### Motor Second ■

#### (THREE-CAR SUBURBAN)
For details see W50092-50133

| W50871 | W50889 | W50907 |
|--------|--------|--------|
| W50872 | W50890 | W50908 |
| W50873 | W50891 | W50909 |
| W50874 | W50892 | W50910 |
| W50875 | W50893 | W50911 |
| W50876 | W50894 | W50912 |
| W50877 | W50895 | W50913 |
| W50878 | W50896 | W50914 |
| W50879 | W50897 | W50915 |
| W50880 | W50898 | W50916 |
| W50881 | W50899 | W50917 |
| W50882 | W50900 | W50918 |
| W50883 | W50901 | W50919 |
| W50884 | W50902 | W50920 |
| W50885 | W50903 | W50921 |
| W50886 | W50904 | W50922 |
| W50887 | W50905 | W50923 |
| W50888 | W50906 | |

### Motor Brake Second ■

#### (TWIN UNITS)

*Built by:* **Derby Works, B.R.**
*Engines:* Two B.U.T. (A.E.C.) 6-cyl. horizontal type of 150 b.h.p.
*Transmission:* **Mechanical.** Cardan shaft and freewheel to four-speed epicyclic gearbox and further cardan shaft to final drive.
*Body:* 57′ 6″ × 9′ 2″.
*Weight:* 28 tons 10 cwt.
*Seats* 2nd: 52.

| M50924 | M50928 | M50932 |
|--------|--------|--------|
| M50925 | M50929 | M50933 |
| M50926 | M50930 | M50934 |
| M50927 | M50931 | M50935 |

## Motor Second (L) ●
### (INTER CITY UNITS)

*Built by:* **Swindon Works, B.R.**
*Engines:* Two B.U.T. 6-cyl. horizontal type of 150 b.h.p.
*Transmission:* **Mechanical.** Cardan shaft and freewheel to four-speed epicyclic gearbox and further cardan shaft to final drive.
*Body:* 64′ 6″ × 9′ 3″. Gangwayed both ends, side driving compartment at one end.
*Weight:*
*Seats 2nd:* 64.

SC50936

## Motor Brake Second ■
### (TWIN UNITS)

*Built by:* **Derby Works, B.R.**
*Engines:* Two B.U.T. (Leyland) 6-cyl. horizontal type of 150 b.h.p.
*Transmission:* **Mechanical.** Cardan shaft and freewheel to four-speed epicyclic gearbox and further cardan shaft to final drive.
*Body:* 57′ 6″ × 9′ 2″.
*Weight:* 28 tons 10 cwt.
*Seats 2nd:* 52.

| | | |
|---|---|---|
| M50938 | M50955 | M50972 |
| M50939 | M50956 | M50973 |
| M50940 | M50957 | M50974 |
| M50941 | M50958 | M50975 |
| M50942 | M50959 | M50976 |
| M50943 | M50960 | M50977 |
| M50944 | M50961 | M50978 |
| M50945 | M50962 | M50979 |
| M50946 | M50963 | M50980 |
| M50947 | M50964 | M50981 |
| M50948 | M50965 | M50982 |
| M50949 | M50966 | M50983 |
| M50950 | M50967 | M50984 |
| M50951 | M50968 | M50985 |
| M50952 | M50969 | M50986 |
| M50953 | M50970 | M50987 |
| M50954 | M50971 | |

## Motor Second ★
### (THREE-CAR SUBURBAN)

*Built by:* **Derby Works, B.R.**
*Engines:* Two Rolls Royce horizontal type of 238 b.h.p.
*Transmission:* **Hydraulic.** Twin-disc torque converter.
*Body:* 64′ 0″ × 9′ 3″. Non-gangwayed, side doors to each seating bay.
*Weight:* 39 tons 10 cwt.
*Seats 2nd:* 95.

| | | |
|---|---|---|
| E50988 | E50995 | E51002 |
| E50989 | E50996 | E51003 |
| E50990 | E50997 | E51004 |
| E50991 | E50998 | E51005 |
| E50992 | E50999 | E51006 |
| E50993 | E51000 | E51007 |
| E50994 | E51001 | |

## Motor Second (L) ●
### (INTER CITY UNITS)

*Built by* : **Swindon Works, B.R.**
*Engines:* Two B.U.T. 6-cyl. horizontal type of 150 b.h.p.
*Transmission:* **Mechanical.** Cardan shaft and freewheel to four-speed epicyclic gearbox and further cardan shaft to final drive.
*Body:* 64′ 6″ × 9′ 3″. Gangwayed both ends, side driving compartment at one end.
*Weight:* 38 tons.
*Seats 2nd:* 64.

| | | |
|---|---|---|
| SC51008 | SC51016 | SC51024 |
| SC51009 | SC51017 | SC51025 |
| SC51010 | SC51018 | SC51026 |
| SC51011 | SC51019 | SC51027 |
| SC51012 | SC51020 | SC51028 |
| SC51013 | SC51021 | SC51029 |
| SC51014 | SC51022 | |
| SC51015 | SC51023 | |

## Motor Brake Second (L) ●
### (INTER CITY UNITS)

*Built by* : **Swindon Works, B.R.**
*Engines:* Two B.U.T. (A.E.C.) 6-cyl. horizontal type of 150 b.h.p.
*Transmission:* **Mechanical.** Cardan shaft and freewheel to four-speed epicyclic gearbox and further cardan shaft to final drive.
*Body:* 64′ 6″ × 9′ 3″.
*Weight:* 38 tons.
*Seats 2nd:* 52.

| SC51030 | SC51038 | SC51046 | W51089 | W51096 | W51103 |
| SC51031 | SC51039 | SC51047 | W51090 | W51097 | W51104 |
| SC51032 | SC51040 | SC51048 | W51091 | W51098 | W51105 |
| SC51033 | SC51041 | SC51049 | W51092 | W51099 | W51106 |
| SC51034 | SC51042 | SC51050 | W51093 | W51100 | W51107 |
| SC51035 | SC51043 | SC51051 | W51094 | W51101 | |
| SC51036 | SC51044 | | W51095 | W51102 | |
| SC51037 | SC51045 | | | | |

## Motor Brake Composite ■
### (THREE-CAR CROSS-COUNTRY)

*Built by:* **Gloucester R.C. & W. Co.**
*Engines:* Two B.U.T. 6-cyl. horizontal type of 150 b.h.p.
*Transmission:* **Mechanical.** Cardan shaft and freewheel to four-speed epicyclic gearbox and further cardan shaft to final drive.
*Body:* 64' 6" × 9' 3".
*Weight:* 36 tons 19 cwt.
*Seats 1st:* 18.
*2nd:* 16.

| W51052 | W51062 | W51072 |
| W51053 | W51063 | W51073 |
| W51054 | W51064 | W51074 |
| W51055 | W51065 | W51075 |
| W51056 | W51066 | W51076 |
| W51057 | W51067 | W51077 |
| W51058 | W51068 | W51078 |
| W51059 | W51069 | W51079 |
| W51060 | W51070 | |
| W51061 | W51071 | |

## Motor Second (L) ■
### (THREE-CAR CROSS-COUNTRY)

*Built by:* **Gloucester R.C. & W. Co.**
*Engines:* Two B.U.T. 6-cyl. horizontal type of 150 b.h.p.
*Transmission:* **Mechanical.** Cardan shaft and freewheel to four-speed epicyclic gearbox and further cardan shaft to final drive.
*Body:* 64' 6" × 9' 3".
*Weight:* 37 tons 10 cwt.
*Seats 2nd:* 68.

| W51080 | W51083 | W51086 |
| W51081 | W51084 | W51087 |
| W51082 | W51085 | W51088 |

## Motor Brake Second ■
### (TWIN UNITS)
For details see SC50339-M50357

| SC51108 | SC51115 | SC51122 |
| SC51109 | SC51116 | SC51123 |
| SC51110 | SC51117 | SC51124 |
| SC51111 | SC51118 | SC51125 |
| SC51112 | SC51119 | SC51126 |
| SC51113 | SC51120 | SC51127 |
| SC51114 | SC51121 | |

## Motor Brake Second ■
### (THREE-CAR SUBURBAN
For details see W50050-91

| W51128 | W51133 | W51138 |
| W51129 | W51134 | W51139 |
| W51130 | W51135 | W51140 |
| W51131 | W51136 | |
| W51132 | W51137 | |

## Motor Second ■
### (THREE-CAR SUBURBAN)
For details see W50092-50133

| W51141 | W51146 | W51151 |
| W51142 | W51147 | W51152 |
| W51143 | W51148 | W51153 |
| W51144 | W51149 | |
| W51145 | W51150 | |

## Motor Brake Second ★
### (E.R. THREE-CAR SUBURBAN)

*Built by:* **Derby Works, B.R.**
*Engines:* Two Rolls Royce horizontal type of 238 b.h.p.
*Transmission:* **Hydraulic.** Twin-disc torque converter.
*Body:* 64' 0" × 9' 3". Non-gangwayed, side doors to each seating bay.
*Weight:* 39 tons 10 cwt.
*Seats 2nd:* 65.

| E51154 | E51161 | E51168 |
|--------|--------|--------|
| E51155 | E51162 | E51169 |
| E51156 | E51163 | E51170 |
| E51157 | E51164 | E51171 |
| E51158 | E51165 | E51172 |
| E51159 | E51166 | E51173 |
| E51160 | E51167 | |

## Motor Brake Second ■
### (TWIN UNITS)
*Built by:* **Metropolitan Cammell.**
*Engines:* Two B.U.T. (A.E.C.) 6-cyl. horizontal type of 150 b.h.p.
*Transmission:* **Mechanical.** Cardan shaft and freewheel to four-speed epicyclic gearbox and further cardan shaft to final drive.
*Body:* 57' 0" × 9' 3".
*Weight:* 32 tons.
*Seats 2nd:* 52.

| M51174 | M51201 | SC51228 |
|--------|--------|---------|
| M51175 | M51202 | SC51229 |
| M51176 | M51203 | SC51230 |
| M51177 | E51204 | SC51231 |
| M51178 | E51205 | SC51232 |
| M51179 | E51206 | SC51233 |
| M51180 | E51207 | SC51234 |
| M51181 | E51208 | SC51235 |
| M51182 | E51209 | SC51236 |
| M51183 | E51210 | SC51237 |
| M51184 | E51211 | SC51238 |
| M51185 | E51212 | SC51239 |
| M51186 | E51213 | SC51240 |
| M51187 | E51214 | SC51241 |
| M51188 | E51215 | SC51242 |
| M51189 | E51216 | SC51243 |
| M51190 | E51217 | SC51244 |
| M51191 | E51218' | SC51245 |
| M51192 | E51219 | SC51246 |
| M51193 | E51220 | SC51247 |
| M51194 | E51221 | SC51248 |
| M51195 | E51222 | SC51249 |
| M51196 | E51223 | SC51250 |
| M51197 | SC51224 | SC51251 |
| M51198 | SC51225 | SC51252 |
| M51199 | SC51226 | SC51253 |
| M51200 | SC51227 | |

## Motor Brake Second ■
### (TWIN UNITS)
*Built by:* **Cravens.**
*Engines:* Two B.U.T. (A.E.C.) 6-cyl. horizontal type of 150 b.h.p.
*Transmission:* **Mechanical.** Cardan shaft and freewheel to four-speed epicyclic gearbox and further cardan shaft to final drive.
*Body:* 57' 6" × 9' 2".
*Weight:* 30 tons.
*Seats 2nd:* 52.

| E51254 | E51270 | E51286 |
|--------|--------|--------|
| E51255 | E51271 | E51287 |
| E51256 | E51272 | E51288 |
| E51257 | E51273 | E51289 |
| E51258 | E51274 | E51290 |
| E51259 | E51275 | E51291 |
| E51260 | E51276 | E51292 |
| E51261 | E51277 | E51293 |
| E51262 | E51278 | E51294 |
| E51263 | E51279 | E51295 |
| E51264 | E51280 | E51296 |
| E51265 | E51281 | E51297 |
| E51266 | E51282 | E51298 |
| E51267 | E51283 | E51299 |
| E51268 | E51284 | E51300 |
| E51269 | E51285 | E51301 |

## Motor Brake Second ■
*Built by:* **Birmingham R.C. & W. Co.**
*Engines:*
*Transmission:* **Mechanical.** Cardan shaft and freewheel to four-speed epicyclic gearbox and further cardan shaft to final drive.
*Body:* 64' 0" × 9' 3". Non-gangwayed, side doors to each seating bay.
*Weight:* 36 tons.
*Seats 2nd:* 65.

| W51302 | W51307 | W51312 |
|--------|--------|--------|
| W51303 | W51308 | W51313 |
| W51304 | W51309 | W51314 |
| W51305 | W51310 | W51315 |
| W51306 | W51311 | W51316 |

## Motor Second ■
*Built by:* **Birmingham R.C. & W. Co.**
*Engines:*
*Transmission:* **Mechanical.** Cardan shaft and freewheel to four-speed epicyclic gearbox and further cardan shaft to final drive.

Body: 64' 0" × 9' 3". Non-gangwayed,
 side doors to each seating bay.
Weight: 36 tons.
Seats 2nd: 91.

| | | |
|---|---|---|
| W51317 | W51322 | W51327 |
| W51318 | W51323 | W51328 |
| W51319 | W51324 | W51329 |
| W51320 | W51325 | W51330 |
| W51321 | W51326 | W51331 |

## Motor Brake Second ■
### (THREE-CAR SUBURBAN)

Built by: **Pressed Steel Co.**
Engines: Two B.U.T. (Leyland) 6-cyl.
 horizontal type of 150 b.h.p.
Transmission: **Mechanical.** Cardan
 shaft and freewheel to four-speed
 epicyclic gearbox and further cardan
 shaft to final drive.
Body: 64' 0" × 9' 3". Non-gangwayed,
 side doors to each seating bay.
Weight: 36 tons.
Seats 2nd: 65.

| | | |
|---|---|---|
| W51332 | W51346 | W51360 |
| W51333 | W51347 | W51361 |
| W51334 | W51348 | W51362 |
| W51335 | W51349 | W51363 |
| W51336 | W51350 | W51364 |
| W51337 | W51351 | W51365 |
| W51338 | W51352 | W51366 |
| W51339 | W51353 | W51367 |
| W51340 | W51354 | W51368 |
| W51341 | W51355 | W51369 |
| W51342 | W51356 | W51370 |
| W51343 | W51357 | W51371 |
| W51344 | W51358 | W51372 |
| W51345 | W51359 | W51373 |

## Motor Second ■
### (THREE-CAR SUBURBAN)

Built by: **Pressed Steel Co.**
Engines: Two B.U.T. (Leyland) 6-cyl.
 horizontal type of 150 b.h.p.
Transmission: **Mechanical.** Cardan
 shaft and freewheel to four-speed
 opicyclic gearbox and further cardan
 shaft to final drive.
Body: 64' 0" × 9' 3". Non-gangwayed
 side doors to each seating bay.
Weight: 36 tons.
Seats 2nd: 91.

| | | |
|---|---|---|
| W51374 | W51388 | W51402 |
| W51375 | W51389 | W51403 |
| W51376 | W51390 | W51404 |
| W51377 | W51391 | W51405 |
| W51378 | W51392 | W51406 |
| W51379 | W51393 | W51407 |
| W51380 | W51394 | W51408 |
| W51381 | W51395 | W51409 |
| W51382 | W51396 | W51410 |
| W51383 | W51397 | W51411 |
| W51384 | W51398 | W51412 |
| W51385 | W51399 | W51413 |
| W51386 | W51400 | W51414 |
| W51387 | W51401 | W51415 |

## Motor Brake Second ■
### (TWIN UNITS)

Built by: **Derby Works, B.R.**
Engines: Two B.U.T. (A.E.C.) 6-cyl.
 horizontal type of 150 b.h.p.
Transmission: **Mechanical.** Cardan
 shaft and freewheel to four-speed
 epicyclic gearbox and further cardan
 shaft to final drive.
Body: 57' 6" × 9' 2".
Weight:
Seats 2nd:

| | | |
|---|---|---|
| M51416 | M51419 | M51422 |
| M51417 | M51420 | M51423 |
| M51418 | M51421 | M51424 |

## Motor Brake Second ■
### (TWIN UNITS)

Built by: **Metropolitan Cammell.**
Engines: Two B.U.T. (Leyland) 6-cyl.
 horizontal type of 150 b.h.p.
Transmission: **Mechanical.** Cardan
 shaft and freewheel to four-speed
 epicyclic gearbox and further cardan
 shaft to final drive.
Body: 57' 0" × 9' 3".
Weight: 32 tons.
Seats 2nd: 52.

| | | |
|---|---|---|
| E51425 | E51429 | E51433 |
| E51426 | E51430 | E51434 |
| E51427 | E51431 | |
| E51428 | E51432 | |

## Motor Brake Second ■
### (THREE OR *FOUR-CAR UNITS)

Built by: **Metropolitan Cammell.**
Engines: Two B.U.T. (Leyland) 6-cyl. horizontal type of 150 b.h.p.
Transmission: **Mechanical** Cardan shaft and freewheel to four-speed epicyclic gearbox and further cardan shaft to final drive.
Body: 57' 0" × 9' 3".
Weight: 32 tons.
Seats 2nd: 52.

| | | |
|---|---|---|
| E51435* | SC51447 | SC51459 |
| E51436* | SC51448 | SC51460 |
| E51437* | SC51449 | SC51461 |
| E51438* | SC51450 | SC51462 |
| E51439* | SC51451 | SC51463 |
| E51440* | SC51452 | SC51464 |
| E51441* | SC51453 | SC51465 |
| E51442* | SC51454 | SC51466 |
| E51443* | SC51455 | SC51467 |
| E51444* | SC51456 | SC51468 |
| SC51445 | SC51457 | SC51469 |
| SC51446 | SC51458 | SC51470 |

## Motor Brake Second ■
### (TWIN UNITS)

Built by: **Cravens.**
Engines: Two B.U.T. (A.E.C.) 6-cyl. horizontal type of 150 b.h.p.
Transmission: **Mechanical.** Cardan shaft and freewheel to four-speed epicyclic gearbox and further cardan shaft to final drive.
Body: 57' 6" × 9' 2".
Weight: 30 tons 10 cwt.
Seats 2nd: 52.

| | | |
|---|---|---|
| E51471 | SC51479 | SC51487 |
| E51472 | SC51480 | SC51488 |
| SC51473 | SC51481 | SC51489 |
| SC51474 | SC51482 | SC51490 |
| SC51475 | SC51483 | SC51491 |
| SC51476 | SC51484 | SC51492 |
| SC51477 | SC51485 | SC51493 |
| SC51478 | SC51486 | SC51494 |

## Motor Composite (L) ■
### (TWIN UNITS)

Built by: **Metropolitan Cammell.**
Engines: Two B.U.T. (Leyland) 6-cyl. horizontal type of 150 b.h.p.

Transmission: **Mechanical.** Cardan shaft and freewheel to four-speed epicyclic gearbox and further cardan shaft to final drive.
Body: 57' 0" × 9' 3".
Weight: 32 tons.
Seats 1st: 12.
  2nd: 53.

| | | |
|---|---|---|
| E51495 | E51499 | E51503 |
| E51496 | E51500 | E51504 |
| E51497 | E51501 | |
| E51498 | E51502 | |

## Motor Composite (L) ■
### (THREE OR *FOUR-CAR UNITS)

Built by: **Metropolitan Cammell.**
Engines: Two B.U.T. (Leyland) 6-cyl. horizontal type of 150 b.h.p.
Transmission: **Mechanical.** Cardan shaft and freewheel to four-speed epicyclic gearbox and further cardan shaft to final drive.
Body: 57' 0" × 9' 3".
Weight: 32 tons.
Seats 1st: 12.
  2nd: 53.

| | | |
|---|---|---|
| E51505* | SC51517 | SC51529 |
| E51506* | SC51518 | SC51530 |
| E51507* | SC51519 | SC51531 |
| E51508* | SC51520 | SC51532 |
| E51509* | SC51521 | SC51533 |
| E51510* | SC51522 | SC51534 |
| E51511* | SC51523 | SC51535 |
| E51512* | SC51524 | SC51536 |
| E51513* | SC51525 | SC51537 |
| E51514* | SC51526 | SC51538 |
| SC51515 | SC51527 | SC51539 |
| SC51516 | SC51528 | SC51540 |

## Motor Brake Second ■
### (THREE-CAR UNITS)

For details see **E51435-SC51470**

| | | |
|---|---|---|
| E51541 | E51544 | E51547 |
| E51542 | E51545 | |
| E51543 | E51546 | |

## Motor Brake Second ■
### (TWIN UNITS)
*Built by:* **Metropolitan Cammell.**
*Engines:* Two B.U.T. (A.E.C.) 6-cyl.
horizontal type of 150 b.h.p.
*Transmission:* **Mechanical.** Cardan
shaft and freewheel to four-speed
epicyclic gearbox and further cardan
shaft to final drive.
*Body:* 57′ 0″ × 9′ 3″.
*Weight:* 31 tons 10 cwt.
*Seats 2nd:* 52.

| | | |
|---|---|---|
| E51548 | E51549 | E51550 |

## Motor Composite (L) ■
### (THREE-CAR UNITS)
**For details see E51505-SC51540**

| | | |
|---|---|---|
| E51551 | E51554 | E51557 |
| E51552 | E51555 | |
| E51553 | E51556 | |

## Motor Composite (L) ■
### (TWIN UNITS)
*Built by:* **Metropolitan Cammell.**
*Engines:* Two B.U.T. (A.E.C.) 6-cyl.
horizontal type of 150 b.h.p.
*Transmission:* **Mechanical.** Cardan
shaft and freewheel to four-speed
epicyclic gearbox and further cardan
shaft to final drive.
*Body:* 57′ 0″ × 9′ 3″.
*Weight:* 31 tons 10 cwt.
*Seats 1st:* 12
*2nd:* 53

| | | |
|---|---|---|
| E51558 | E51559 | E51560 |

## Motor Composite (L) ■
### (TWIN UNITS)
*Built by:* **Derby Works, B.R.**
*Engines:* Two B.U.T. (A.E.C.) 6-cyl.
horizontal type of 150 b.h.p.
*Transmission:* **Mechanical.** Cardan
shaft and freewheel to four-speed
epicyclic gearbox and further cardan
shaft to final drive.
*Body:* 57′ 6″ × 9′ 2″.
*Weight:* 27 tons.
*Seats 1st:* 12.
*2nd:* 53.

| | | |
|---|---|---|
| M51561 | M51565 | M51569 |
| M51562 | M51566 | M51570 |
| M51563 | M51567 | M51571 |
| M51564 | M51568 | M51572 |

## Motor Brake Second ■
### (FOUR-CAR SUBURBAN)
*Built by:* **Derby Works, B.R.**
*Engines:* Two Rolls Royce 8-cyl.
horizontal type of 238 b.h.p.
*Transmission:* **Hydraulic.** Torque con-
verter.
*Body:* 64′ 0″ × 9′ 3″.
Non-gangwayed, side doors to each
seating bay.
*Weight:* 40 tons.
*Seats 2nd:* 76.

| | | |
|---|---|---|
| M51591 | M51611 | M51631 |
| M51592 | M51612 | M51632 |
| M51593 | M51613 | M51633 |
| M51594 | M51614 | M51634 |
| M51595 | M51615 | M51635 |
| M51596 | M51616 | M51636 |
| M51597 | M51617 | M51637 |
| M51598 | M51618 | M51638 |
| M51599 | M51619 | M51639 |
| M51600 | M51620 | M51640 |
| M51601 | M51621 | M51641 |
| M51602 | M51622 | M51642 |
| M51603 | M51623 | M51643 |
| M51604 | M51624 | M51644 |
| M51605 | M51625 | M51645 |
| M51606 | M51626 | M51646 |
| M51607 | M51627 | M51647 |
| M51608 | M51628 | M51648 |
| M51609 | M51629 | M51649 |
| M51610 | M51630 | M51650 |

## Motor Brake Second ■
### (FOUR-CAR SUBURBAN)
*Built by:* **Derby Works, B.R.**
*Engines:* Two B.U.T. (Leyland) 6-cyl.
horizontal type of 230 b.h.p.
*Transmission:* **Mechanical.** Cardan
shaft and freewheel to four-speed
epicyclic gearbox and further cardan
shaft to final drive.
*Body:* 64′ 0″ × 9′ 3″. Non-gangwayed,
side doors to each seating bay.
*Weight:* 38 tons.
*Seats 2nd:* 78.

| | | |
|---|---|---|
| M51651 | M51655 | M51659 |
| M51652 | M51656 | M51660 |
| M51653 | M51657 | M51661 |
| M51654 | M51658 | M51662 |

| M51663 | M51669 | M51675 |
|--------|--------|--------|
| M51664 | M51670 | M51676 |
| M51665 | M51671 | M51677 |
| M51666 | M51672 | M51678 |
| M51667 | M51673 | M51679 |
| M51668 | M51674 | M51680 |

## Motor Brake Second
### (TWIN UNITS)

*Built by:* **Cravens.**
*Engine:* One Rolls Royce 8-cyl. horizontal type of 238 b.h.p.
*Transmission:* **Mechanical.**
*Body:* 57' 6" × 9' 2".
*Weight:*
*Seats* 2nd: 52.

| M51681 | M51690 | M51699 |
|--------|--------|--------|
| M51682 | M51691 | M51700 |
| M51683 | M51692 | M51701 |
| M51684 | M51693 | M51702 |
| M51685 | M51694 | M51703 |
| M51686 | M51695 | M51704 |
| M51687 | M51696 | M51705 |
| M51688 | M51697 |        |
| M51689 | M51698 |        |

## Motor Composite (L)
### (TWIN UNITS)

*Built by :* **Cravens.**
*Engine:* One Rolls Royce 8-cyl. horizontal type of 238 b.h.p.
*Transmission:* **Mechanical.**
*Body:* 57' 6" × 9' 2".
*Weight:*
*Seats* 1st: 12.
     2nd: 51.

| M51706 | M51715 | M51724 |
|--------|--------|--------|
| M51707 | M51716 | M51725 |
| M51708 | M51717 | M51726 |
| M51709 | M51718 | M51727 |
| M51710 | M51719 | M51728 |
| M51711 | M51720 | M51729 |
| M51712 | M51721 | M51730 |
| M51713 | M51722 |        |
| M51714 | M51723 |        |

## Motor Brake Second
### (TWIN UNITS)

*Built by:* **Cravens.**
*Engine:* One Rolls Royce 8-cyl. horizontal type of 238 b.h.p.
*Transmission:* **Hydraulic.** Torque converter.
*Body:* 57' 6" × 9' 2".
*Weight:*
*Seats* 2nd: 52.

| M51731 | M51740 | M51749 |
|--------|--------|--------|
| M51732 | M51741 | M51750 |
| M51733 | M51742 | M51751 |
| M51734 | M51743 | M51752 |
| M51735 | M51744 | M51753 |
| M51736 | M51745 | M51754 |
| M51737 | M51746 | M51755 |
| M51738 | M51747 |        |
| M51739 | M51748 |        |

## Motor Composite (L)
### (TWIN UNITS)

*Built by:* **Cravens.**
*Engine:* One Rolls Royce 8-cyl. horizontal type of 238 b.h.p.
*Transmission:* **Hydraulic.** Torque converter.
*Body:* 57' 6" × 9' 2".
*Weight:*
*Seats* 1st: 12.
     2nd: 51.

| M51756 | M51765 | M51774 |
|--------|--------|--------|
| M51757 | M51766 | M51775 |
| M51758 | M51767 | M51776 |
| M51759 | M51768 | M51777 |
| M51760 | M51769 | M51778 |
| M51761 | M51770 | M51779 |
| M51762 | M51771 | M51780 |
| M51763 | M51772 |        |
| M51764 | M51773 |        |

## Motor Brake Composite ■
### (THREE-CAR CROSS-COUNTRY)

*Built by:* **Swindon Works, B.R.**
*Engines:* Two B.U.T. 6-cyl. horizontal type of 150 b.h.p.

*Transmission:* **Mechanical.** Cardan shaft and freewheel to four-speed epicyclic gearbox and further cardan shaft to final drive.
*Body:* 64′ 6″ × 9′ 3″.
*Weight:* 36 tons 7 cwt.
*Seats* 1st: 18.
　　　2nd: 16.

| | | |
|---|---|---|
| SC51781 | SC51784 | SC51787 |
| SC51782 | SC51785 | |
| SC51783 | SC51786 | |

## Motor Second (L) ■
### (THREE-CAR CROSS-COUNTRY)

*Built by:* **Swindon Works, B.R.**
*Engines:* Two B.U.T. 6-cyl. horizontal type of 150 b.h.p.
*Transmission:* **Mechanical.** Cardan shaft and freewheel to four-speed epicyclic gearbox and further cardan shaft to final drive.
*Body:* 64′ 6″ × 9′ 3″.
*Weight:* 36 tons 10 cwt.
*Seats* 2nd: 68.

| | | |
|---|---|---|
| SC51788 | SC51791 | SC51794 |
| SC51789 | SC51792 | |
| SC51790 | SC51793 | |

## Motor Brake Second ■
### (THREE-CAR UNITS)

*Built by:* **Metropolitan Cammell.**
*Engines:* Two B.U.T. (A.E.C.) 6-cyl. horizontal type of 150 b.h.p.
*Transmission:* **Mechanical.** Cardan shaft and freewheel to four-speed epicyclic gearbox and further cardan shaft to final drive.
*Body:* 57′ 0″ × 9′ 3″.
*Weight:* 32 tons.
*Seats* 2nd: 52.

| | | |
|---|---|---|
| SC51795 | SC51798 | SC51801 |
| SC51796 | SC51799 | |
| SC51797 | SC51800 | |

## Motor Composite (L) ■
### (THREE-CAR UNITS)

*Built by:* **Metropolitan Cammell.**
*Engines:* Two B.U.T. (A.E.C.) 6-cyl. horizontal type of 150 b.h.p.
*Transmission:* **Mechanical.** Cardan shaft and freewheel to four-speed epicyclic gearbox and further cardan shaft to final drive.

*Body:* 57′ 0″ × 9′ 3″.
*Weight:* 32 tons.
*Seats* 1st: 12.
　　　2nd: 53.

| | | |
|---|---|---|
| SC51802 | SC51805 | SC51808 |
| SC51803 | SC51806 | |
| SC51804 | SC51807 | |

## Motor Brake Second ■
### (FOUR-CAR SUBURBAN)

*Built by:* **Derby Works, B.R.**
*Engines:* Two B.U.T. 6-cyl. horizontal type of 230 b.h.p.
*Transmission:* **Mechanical.** Cardan shaft and freewheel to four-speed epicyclic gearbox and further cardan shaft to final drive.
*Body:* 64′ 0″ × 9′ 3″.
　Non-gangwayed, side doors to each seating bay.
*Weight:* 38 tons.
*Seats* 2nd: 78.

| | | |
|---|---|---|
| M51849 | M51867 | M51885 |
| M51850 | M51868 | M51886 |
| M51851 | M51869 | M51887 |
| M51852 | M51870 | M51888 |
| M51853 | M51871 | M51889 |
| M51854 | M51872 | M51890 |
| M51855 | M51873 | M51891 |
| M51856 | M51874 | M51892 |
| M51857 | M51875 | M51893 |
| M51858 | M51876 | M51894 |
| M51859 | M51877 | M51895 |
| M51860 | M51878 | M51896 |
| M51861 | M51879 | M51897 |
| M51862 | M51880 | M51898 |
| M51863 | M51881 | M51899 |
| M51864 | M51882 | M51900 |
| M51865 | M51883 | |
| M51866 | M51884 | |

## Motor Brake Second ■
### (TWIN UNITS)

*Built by:* **Derby Works, B.R.**
*Engines:* Two B.U.T. (A.E.C.) 6-cyl. horizontal type of 150 b.h.p.
*Transmission:* **Mechanical.** Cardan shaft and freewheel to four-speed epicyclic gearbox and further cardan shaft to final drive.

Body: 57' 6" × 9' 2".
Weight: 28 tons 10 cwt.
Seats 2nd: 52.

| | | |
|---|---|---|
| M51901 | M51916 | M51931 |
| M51902 | M51917 | M51932 |
| M51903 | M51918 | M51933 |
| M51904 | M51919 | M51934 |
| M51905 | M51920 | M51935 |
| M51906 | M51921 | M51936 |
| M51907 | M51922 | M51937 |
| M51908 | M51923 | M51938 |
| M51909 | M51924 | M51939 |
| M51910 | M51925 | M51940 |
| M51911 | M51926 | M51941 |
| M51912 | M51927 | M51942 |
| M51913 | M51928 | M51943 |
| M51914 | M51929 | |
| M51915 | M51930 | |

## Motor Composite ■
### (TRANS-PENNINE UNITS)

*Built by:* **Swindon Works, B.R.**
*Engines:* Two B.U.T. (Leyland) 6-cyl. horizontal type of 230 b.h.p.
*Transmission:* **Mechanical.** Cardan shaft and freewheel to four-speed epicyclic gearbox and further cardan shaft to final drive.
*Body:* 64' 6" × 9' 3".
*Weight:*
*Seats 1st:* 21.
  *2nd:* 36.

| | | |
|---|---|---|
| E51951 | E51957 | E51963 |
| E51952 | E51958 | E51964 |
| E51953 | E51959 | E51965 |
| E51954 | E51960 | E51966 |
| E51955 | E51961 | E51967 |
| E51956 | E51962 | |

## Motor Brake Second (K) ■
### (non-driving)
### (TRANS-PENNINE UNITS)

*Built by:* **Swindon Works, B.R.**
*Engines:* Two B.U.T. (Leyland) 6-cyl. horizontal type of 230 b.h.p.
*Transmission:* **Mechanical.** Cardan shaft and freewheel to four-speed epicyclic gearbox and further cardan shaft to final drive.

Body: 64' 6" × 9' 3".
Weight:
Seats 2nd: 48.

| | | |
|---|---|---|
| E51968 | E51974 | E51980 |
| E51969 | E51975 | E51981 |
| E51970 | E51976 | E51982 |
| E51971 | E51977 | E51983 |
| E51972 | E51978 | E51984 |
| E51973 | E51979 | |

## Motor Brake Second

*Built by:* **Derby Works, B.R.**
*Engines:*
*Transmission:*
*Body:*
*Weight:*
*Seats 2nd:*

| | | |
|---|---|---|
| SC51985 | SC51988 | SC51991 |
| SC51986 | SC51989 | SC51992 |
| SC51987 | SC51990 | |

## Motor Composite (L)

*Built by:* **Derby Works, B.R.**
*Engines:*
*Transmission:*
*Body:*
*Weight:*
*Seats 2nd:*

| | | |
|---|---|---|
| SC52011 | SC52014 | SC52017 |
| SC52012 | SC52015 | SC52018 |
| SC52013 | SC52016 | |

## Motor Composite (L) ■
### (TWIN UNITS)

*Built by:* **Derby Works, B.R.**
*Engines:* Two B.U.T. 6-cyl. horizontal type of 150 b.h.p.
*Transmission:* **Mechanical.** Cardan shaft and freewheel to four-speed epicyclic gearbox and further cardan shaft to final drive.
*Body:* 57' 6" × 9' 2".
*Weight:*
*Seats 1st:* 12.
  *2nd:* 53.

| | | |
|---|---|---|
| M52037 | M52041 | M52045 |
| M52038 | M52042 | M52046 |
| M52039 | M52043 | M52047 |
| M52040 | M52044 | M52048 |

| M52049 | M52053 | M52057 |
|--------|--------|--------|
| M52050 | M52054 | M52058 |
| M52051 | M52055 | M52059 |
| M52052 | M52056 |        |

## Motor Brake Second ■
### (SINGLE UNITS)

*Built by:* **Gloucester R.C. & W. Co.**
*Engines:* Two B.U.T. (A.E.C.) 6-cyl.
 horizontal type of 150 b.h.p.
*Transmission:* **Mechanical.** Cardan
 shaft and freewheel to four-speed
 epicyclic gearbox and further cardan
 shaft to final drive.
*Body:* 64′ 6″ × 9′ 3″.
 Non-gangwayed, side doors to each
 seating bay.
*Weight:* 35 tons.
*Seats 2nd:* 65.

| W55000 | W55007 | W55014 |
|--------|--------|--------|
| W55001 | W55008 | W55015 |
| W55002 | W55009 | W55016 |
| W55003 | W55010 | W55017 |
| W55004 | W55011 | W55018 |
| W55005 | W55012 | W55019 |
| W55006 | W55013 |        |

## Motor Brake Second ■

*Built by:* **Pressed Steel Co. Ltd.**
*Engines:*
*Transmission:* **Mechanical.**
*Body:* 64′ 6″ × 9′ 3″. Non-gangwayed.
*Weight:*
*Seats 2nd:*

| W55020 | W55025 | W55030 |
|--------|--------|--------|
| W55021 | W55026 | W55031 |
| W55022 | W55027 | W55032 |
| W55023 | W55028 | W55033 |
| W55024 | W55029 |        |

## Motor Parcels Van ■

*Built by:* **Gloucester R.C. & W. Co.**
*Engines:* Two B.U.T. (A.E.C.) 6-cyl.
 horizontal type of 230 b.h.p.
*Transmission:* **Mechanical.** Carden
 shaft and freewheel to four-speed
 epicyclic gearbox and further cardan
 shaft to final drive.

*Body:* 64′ 6″ × 9′ 3″.
 Non-gangwayed.
*Weight:* 40 tons.

| M55987 | M55988 | M55990 |
|--------|--------|--------|

## Motor Parcels Van ■

*Built by:* **Gloucester R.C. & W. Co.**
*Engines:* Two B.U.T. (A.E.C.) 6-cyl.
 horizontal type of 230 b.h.p.
*Transmission:* **Mechanical.** Cardan
 shaft and freewheel to four-speed
 epicyclic gearbox and further cardan
 shaft to final drive.
*Body:* 64′ 6″ × 9′ 3″.
*Weight:* 41 tons.

| W55991 | W55993 | W55995 |
|--------|--------|--------|
| W55992 | W55994 | W55996 |

## Motor Parcels Van ◆

*Built by:* **Cravens.**
*Engines:* Two B.U.T. (A.E.C.) 6-cyl.
 horizontal type of 150 b.h.p.
*Transmission.* **Mechanical.** Cardan
 shaft and freewheel to four-speed
 epicyclic gearbox and further cardan
 shaft to final drive.
*Body:* 57′ 6″ × 9′ 3″.
 Non-gangwayed.
*Weight:* 30 tons.

| M55997 | M55998 | M55999 |
|--------|--------|--------|

## Driving Trailer ■
## Composite (L)
### (TWIN UNITS)

*Built by:* **Derby Works, B.R.**
*Body:* 64′ 6″ × 9′ 3″.
*Weight:* 29 tons or 31 tons.*
*Seats 1st:* 12.
 *2nd:* 62.

| E56000 | E56012 | E56024 |
|--------|--------|--------|
| E56001* | E56013 | E56025 |
| E56002 | E56014 | E56026 |
| E56003 | E56015 | E56027* |
| E56004* | E56016 | E56028 |
| E56005* | E56017 | E56029 |
| E56006 | E56018 | E56030 |
| E56007* | E56019 | E56031 |
| E56008* | E56020 | E56032 |
| E56009* | E56021 | E56033 |
| E56010 | E56022 | E56034 |
| E56011 | E56023* | E56035 |

| E56036 | E56041 | E56046 |
|--------|--------|--------|
| E56037 | E56042 | E56047 |
| E56038 | E56043 | E56048 |
| E56039 | E56044 | E56049 |
| E56040 | E56045 | |

## Driving Trailer Composite (L) ■
### (TWIN UNITS)

*Built by:* **Metropolitan Cammell.**
*Body:* 57′ 0″ × 9′ 3″.
*Weight:* 25 tons.
*Seats 1st:* 12.
   *2nd:* 53.

| E56050 | E56065 | E56080 |
|--------|--------|--------|
| E56051 | E56066 | E56081 |
| E56052 | E56067 | E56082 |
| E56053 | E56068 | E56083 |
| E56054 | E56069 | E56084 |
| E56055 | E56070 | E56085 |
| E56056 | E56071 | E56086 |
| E56057 | E56072 | E56087 |
| E56058 | E56073 | E56088 |
| E56059 | E56074 | E56089 |
| E56060 | E56075 | M56090 |
| E56061 | E56076 | M56091 |
| E56062 | E56077 | M56092 |
| E56063 | E56078 | M56093 |
| E56064 | E56079 | |

## Driving Trailer Composite (L) ▣
### (TWIN UNITS)

*Built by:* **Gloucester R.C. & W. Co.**
*Body:* 57′ 6″ × 9′ 3″.
*Weight:* 25 tons.
*Seats 1st:* 12.
   *2nd:* 54.

| SC56094 | SC56101 | M56108 |
|---------|---------|--------|
| SC56095 | SC56102 | M56109 |
| SC56096 | SC56103 | M56110 |
| SC56097 | SC56104 | M56111 |
| SC56098 | M56105 | M56112 |
| SC56099 | M56106 | M56113 |
| SC56100 | M56107 | |

## Driving Trailer Composite (L) ■
### (TWIN UNITS)

*Built by:* **Cravens.**
*Body:* 57′ 6″ × 9′ 2″.
*Weight:* 23 tons.
*Seats 1st:* 12.
   *2nd:* 51.
   *54\*.*

| E56114 | E56126 | E56138 |
|--------|--------|--------|
| E56115 | E56127 | E56139 |
| E56116 | E56128 | E56140 |
| E56117 | E56129 | E56141 |
| E56118 | E56130 | E56142 |
| E56119 | E56131 | E56143 |
| E56120 | E56132 | E56144 |
| E56121 | E56133 | M56145\* |
| E56122 | E56134 | M56146\* |
| E56123 | E56135 | M56147\* |
| E56124 | E56136 | M56148\* |
| E56125 | E56137 | M56149\* |

## Driving Trailer Composite (L) ■
### (TWIN UNITS)

*Built by:* **Park Royal Vehicles.**
*Body:* 57′ 6″ × 9′ 3″.
*Weight:* 26 tons 7 cwt.
*Seats 1st:* 16.
   *2nd:* 48.

| M56150 | M56157 | M56164 |
|--------|--------|--------|
| M56151 | M56158 | M56165 |
| M56152 | M56159 | M56166 |
| M56153 | M56160 | M56167 |
| M56154 | M56161 | M56168 |
| M56155 | M56162 | M56169 |
| M56156 | M56163 | |

## Driving Trailer Composite (L) ■
### (TWIN UNITS)

*Built by:* **D. Wickham & Co. Ltd.**
*Body:* 57′ 0″ × 9′ 3″.
*Weight:* 20 tons 10 cwt.
*Seats 1st:* 16.
   *2nd:* 50.

| E56170 | E56172 | E56174 |
|--------|--------|--------|
| E56171 | E56173 | |

### Driving Trailer Composite (L) ■
#### (TWIN UNITS)

*Built by:* **Birmingham R.C. & W. Co.**
*Body:* 57′ 6″ × 9′ 3″.
*Weight:*
*Seats 1st:* 12.
*2nd:* 54.

| | | |
|---|---|---|
| M56175 | M56179 | M56183 |
| M56176 | M56180 | M56184 |
| M56177 | M56181 | |
| M56178 | M56182 | |

### Driving Trailer Composite (L) ■
#### (TWIN UNITS)

*Built by:* **Birmingham R.C. & W. Co.**
*Body:* 57′ 6″ × 9′ 3″.
*Weight:* 24 tons.
*Seats 1st:* 12.
*2nd:* 54.

| | | |
|---|---|---|
| E56185 | E56187 | E56189 |
| E56186 | E56188 | |

### Driving Trailer Composite (L) ■
#### (TWIN UNITS)

*Built by:* **Derby Works, B.R.**
*Body:* 57′ 6″ × 9′ 2″.
*Weight:* 22 tons.
*Seats 1st:* 12.
*2nd:* 53.

| | | |
|---|---|---|
| E56190 | E56199 | E56208 |
| E56191 | E56200 | E56209 |
| E56192 | E56201 | E56210 |
| E56193 | E56202 | M56211 |
| E56194 | E56203 | M56212 |
| E56195 | E56204 | M56213 |
| E56196 | E56205 | M56214 |
| E56197 | E56206 | M56215 |
| E56198 | E56207 | |

### Driving Trailer Composite (L) ■
#### (TWIN UNITS)

*Built by:* **Metropolitan Cammell.**
*Body:* 57′ 0″ × 9′ 3″.
*Weight:* 25 tons.
*Seats 1st:* 12.
*2nd:* 45.

| | | |
|---|---|---|
| E56218 | E56219 | E56220 |

### Driving Trailer Composite (L) ■
#### (TWIN UNITS)

*Built by:* **Derby Works, B.R.**
*Body:* 57′ 6″ × 9′ 2″.
*Weight:* 22 tons.
*Seats 1st:* 12.
*2nd:* 53.

| | | |
|---|---|---|
| M56221 | M56241 | M56261 |
| M56222 | M56242 | M56262 |
| M56223 | M56243 | M56263 |
| M56224 | M56244 | M56264 |
| M56225 | M56245 | M56265 |
| M56226 | M56246 | M56266 |
| M56227 | M56247 | M56267 |
| M56228 | M56248 | M56268 |
| M56229 | M56249 | M56269 |
| M56230 | M56250 | M56270 |
| M56231 | M56251 | M56271 |
| M56232 | M56252 | M56272 |
| M56233 | M56253 | M56273 |
| M56234 | M56254 | M56274 |
| M56235 | M56255 | M56275 |
| M56236 | M56256 | M56276 |
| M56237 | M56257 | M56277 |
| M56238 | M56258 | M56278 |
| M56239 | M56259 | M56279 |
| M56240 | M56260 | |

### Driving Trailer Second ■
**(For use with Single Unit cars Nos. W55000, etc.)**

*Built by:*
*Body:* 64′ 0″ × 9′ 3″. Non-gangwayed, side doors to each seating bay.
*Weight:*
*Seats 2nd:* 95.

W56280

### Driving Trailer Second ■
**(For use with Single Unit cars Nos. W55000, etc.)**

*Built by:* **Gloucester R.C. & W. Co.**
*Body:* 64′ 0″ × 9′ 3″.
Non-gangwayed, side doors to each seating bay.
*Weight:*
*Seats 2nd:* 95.

Metropolitan-Vickers (A.E.I.) 2,500 h.p. 25 kV a.c. AIA-AIA electric locomotive
No. E2001 (rebuilt from Gas Turbine No. 18100)　　　　　　　　　　　[A. Swain

A.E.I. (B.T.H.) 3,300 h.p. 25 kV a.c. Bo-Bo Type A electric locomotive No. E3002
　　　　　　　　　　　　　　　　　　　　　　　　　　　　　[M. Mensing

English Electric 3,300 h.p. 25 kV a.c. Bo-Bo Type A electric locomotive No. E3024
　　　　　　　　　　　　　　　　　　　　　　　　　　　[English Electric

Swindon-built Inter-City unit at Gloucester (Central) showing a leading motor brake second

[P. J. Sharpe]

[P. J. Sharpe]

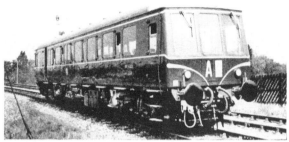

Gloucester R C. & W. Co. single-uuit motor brake second No. W55001 [*P. J. Sharpe*

Gloucester R.C. & W Co. driving trailer second No. W56299 [*P. J. Sharpe*

Pressed Steel single-unit motor brake second No. 55020 [*P. J. Sharpe*

Gloucester R C. & W. Co. parcels car No. M55989                    [P. J. Sharpe]

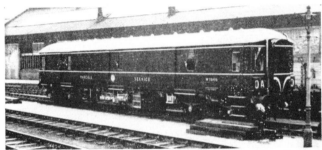

Gloucester R.C & W. Co. gangwayed parcels car No. W55993          [P J. Sharpe]

Cravens parcels car No. M55998 at Wolverhampton (High Level)      [J. B Bucknall]

B.U.T. four-wheel light-weight three-car set at Watford Junction with motor second M79745 nearest the camera
[P. J. Sharpe

Hampshire three-car diesel-electric unit No. 1118 on a Southampton – Portsmouth service
[J. C. Haydon

North Tyneside single-unit motor brake second E29165E [*P. J. Sharpe*

*Above:* Driving trailer second No. M29237M of a Manchester–Altrincham three-car set.
*Below:* A three-car set of the same stock led by motor brake second No. M28574M [*P. J. Sharpe*

B R. Standard 2-HAP unit No. 6025 at London Bridge on a Charing Cross–Ramsgate train                                                [P. J. Sharpe

B.R. Standard 4-CEP unit No. 7126 at Bromley South                    [P. J. Sharpe

B.R. Standard 2-EPB unit No. 5718 at Lovers Walk, Brighton        [W. M. J. Jackson

Motor brake second of an S R. 1925 Eastern Section 4-SUB unit No. 4343  [P. J. Sharpe

S.R. 4-LAV unit No. 2926 (with one 1939-type 2-HAL motor coach)  [J. C. Haydon

S.R. 4-LAV unit No. 2924  [J. C. Haydon

| W56291 | W56294 | W56297 | SC56401 | SC56405 | SC56409 |
| W56292 | W56295 | W56298 | SC56402 | SC56406 | SC56410 |
| W56293 | W56296 | W56299 | SC56403 | SC56407 | SC56411 |
| | | | SC56404 | SC56408 | |

## Driving Trailer Composite (L) ■
### (TWIN UNITS)

For Details see SC56094-M56113

| SC56300 | SC56307 | SC56314 |
| SC56301 | SC56308 | SC56315 |
| SC56302 | SC56309 | SC56316 |
| SC56303 | SC56310 | SC56317 |
| SC56304 | SC56311 | SC56318 |
| SC56305 | SC56312 | SC56319 |
| SC56306 | SC56313 | |

## Driving Trailer Composite (L) ■
### (TWIN UNITS)

Built by: **Metropolitan Cammell.**
Body: 57′ 0″ × 9′ 3″.
Weight: 25 tons.
Seats 1st: 12. 2nd: 53.

| M56332 | M56355 | E56378 |
| M56333 | M56356 | E56379 |
| M56334 | M56357 | E56380 |
| M56335 | M56358 | E56381 |
| M56336 | M56359 | SC56382 |
| M56337 | M56360 | SC56383 |
| M56338 | M56361 | SC56384 |
| M56339 | E56362 | SC56385 |
| M56340 | E56363 | SC56386 |
| M56341 | E56364 | SC56387 |
| M56342 | E56365 | SC56388 |
| M56343 | E56366 | SC56389 |
| M56344 | E56367 | SC56390 |
| M56345 | E56368 | SC56391 |
| M56346 | E56369 | SC56392 |
| M56347 | E56370 | SC56393 |
| M56348 | E56371 | SC56394 |
| M56349 | E56372 | SC56395 |
| M56350 | E56373 | SC56396 |
| M56351 | E56374 | SC56397 |
| M56352 | E56375 | SC56398 |
| M56353 | E56376 | SC56399 |
| M56354 | E56377 | SC56400 |

## Driving Trailer Composite (L) ■

Built by: **Cravens.**
Body: 57′ 6″ × 9′ 2″.
Weight: 24 tons.
Seats 1st: 12. 2nd: 51.

| E56412 | E56436 | E56460 |
| E56413 | E56437 | E56461 |
| E56414 | E56438 | SC56462 |
| E56415 | E56439 | SC56463 |
| E56416 | E56440 | SC56464 |
| E56417 | E56441 | SC56465 |
| E56418 | E56442 | SC56466 |
| E56419 | E56443 | SC56467 |
| E56420 | E56444 | SC56468 |
| E56421 | E56445 | SC56469 |
| E56422 | E56446 | SC56470 |
| E56423 | E56447 | SC56471 |
| E56424 | E56448 | SC56472 |
| E56425 | E56449 | SC56473 |
| E56426 | E56450 | SC56474 |
| E56427 | E56451 | SC56475 |
| E56428 | E56452 | SC56476 |
| E56429 | E56453 | SC56477 |
| E56430 | E56454 | SC56478 |
| E56431 | E56455 | SC56479 |
| E56432 | E56456 | SC56480 |
| E56433 | E56457 | SC56481 |
| E56434 | E56458 | SC56482 |
| E56435 | E56459 | SC56483 |

## Driving Trailer Composite (L) ■
### (TWIN UNITS)

Built by: **Derby Works, B.R.**
Body: 57′ 6″ × 9′ 2″.
Weight: 22 tons.
Seats 1st: 12.
2nd: 53.

| M56484 | M56486 | M56488 |
| M56485 | M56487 | M56489 |

| | | |
|---|---|---|
| M56490 | M56495 | M56500 |
| M56491 | M56496 | M56501 |
| M56492 | M56497 | M56502 |
| M56493 | M56498 | M56503 |
| M56494 | M56499 | M56504 |

## Trailer Composite ■
### (THREE-CAR SUBURBAN)
*Built by:* **Derby Works, B.R.**
*Body:* 63′ 8¼″ × 9′ 3″. Non-gangwayed,
side doors to each seating bay.
*Weight:* 28 tons 10 cwt.
*Seats* 1st: 28.
2nd: 74.

| | | |
|---|---|---|
| W59000 | W59011 | W59022 |
| W59001 | W59012 | W59023 |
| W59002 | W59013 | W59024 |
| W59003 | W59014 | W59025 |
| W59004 | W59015 | W59026 |
| W59005 | W59016 | W59027 |
| W59006 | W59017 | W59028 |
| W59007 | W59018 | W59029 |
| W59008 | W59019 | W59030 |
| W59009 | W59020 | W59031 |
| W59010 | W59021 | |

## Trailer Second ■
### (THREE-CAR SUBURBAN)
*Built by:* **Derby Works, B.R.**
*Body:* 63′ 8¾″ × 9′ 3″. Non-gangwayed,
side doors to each seating bay.
*Weight:* 28 tons 10 cwt.
*Seats* 2nd: 106.

| | | |
|---|---|---|
| W59032 | W59036 | W59040 |
| W59033 | W59037 | W59041 |
| W59034 | W59038 | |
| W59035 | W59039 | |

## Trailer Second (L) ■
### (FOUR-CAR UNITS)
*Built by:* **Metropolitan Cammell.**
*Body:* 57′ 0″ × 9′ 3″.
*Weight:* 25 tons.
*Seats* 2nd: 61.

| | | |
|---|---|---|
| E59042 | E59045 | E59048 |
| E59043 | E59046 | |
| E59044 | E59047 | |

## Trailer Brake Second (L) ■
### (FOUR-CAR UNITS)
*Built by:* **Metropolitan Cammell.**
*Body:* 57 0″ × 9′ 3″.
*Weight:* 25 tons.
*Seats* 2nd: 45.

| | | |
|---|---|---|
| E59049 | E59052 | E59055 |
| E59050 | E59053 | |
| E59051 | E59054 | |

## Trailer Second (L) ■
### (FOUR-CAR UNITS)
*Built by:* **Metropolitan Cammell.**
*Body:* 57′ 0″ × 9′ 3″.
*Weight:* 25 tons.
*Seats* 2nd: 71.

| | | |
|---|---|---|
| E59060 | E59065 | E59070 |
| E59061 | E59066 | E59071 |
| E59062 | E59067 | E59072 |
| E59063 | E59068 | |
| E59064 | E59069 | |

## Trailer Brake Second ■
### (FOUR-CAR UNITS)
*Built by:* **Metropolitan Cammell.**
*Body:* 57′ 0″ × 9′ 3″.
*Weight:* 25 tons.
*Seats* 2nd: 53.

| | | |
|---|---|---|
| E59073 | E59078 | E59083 |
| E59074 | E59079 | E59084 |
| E59075 | E59080 | E59085 |
| E59076 | E59081 | |
| E59077 | E59082 | |

## Trailer Second (L) ■
### (FOUR-CAR UNITS)
### For details see E59042-8

| | | |
|---|---|---|
| E59086 | E59088 | E59090 |
| E59087 | E59089 | E59091 |

## Trailer Brake Second (L) ■
### (FOUR-CAR UNITS)
### For details see E59049-55)

| | | |
|---|---|---|
| E59092 | E59094 | E59096 |
| E59093 | E59095 | E59097 |

## Trailer Second (L) ■
### (THREE-CAR UNITS)
*Built by:* **Metropolitan Cammell.**
*Body:* 57′ 0″ × 9′ 3″.
*Weight:* 24 tons 10 cwt.
*Seats* 2nd: 71.

| | | |
|---|---|---|
| E59100 | E59104 | E59108 |
| E59101 | E59105 | E59109 |
| E59102 | E59106 | |
| E59103 | E59107 | |

## Trailer Brake Second (L) ∎
### (FOUR-CAR UNITS)
*Built by:* **Metropolitan Cammell.**
*Body:* 57′ 0″ × 9′ 3″.
*Weight:* 25 tons.
*Seats 2nd:* 53.

| | |
|---|---|
| E59112 | E59113 |

## Trailer Composite (L) ∎
### (THREE-CAR UNITS)
*Built by:* **Metropolitan Cammell.**
*Body:* 57′ 0″ × 9′ 3″.
*Weight:* 25 tons.
*Seats 1st:* 12.
*2nd:* 53.

| | | |
|---|---|---|
| M59114 | M59120 | M59126 |
| M59115 | M59121 | M59127 |
| M59116 | M59122 | M59128 |
| M59117 | M59123 | M59129 |
| M59118 | M59124 | M59130 |
| M59119 | M59125 | M59131 |

## Trailer Composite (L) ∎
### (THREE-CAR UNITS)
*Built by:* **Birmingham R. C. & W. Co.**
*Body:* 57′ 0″ × 9′ 3″.
*Weight:* 24 tons.
*Seats 1st:* 12.
*2nd:* 54.

| | | |
|---|---|---|
| M59132 | M59151 | M59170 |
| M59133 | M59152 | M59171 |
| M59134 | M59153 | M59172 |
| M59135 | M59154 | M59173 |
| M59136 | M59155 | M59174 |
| M59137 | M59156 | M59175 |
| M59138 | M59157 | M59176 |
| M59139 | M59158 | M59177 |
| M59140 | M59159 | M59178 |
| M59141 | M59160 | M59179 |
| M59142 | M59161 | M59180 |
| M59143 | M59162 | M59181 |
| M59144 | M59163 | M59182 |
| M59145 | M59164 | M59183 |
| M59146 | M59165 | M59184 |
| M59147 | M59166 | M59185 |
| M59148 | M59167 | M59186 |
| M59149 | M59168 | M59187 |
| M59150 | M59169 | |

## Trailer Second (L) ∎
### (FOUR-CAR UNITS)
*Built by:* **Birmingham R.C. & W. Co.**
*Body:* 57′ 0″ × 9′ 3″.
*Weight:* 24 tons.
*Seats 2nd:* 69.

| | | |
|---|---|---|
| E59188 | E59195 | E59202 |
| E59189 | E59196 | E59203 |
| E59190 | E59197 | E59204 |
| E59191 | E59198 | E59205 |
| E59192 | E59199 | E59206 |
| E59193 | E59200 | E59207 |
| E59194 | E59201 | E59208 |

## Trailer Brake Second (L) ∎
### (FOUR-CAR UNITS)
*Built by:* **Birmingham R. C. & W. Co.**
*Body:* 57′ 0″ × 9′ 3″.
*Weight:* 25 tons.
*Seats 2nd:* 51.

| | | |
|---|---|---|
| E59209 | E59216 | E59223 |
| E59210 | E59217 | E59224 |
| E59211 | E59218 | E59225 |
| E59212 | E59219 | E59226 |
| E59213 | E59220 | E59227 |
| E59214 | E59221 | E59228 |
| E59215 | E59222 | E59229 |

## Trailer Second (L) ∎
### (FOUR-CAR UNITS)
### For details see E59188-E59208

| | | |
|---|---|---|
| E59230 | E59232 | E59234 |
| E59231 | E59233 | |

## Trailer Brake Second (L) ∎
### (FOUR-CAR UNITS)
### For details see E59209-29

| | | |
|---|---|---|
| E59240 | E59242 | E59244 |
| E59241 | E59243 | |

## Trailer Brake Second (L) ∎
### (FOUR-CAR UNITS)
*Built by:* **Derby Works, B.R.**
*Body:* 57′ 6″ × 9′ 2″.
*Weight:* 22 tons 10 cwt.
*Seats 2nd:* 50.

| | | |
|---|---|---|
| E59245 | E59247 | E59249 |
| E59246 | E59248 | E59250 |

## Trailer Buffet Second (L) ■
### (THREE-CAR CROSS-COUNTRY)
Built by: **Swindon Works, B.R.**
Body: 64' 6" × 9' 3".
Open second with small buffet and counter at one end.
Weight: 31 tons.
Seats 2nd: 60.
Buffet: 4.

| | | |
|---|---|---|
| W59255 | W59271 | W59287 |
| W59256 | W59272 | W59288 |
| W59257 | W59273 | W59289 |
| W59258 | W59274 | W59290 |
| W59259 | W59275 | W59291 |
| W59260 | W59276 | W59292 |
| W59261 | W59277 | W59293 |
| W59262 | W59278 | W59294 |
| W59263 | W59279 | W59295 |
| W59264 | W59280 | W59296 |
| W59265 | W59281 | W59297 |
| W59266 | W59282 | W59298 |
| W59267 | W59283 | W59299 |
| W59268 | W59284 | W59300 |
| W59269 | W59285 | W59301 |
| W59270 | W59286 | |

## Trailer Second (L) ■
### (THREE-CAR UNITS)
Built by: **Metropolitan Cammell.**
Body: 57' 0" × 9' 3".
Weight: 25 tons.
Seats 2nd: 71.

| | | |
|---|---|---|
| E59302 | E59303 | E59304 |

## Trailer Second (L) ▣
### (FOUR-CAR UNITS)
Built by: **Metropolitan Cammell.**
Body: 57' 0" × 9' 3".
Weight: 25 tons.
Seats 2nd: 71.

| | |
|---|---|
| E59305 | E59306 |

## Trailer Second (L) ▣ or Trailer Composite (L)*
### (THREE-CAR UNITS)
Built by **Cravens.**
Body: 57' 6" × 9' 2".
Weight: 23 tons.
Seats 2nd: 69.
　1st: 12*.
　2nd: 54*.

| | | |
|---|---|---|
| M59307* | M59314 | M59321* |
| M59308 | M59315 | M59322* |
| M59309 | M59316* | M59323 |
| M59310* | M59317* | M59324 |
| M59311 | M59318* | M59325 |
| M59312 | M59319 | |
| M59313 | M59320* | |

## Trailer Composite ■
### (THREE-CAR SUBURBAN)
For details see W59000-31

| | | |
|---|---|---|
| W59326 | W59343 | W59360 |
| W59327 | W59344 | W59361 |
| W59328 | W59345 | W59362 |
| W59329 | W59346 | W59363 |
| W59330 | W59347 | W59364 |
| W59331 | W59348 | W59365 |
| W59332 | W59349 | W59366 |
| W59333 | W59350 | W59367 |
| W59334 | W59351 | W59368 |
| W59335 | W59352 | W59369 |
| W59336 | W59353 | W59370 |
| W59337 | W59354 | W59371 |
| W59338 | W59355 | W59372 |
| W59339 | W59356 | W59373 |
| W59340 | W59357 | W59374 |
| W59341 | W59358 | W59375 |
| W59342 | W59359 | W59376 |

## Trailer Second (L) ▣
### (THREE* AND FOUR-CAR UNITS)
Built by: **Derby Works, B.R.**
Body: 57' 6" × 9' 2".
Weight: { 22 tons.
　　　　 { 22 tons 10 cwt.*
Seats 2nd: 68.

| | | |
|---|---|---|
| E59380 | E59384 | E59388* |
| E59381 | E59385 | E59389* |
| E59382 | E59386* | E59390* |
| E59383 | E59387* | |

## Trailer First (K) ●
### (INTER-CITY UNITS)
*Built by:* Swindon Works, B.R.
Body: 64' 6" × 9' 3".
Weight:
Seats 1st: 42.

| | | |
|---|---|---|
| SC59391 | SC59395 | SC59399 |
| SC59392 | SC59396 | SC59400 |
| SC59393 | SC59397 | |
| SC59394 | SC59398 | |

## Trailer Composite (L) ●
### (INTER CITY UNITS)
*Built by:* Swindon Works, B.R.
Body: 64' 6" × 9' 3".
Weight:
Seats 1st: 18.
2nd: 32.

| | | |
|---|---|---|
| SC59402 | SC59406 | SC59410 |
| SC59403 | SC59407 | SC59411 |
| SC59404 | SC59408 | SC59412 |
| SC59405 | SC59409 | |

## Trailer Buffet Second (L) ▣
### (THREE-CAR CROSS COUNTRY)
*Built by:* Gloucester R.C. & W. Co.
Body: 64' 6" × 9' 3".
Open second with small buffet and counter at one end.
Weight: 31 tons 8 cwt.
Seats 2nd: 60 or 64.

| | | |
|---|---|---|
| W59413 | W59422 | W59431 |
| W59414 | W59423 | W59432 |
| W59415 | W59424 | W59433 |
| W59416 | W59425 | W59434 |
| W59417 | W59426 | W59435 |
| W59418 | W59427 | W59436 |
| W59419 | W59428 | W59437 |
| W59420 | W59429 | |
| W59421 | W59430 | |

## Trailer Composite ▣
### (THREE-CAR SUBURBAN)
For details see W59000-31

| | | |
|---|---|---|
| W59438 | W59442 | W59446 |
| W59439 | W59443 | W59447 |
| W59440 | W59444 | W59448 |
| W59441 | W59445 | |

## Trailer Second ★
### (THREE-CAR SUBURBAN)
*Built by:* Derby Works, B.R.
Body: 63' 8½" × 9' 3". Non-gangwayed, side doors to each seating bay.
Weight: 28 tons 10 cwt.
Seats 2nd: 110.

| | | |
|---|---|---|
| E59449 | E59456 | E59463 |
| E59450 | E59457 | E59464 |
| E59451 | E59458 | E59465 |
| E59452 | E59459 | E59466 |
| E59453 | E59460 | E59467 |
| E59454 | E59461 | E59468 |
| E59455 | E59462 | |

## Trailer Composite (L) ■
*Built by:* Birmingham R.C. & W. Co.
Body:
Weight:
Seats 1st:
2nd:

| | | |
|---|---|---|
| W59469 | W59474 | W59479 |
| W59470 | W59475 | W59480 |
| W59471 | W59476 | W59481 |
| W59472 | W59477 | W59482 |
| W59473 | W59478 | W59483 |

## Trailer Composite (L) ■
### (THREE-CAR SUBURBAN)
*Built by:* Pressed Steel Co.
Body:
Weight: 30 tons.
Seats 1st: 24.
2nd: 50.

| | | |
|---|---|---|
| W59484 | W59497 | W59510 |
| W59485 | W59498 | W59511 |
| W59486 | W59499 | W59512 |
| W59487 | W59500 | W59513 |
| W59488 | W59501 | W59514 |
| W59489 | W59502 | W59515 |
| W59490 | W59503 | W59516 |
| W59491 | W59504 | W59517 |
| W59492 | W59505 | W59518 |
| W59493 | W59506 | W59519 |
| W59494 | W59507 | W59520 |
| W59495 | W59508 | W59521 |
| W59496 | W59509 | W59522 |

## Trailer Composite (L) ■

(THREE- OR *FOUR-CAR UNITS)

Built by: **Metropolitan Cammell.**
Body: 57′ 0″ × 9′ 3″.
Weight: 25 tons.
Seats 1st: 12.
2nd: 53.

| | | |
|---|---|---|
| E59523* | E59539* | SC59555 |
| E59524* | E59540* | SC59556 |
| E59525* | E59541* | SC59557 |
| E59526* | E59542* | SC59558 |
| E59527* | SC59543 | SC59559 |
| E59528* | SC59544 | SC59560 |
| E59529* | SC59545 | SC59561 |
| E59530* | SC59546 | SC59562 |
| E59531* | SC59547 | SC59563 |
| E59532* | SC59548 | SC59564 |
| E59533* | SC59549 | SC59565 |
| E59534* | SC59550 | SC59566 |
| E59535* | SC59551 | SC59567 |
| E59536* | SC59552 | SC59568 |
| E59537* | SC59553 | |
| E59538* | SC59554 | |

## Trailer Second (L) ■

(THREE-CAR UNITS)

Built by: **Metropolitan Cammell.**
Body: 57′ 0″ × 9′ 3″.
Weight: 24 tons 10 cwt.
Seats 2nd: 71.

| | | |
|---|---|---|
| E59569 | E59571 | E59572 |
| E59570 | | |

## Trailer Buffet Second (L) ■

Built by: **Metropolitan-Cammell.**
Body: 57′ 0″ × 9′ 3″.
Weight: 26 tons 10 cwt.
Seats 2nd: 53.

| | | |
|---|---|---|
| E59573 | E59575 | E59577 |
| E59574 | E59576 | E59578 |

## Trailer Second (L)

Built by: **Swindon Works, B.R.**
Body:
Weight:
Seats 2nd:

| | | |
|---|---|---|
| W59579 | W59580 | W59581 |

## Trailer Second (L) ■

(FOUR-CAR SUBURBAN)

Built by: **Derby Works, B.R.**
Body: 63′ 10″ × 9′ 3″. Non-gangwayed, side door to each seating bay. Intermediate lavatories on each side of central passageway.
Weight: 30 tons.
Seats 2nd: 90.

| | | |
|---|---|---|
| M59589 | M59599 | M59609 |
| M59590 | M59600 | M59610 |
| M59591 | M59601 | M59611 |
| M59592 | M59602 | M59612 |
| M59593 | M59603 | M59613 |
| M59594 | M59604 | M59614 |
| M59595 | M59605 | M59615 |
| M59596 | M59606 | M59616 |
| M59597 | M59607 | M59617 |
| M59598 | M59608 | M59618 |

## Trailer Second ■

(FOUR-CAR SUBURBAN)

Built by: **Derby Works, B.R.**
Body: 63′ 8½″ × 9′ 3″. Non-gangwayed, side doors to each seating bay.
Weight: 29 tons.
Seats 2nd: 106.

| | | |
|---|---|---|
| M59619 | M59634 | M59649 |
| M59620 | M59635 | M59650 |
| M59621 | M59636 | M59651 |
| M59622 | M59637 | M59652 |
| M59623 | M59638 | M59653 |
| M59624 | M59639 | M59654 |
| M59625 | M59640 | M59655 |
| M59626 | M59641 | M59656 |
| M59627 | M59642 | M59657 |
| M59628 | M59643 | M59658 |
| M59629 | M59644 | M59659 |
| M59630 | M59645 | M59660 |
| M59631 | M59646 | M59661 |
| M59632 | M59647 | M59662 |
| M59633 | M59648 | M59663 |

## Trailer Composite (L) ■
### (FOUR-CAR SUBURBAN)
*Built by:* **Derby Works, B R.**
*Body:* 63′ 6″ × 9′ 3″.
*Weight* 30 tons.
*Seats* 1st: 30.
    2nd: 40.

| | | |
|---|---|---|
| M59664 | M59669 | M59674 |
| M59665 | M59670 | M59675 |
| M59666 | M59671 | M59676 |
| M59667 | M59672 | M59677 |
| M59668 | M59673 | M59678 |

## Trailer Buffet Second (L) ■
### (THREE-CAR CROSS COUNTRY)
*Built by:* **Swindon Works, B.R.**
*Body:* 64′ 6″ × 9′ 3″.
Open second with small buffet and counter at one end.
*Weight:* 30 tons 12 cwt.
*Seats* 2nd: 60.
*Buffet:* 4.

| | | |
|---|---|---|
| SC59679 | SC59682 | SC59685 |
| SC59680 | SC59683 | |
| SC59681 | SC59684 | |

## Trailer Composite (L) ■
### (THREE-CAR UNITS)
*Built by:* **Metropolitan Cammell.**
*Body:* 57′ 0″ × 9′ 3″.
*Weight:* 25 tons.
*Seats* 1st: 12.
    2nd: 53.

| | | |
|---|---|---|
| SC59686 | SC59689 | SC59692 |
| SC59687 | SC59690 | |
| SC59688 | SC59691 | |

## Trailer Second ■
### (FOUR-CAR SUBURBAN)
*Built by:* **Derby Works, B.R.**
*Body:* 63′ 6″ × 9′ 3″.
*Weight:* 28 tons.
*Seats* 2nd: 106.

| | | |
|---|---|---|
| M59713 | M59715 | M59717 |
| M59714 | M59716 | M59718 |

## Trailer Composite (L) ■
### (FOUR-CAR SUBURBAN)
*Built by:* **Derby Works, B.R.**
*Body:* 63′ 6″ × 9′ 3″.
*Weight:* 30 tons.
*Seats* 1st: 30.
    2nd: 40.

| | | |
|---|---|---|
| M59719 | M59721 | M59723 |
| M59720 | M59722 | M59724 |

## Trailer Second Suburban ■
### (FOUR-CAR SUBURBAN)
### For details see M59713-8

| | | |
|---|---|---|
| M59725 | M59732 | M59739 |
| M59726 | M59733 | M59740 |
| M59727 | M59734 | M59741 |
| M59728 | M59735 | M59742 |
| M59729 | M59736 | M59743 |
| M59730 | M59737 | M59744 |
| M59731 | M59738 | |

## Trailer Composite ■
### (FOUR-CAR SUBURBAN)
### For details see M59719-24

| | | |
|---|---|---|
| M59745 | M59752 | M59759 |
| M59746 | M59753 | M59760 |
| M59747 | M59754 | M59761 |
| M59748 | M59755 | M59762 |
| M59749 | M59756 | M59763 |
| M59750 | M59757 | M59764 |
| M59751 | M59758 | |

## Trailer Second (L) ■
### (TRANS-PENNINE UNITS)
*Built by:* **Swindon Works, B.R.**
*Body:* 64′ 6″ × 9′ 3″
*Weight:*
*Seats:* 64.

| | | |
|---|---|---|
| E59765 | E59768 | E59771 |
| E59766 | E59769 | E59772 |
| E59767 | E59770 | E59773 |

## Trailer Buffet First (L) ■
### (TRANS-PENNINE UNITS)
*Built by:* **Swindon Works, B.R.**
*Body:* 64' 6" × 9' 3".
*Weight:*
*Seats:* 18.
*Buffet:* 8.

| | | |
|---|---|---|
| E59774 | E59777 | E59780 |
| E59775 | E59778 | E59781 |
| E59776 | E59779 | |

## Trailer Second (L)
*Built by:* **Derby Works, B.R.**
*Body:*
*Weight:*
*Seats 2nd:*

| | | |
|---|---|---|
| SC59782 | SC59785 | SC59788 |
| SC59783 | SC59786 | SC59789 |
| SC59784 | SC59787 | |

## Motor Brake Second
### (HASTINGS UNITS)
Unit numbers 1001–7*
1011–9†
1031–7‡

*Built by:* **Eastleigh Works, B.R.**
*Engine:* English Electric 4-cyl. type 4SRKT Mark 11 of 500 b.h.p. at 850 r.p.m.
*Transmission:* **Electric.** Two nose-suspended axle-hung traction motors.
*Body:* 58' 0 " × 8' 2½".*
64' 6" × 8' 2½".†‡
Guard's, luggage compartment, engine room and full width driving compartment at outer end of car.
*Weight:* 54 tons 2 cwt.*
55 tons 0 cwt.†‡
*Seats 2nd:* 22.*
30.†‡

| | | |
|---|---|---|
| S60000* | S60009* | S60018† |
| S60001* | S60010* | S60019† |
| S60002* | S60011* | S60020† |
| S60003* | S60012* | S60021† |
| S60004* | S60013* | S60022† |
| S60005* | S60014† | S60023† |
| S60006* | S60015† | S60024† |
| S60007* | S60016† | S60025† |
| S60008* | S60017† | S60026† |

| | | |
|---|---|---|
| S60027† | S60034‡ | S60041‡ |
| S60028† | S60035‡ | S60042‡ |
| S60029† | S60036‡ | S60043‡ |
| S60030† | S60037‡ | S60044‡ |
| S60031† | S60038‡ | S60045‡ |
| S60032‡ | S60039† | |
| S60033‡ | S60040† | |

## Motor Brake First (L)
### (PULLMAN UNITS)
*Built by:* **Metropolitan Cammell.**
*Engine:* One North British/M.A.N. 12-cyl. pressure-charged V-type L12V18/21BS of 1,000 b.h.p.
*Transmission:* **Electric.** Two 425 h.p. G.E.C. traction motors driving through Brown-Boveri spring-drive.
*Body:* 66' 5½" × 9' 3". Guard's, luggage compartment, engine room and full width driving cab at outer end of car.
*Weight:* 67 tons 10 cwt.
*Seats 1st:* 12.

| | | |
|---|---|---|
| M60090 | M60092 | M60093 |
| M60091 | | |

## Motor Brake Second (L)
### (PULLMAN UNITS)
*Built by:* **Metropolitan Cammell.**
*Engine:* One North British/M.A.N. 12-cyl. pressure-charged V-type L12V18/21BS of 1,000 b.h.p.
*Transmission:* **Electric.** Two 425 h.p. G.E.C. traction motors driving through Brown-Boveri spring-drive.
*Body:* 66' 5½" × 9' 3". Guard's, luggage compartment, engine room and full width driving cab at outer end of car.
*Weight:* 67 tons 10 cwt.
*Seats 2nd:* 18.

| | | |
|---|---|---|
| W60094 | W60096 | W60098 |
| W60095 | W60097 | W60099 |

## Motor Brake Second
### (TWIN* OR THREE-CAR UNITS)
Unit numbers ⎰ 1101–18
⎱ 1119–22*
1123–6

Built by: **Eastleigh Works, B.R.**
Engine: English Electric 4-cyl. type
4SRKT Mark II of 600 b.h.p. at 850
r.p.m.
Transmission. **Electric.** Two nose-
suspended axle-hung traction motors.
Body: 64′ 0″ × 9′ 3″.
Guard's, luggage compartment, en-
gine room and full width driving
compartment at outer end of car.
Non-gangwayed, side door to each
seating bay.
Weight: 56 tons 0 cwt.
Seats 2nd: 52.

| | | |
|---|---|---|
| S60100 | S60109 | S60118* |
| S60101 | S60110 | S60119* |
| S60102 | S60111 | S60120* |
| S60103 | S60112 | S60121* |
| S60104 | S60113 | S60122 |
| S60105 | S60114 | S60123 |
| S60106 | S60115 | S60124 |
| S60107 | S60116 | S60125 |
| S60108 | S60117 | |

## Trailer Second (L)
### (HASTINGS UNITS)

Unit numbers     1001-7*
                 1011-9†
                 1031-7‡

Built by: **Eastleigh Works, B.R.**
Body: 58′ 0″ × 8′ 2½″.*
       64′ 6″ × 8′ 2½″.††‡
Weight: 29 tons.*
          30 tons.††‡
Seats 2nd: 52.*
          60.††

| | | |
|---|---|---|
| S60500* | S60513* | S60526† |
| S60501* | S60514* | S60527† |
| S60502* | S60515* | S60528† |
| S60503* | S60516* | S60529† |
| S60504* | S60517* | S60530† |
| S60505* | S60518* | S60531† |
| S60506* | S60519* | S60532† |
| S60507* | S60520* | S60533† |
| S60508* | S60521† | S60534† |
| S60509* | S60522† | S60535† |
| S60510* | S60523† | S60536† |
| S60511* | S60524† | S60537† |
| S60512* | S60525† | S60538† |

| | | |
|---|---|---|
| S60539† | S60547† | S60555‡ |
| S60540† | S60548‡ | S60556‡ |
| S60541† | S60549‡ | S60557‡ |
| S60542† | S60550‡ | S60558‡ |
| S60543† | S60551‡ | S60559‡ |
| S60544† | S60552‡ | S60560‡ |
| S60545† | S60553‡ | S60561‡ |
| S60546† | S60554‡ | |

## Motor Parlour Second (L)
### (Non-driving)
### PULLMAN UNITS

Built by: **Metropolitan Cammell.**
Transmission: **Electric.** Two 425 h.p.
G.E.C. traction motors driving
through Brown-Boveri spring drive.
Body: 65′ 6″ × 9′ 3″.
Weight: 45 tons 10 cwt.
Seats 2nd: 42.

| | | |
|---|---|---|
| W60644 | W60646 | W60648 |
| W60645 | W60647 | W60649 |

## Trailer Second
### (THREE-CAR UNITS)

Unit numbers 1101-18/23-26

Built by: **Eastleigh Works, B.R.**
Body: 63′ 6″ × 9′ 3″.
Weight:
Seats 2nd: 104.

| | | |
|---|---|---|
| S60650 | S60658 | S60666 |
| S60651 | S60659 | S60667 |
| S60652 | S60660 | S60668 |
| S60653 | S60661 | S60669 |
| S60654 | S60662 | S60670 |
| S60655 | S60663 | S60671 |
| S60656 | S60664 | |
| S60657 | S60665 | |

## Trailer First (K)
### (HASTINGS UNITS)

Unit numbers     1001-7*
                 1011-9†
                 1031-7‡

Built by: **Eastleigh Works, B.R.**
Body: 58′ 0″ × 8′ 2½″.*
     64′ 6″ × 8′ 2½″.††

Side corridor with seven* (eight††)
first class compartments with side
door to each compartment.
Weight: 30 tons.*
      31 tons.†‡
Seats 1st: 42.*
      48.††

| | | |
|---|---|---|
| S60700* | S60708† | S60716‡ |
| S60701* | S60709† | S60717‡ |
| S60702* | S60710† | S60718‡ |
| S60703* | S60711† | S60719‡ |
| S60704* | S60712† | S60720‡ |
| S60705* | S60713† | S60721‡ |
| S60706* | S60714† | S60722‡ |
| S60707† | S60715† | |

## Motor Kitchen First (L)
### (Non-driving)
### PULLMAN UNITS

Built by: **Metropolitan Cammell.**
Transmission: **Electric.** Two 425 h.p.
G.E.C. traction motors driving
through Brown-Boveri spring drive.
Body: 65′ 6″ × 9′ 3″.
Weight: 49 tons.
Seats 1st: 18.

| | | |
|---|---|---|
| M60730 | M60732 | M60733 |
| M60731 | | |

## Trailer Kitchen First (L)
### (PULLMAN UNITS)

Built by: **Metropolitan Cammell.**
Body: 65′ 6″ × 9′ 3″.
Weight: 36 tons.
Seats 1st: 18.

| | | |
|---|---|---|
| W60734 | W60736 | W60738 |
| W60735 | W60737 | W60739 |

## Trailer Parlour First (L)
### (PULLMAN UNITS)

Built by: **Metropolitan Cammell.**
Body: 65′ 6″ × 9′ 3″.
Weight: 33 tons.
Seats 1st: 36.

| | | |
|---|---|---|
| M60740 | W60744 | W60748 |
| M60741 | W60745 | W60749 |
| M60742 | W60746 | |
| M60743 | W60747 | |

## Trailer Buffet
### (HASTINGS UNITS)

Unit numbers   1031-7

Built by: **Eastleigh Works, B.R.**
Body: 64′ 6″ × 8′ 2½″.
Buffet with kitchen and bar; self-
contained seating saloon.
Weight: 35 tons.
Seats: 21.

| | | |
|---|---|---|
| S60750 | S60753 | S60756 |
| S60751 | S60754 | |
| S60752 | S60755 | |

## Driving Trailer
## Composite (L)
### (TWIN* OR THREE-CAR UNITS)

Unit numbers   1101–18
                   1119–22*
                   1123–6

Built by: **Eastleigh Works, B.R.**
Body: 64′ 0″ × 9′ 3″.
Non-gangwayed, side door to each
seating bay or compartment. 5-bay
2nd saloon and 2 1st compartments
with intermediate lavatories, also a
2nd class compartment next to driving
compartment.
Weight: 32 tons 0 cwt.
Seats 1st: 13.
     2nd: 62.

| | | |
|---|---|---|
| S60800 | S60809 | S60818* |
| S60801 | S60810 | S60819 |
| S60802 | S60811 | S60820* |
| S60803 | S60812 | S60821* |
| S60804 | S60813 | S60822 |
| S60805 | S60814 | S60823 |
| S60806 | S60815 | S60824 |
| S60807 | S60816 | S60825 |
| S60808 | S60817 | |

## Motor Brake Second ▲
### (TWIN UNITS)
*Built by:* **Derby Works, B.R.**
*Engines:* Two B.U.T. (Leyland) 6-cyl.
horizontal type of 125 b.h.p.
*Transmission:* **Hydro-Mechanical.**
Lysholm Smith (Leyland) torque
converter to final drive.
*Body:* 57′ 6″ × 9′ 2″.
*Weight:* 26 tons.
*Seats 2nd:* 61.

| E79000 | E79003 | E79006 |
|--------|--------|--------|
| E79001 | E79004 | E79007 |
| E79002 | E79005 |        |

## Motor Brake Second ◆
### (TWIN UNITS)
*Built by:* **Derby Works, B.R.**
*Engines:* Two B.U.T. (A.E.C.) 6-cyl.
horizontal type of 150 b.h.p.
*Transmission:* **Mechanical.** Cardan
shaft and freewheel to four-speed
epicyclic gearbox and further cardan
shaft to final drive.
*Body:* 57′ 6″ × 9′ 2″.
*Weight:* 27 tons.
*Seats 2nd:* 61.
　　　　　56*.

| M79008 | E79021* | E79034* |
|--------|---------|---------|
| M79009 | E79022* | E79035* |
| M79010 | E79023* | E79036* |
| M79011 | E79024* | E79037* |
| M79012 | E79025* | E79038* |
| M79013 | E79026* | E79039* |
| M79014 | E79027* | E79040* |
| M79015 | E79028* | E79041* |
| M79016 | E79029* | E79042* |
| M79017 | E79030* | E79043* |
| M79018 | E79031* | E79044* |
| M79019 | E79032* | E79045* |
| M79020 | E79033* | E79046* |

## Motor Brake Second ◆
### (TWIN UNITS)
*Built by:* **Metropolitan Cammell.**
*Engines:* Two B.U.T. (A.E.C.) 6-cyl.
horizontal type of 150 b.h.p.
*Transmission:* **Mechanical.** Cardan
shaft and freewheel to four-speed
epicyclic gearbox and further cardan
shaft to final drive.
*Body:* 57′ 0″ × 9′ 3″.
*Weight:* 26 tons 10 cwt.
*Seats 2nd:* 57.
　　　　　53*.

| E79047 | E79059 | E79071 |
|--------|--------|--------|
| E79048 | E79060 | E79072 |
| E79049 | E79061 | E79073 |
| E79050 | E79062 | E79074 |
| E79051 | E79063 | E79075 |
| E79052 | E79064 | M79076* |
| E79053 | E79065 | M79077* |
| E79054 | E79066 | M79078* |
| E79055 | E79067 | M79079* |
| E79056 | E79068 | M79080* |
| E79057 | E79069 | M79081* |
| E79058 | E79070 | M79082* |

## Motor Brake Second (L) ●
### (INTER-CITY UNITS)
*Built by:* **Swindon Works, B.R.**
*Engines:* Two B.U.T. (A.E.C.) 6-cyl.
horizontal type of 150 b.h.p.
*Transmission:* **Mechanical.** Cardan
shaft and freewheel to four-speed
epicyclic gearbox and further cardan
shaft to final drive.
*Body:* 64′ 6″ × 9′ 3″.
Guard's and luggage compartment at
outer end. Two types of car;
"leading"* with full width driving
compartment, gangwayed at inner
end only; "intermediate"† with
side driving compartment gangwayed
at both ends.
*Weight:* 38 tons.
*Seats 2nd:* 52.

| SC79083† | SC79093* | SC79103* |
|----------|----------|----------|
| SC79084† | SC79094* | SC79104* |
| SC79085† | SC79095† | SC79105* |
| SC79086† | SC79096† | SC79106* |
| SC79087† | SC79097* | SC79107* |
| SC79088† | SC79098† | SC79108* |
| SC79089† | SC79099* | SC79109* |
| SC79090† | SC79100† | SC79110* |
| SC79091* | SC79101* | SC79111* |
| SC79092* | SC79102* |          |

## Motor Brake Second ◆
### (TWIN UNITS)
*Built by:* **Derby Works, B.R.**
*Engines:* Two B.U.T. 6-cyl. horizontal
type of 150 b.h.p.

Transmission: **Mechanical.** Cardan shaft and freewheel to four-speed epicyclic gearbox and further cardan shaft to final drive.
Body: 57′ 6″ × 9′ 2″.
Weight: 27 tons.
Seats 2nd: 52.

| | | |
|---|---|---|
| M79118 | M79129 | M79140 |
| M79119 | M79130 | M79141 |
| M79120 | M79131 | M79142 |
| M79121 | M79132 | M79143 |
| M79122 | M79133 | M79144 |
| M79123 | M79134 | M79145 |
| M79124 | M79135 * | M79146 |
| M79125 | M79136 | M79147 |
| M79126 | M79137 | M79148 |
| M79127 | M79138 | M79149 |
| M79128 | M79139 | |

*Fitted with Self Changing Gears Ltd. automatic four-speed gearbox.*

## Motor Second
### (FOUR-CAR UNITS)
Built by: **Derby Works, B.R.**
Engines: Two B.U.T. (A.E.C.) 6-cyl. horizontal type of 150 b.h.p.
Transmission: **Mechanical.** Cardan shaft and freewheel to four-speed epicyclic gearbox and further cardan shaft to final drive.
Body: 57′ 6″ × 9′ 2″.
Weight: 26 tons.
Seats 2nd: 64.

| | | |
|---|---|---|
| E79150 | E79152 | E79154 |
| E79151 | E79153 | |

## Motor Second (L) ●
### (INTER-CITY UNITS)
Built by: **Swindon Works, B.R.**
Engines: Two B.U.T. (A.E.C.) 6-cyl. horizontal type of 150 b.h.p.
Transmission: **Mechanical.** Cardan shaft and freewheel to four-speed epicyclic gearbox and further cardan shaft to final drive.
Body: 64′ 6″ × 9′ 3″.
  Gangways both ends. Side driving compartment at one end.
Weight: 39 tons 3 cwt.
Seats 2nd: 64.

| | | |
|---|---|---|
| SC79155 | SC79160 | SC79165 |
| SC79156 | SC79161 | SC79166 |
| SC79157 | SC79162 | SC79167 |
| SC79158 | SC79163 | SC79168 |
| SC79159 | SC79164 | |

## Motor Brake Second ◆
### (TWIN UNITS)
**For details see M79118-49**

| | | |
|---|---|---|
| M79169 | M79174 | M79179 |
| M79170 | M79175 | M79180 |
| M79171 | M79176 | M79181 |
| M79172 | M79177 | |
| M79173 | M79178 | |

## Motor Brake Second ◆
### (TWIN UNITS)
**For details see M79008-20**

| | | |
|---|---|---|
| M79184 | M79186 | M79188 |
| M79185 | M79187 | |

## Motor Composite (L) ◆
### (TWIN UNITS)
Built by: **Derby Works, B.R.**
Engines: Two B.U.T. (A.E.C.) 6-cyl. horizontal type of 150 b.h.p.
Transmission: **Mechanical.** Cardan shaft and freewheel to four-speed epicyclic gearbox and further cardan shaft to final drive.
Body: 57′ 6″ × 9′ 2″.
Weight: 27 tons.
Seats 1st: 12.
   2nd: 53.

| | | |
|---|---|---|
| M79189 | M79191 | M79193 |
| M79190 | M79192 | |

## Driving Trailer ◆
## Composite (L)
### (TWIN UNITS)
Built by: **Derby Works, B.R.**
Body: 57′ 6″ × 9′ 2″.
Weight: 20 tons.
Seats 1st: 16.
   2nd: 53.

| | | |
|---|---|---|
| E79250 | E79255 | E79260 |
| E79251 | E79256 | E79261 |
| E79252 | E79257 | E79262 |
| E79253 | E79258 | |
| E79254 | E79259 | |

## Driving Trailer Second (L) ◆
### (TWIN UNITS)

*Built by:* **Metropolitan Cammell.**
*Body:* 57″ 0′ × 9′ 3″.
*Weight:* 25 tons.
*Seats 2nd:* 71.

| | | |
|---|---|---|
| E79263 | E79273 | E79283 |
| E79264 | E79274 | E79284 |
| E79265 | E79275 | E79285 |
| E79266 | E79276 | E79286 |
| E79267 | E79277 | E79287 |
| E79268 | E79278 | E79288 |
| E79269 | E79279 | E79289 |
| E79270 | E79280 | E79290 |
| E79271 | E79281 | E79291 |
| E79272 | E79282 | |

## Trailer Brake Second (L) ◆
### (FOUR-CAR UNITS)

*Built by:* **Derby Works, B.R.**
*Body:* 57′ 6″ × 9′ 2″.
*Weight:* 20 tons 10 cwt.
*Seats 2nd:* 45.

| | | |
|---|---|---|
| E79325 | E79327 | E79329 |
| E79326 | E79328 | |

## Trailer Second (L) ◆
### (FOUR-CAR UNITS)

*Built by:* **Derby Works, B.R.**
*Body:* 57′ 6″ × 9′ 2″.
*Weight:* 20 tons 10 cwt.
*Seats 2nd:* 61.

| | | |
|---|---|---|
| E79400 | E79402 | E79404 |
| E79401 | E79403 | |

## Trailer Buffet First (K) ●
### (INTER-CITY UNITS)

*Built by:* **Swindon Works, B.R.**
*Body:* 64′ 6″ × 9′ 3″.
  Side corridor with three first class
  compartments. Buffet with kitchen,
  bar and saloon.
*Weight:* 34 tons.
*Seats 1st:* 18.
  *Buffet:* 12.

| | | |
|---|---|---|
| SC79440 | SC79443 | SC79446 |
| SC79441 | SC79444 | SC79447 |
| SC79442 | SC79445 | |

## Trailer First (K) ●
### (INTER-CITY UNITS)

*Built by:* **Swindon Works, B.R.**
*Body:* 64′ 6″ × 9′ 3″.
  Side corridor with seven first class
  compartments and end doors.
*Weight:* 33 tons 9 cwt.
*Seats 1st:* 42.

| | | |
|---|---|---|
| SC79470 | SC79475 | SC79480 |
| SC79471 | SC79476 | SC79481 |
| SC79472 | SC79477 | SC79482 |
| SC79473 | SC79478 | |
| SC79474 | SC79479 | |

## Motor Composite (L) ▲
### (TWIN UNITS)

*Built by:* **Derby Works, B.R.**
*Engines:* Two B.U.T. (Leyland) 6-cyl.
  horizontal type of 125 b.h.p.
*Transmission:* **Hydro-Mechanical.**
  Lysholm Smith (Leyland) torque
  converter to final drive.
*Body:* 57′ 6″ × 9′ 2″.
*Weight:*
*Seats 1st:* 16.
  *2nd:* 53.

| | | |
|---|---|---|
| E79500 | E79503 | E79506 |
| E79501 | E79504 | E79507 |
| E79502 | E79505 | |

## Motor Composite ◆
### (FOUR-CAR UNITS)

*Built by:* **Derby Works, B.R.**
*Engines:* Two B.U.T. (A.E.C.) 6-cyl.
  horizontal type of 150 b.h.p.
*Transmission:* **Mechanical.** Cardan
  shaft and freewheel to four-speed
  epicyclic gearbox and further cardan
  shaft to final drive.
*Body:* 57′ 6″ × 9′ 2″.
*Weight:* 26 tons 10 cwt.
*Seats 1st:* 20.
  *2nd:* 36.

| | | |
|---|---|---|
| E79508 | E79510 | E79512 |
| E79509 | E79511 | |

## Driving Trailer Composite (L) ◆
### (TWIN UNITS)

*Built by:* **Derby Works, B.R.**
Body: 57′ 6″ × 9′ 2″.
Weight: 21 tons.
Seats 1st:   9.
16*.
2nd: 53.

| | | |
|---|---|---|
| M79600 | M79609 | E79618* |
| M79601 | M79610 | E79619* |
| M79602 | M79611 | E79620* |
| M79603 | M79612 | E79621* |
| M79604 | E79613* | E79622* |
| M79605 | E79614* | E79623* |
| M79606 | E79615* | E79624* |
| M79607 | E79616* | E79625* |
| M79608 | E79617* | |

## Driving Trailer Composite (L) ◆
### (TWIN UNITS)

*Built by:* **Metropolitan Cammell.**
Body: 57′ 0″ × 9′ 3″.
Weight: 25 tons.
Seats 1st:  12.
2nd: 53.

| | | |
|---|---|---|
| M79626 | M79629 | M79632 |
| M79627 | M79630 | |
| M79628 | M79631 | |

## Driving Trailer Composite (L) ◆
### (TWIN UNITS)
**For Details see M79600-E79625**

| | | |
|---|---|---|
| M79639 | M79646 | M79653 |
| M79640 | M79647 | M79654 |
| M79641 | M79648 | M79655 |
| M79642 | M79649† | M79656 |
| M79643 | M79650 | M79657 |
| M79644 | M79651 | E79658* |
| M79645 | M79652 | E79659* |

†This vehicle has been fitted internally for use as an inspection saloon including a pantry, and is not in public service. It has been rewired to work with "Blue Square" type motorcoaches.

| | | |
|---|---|---|
| E79660* | M79669 | M79677 |
| E79661* | M79670 | M79678 |
| M79662 | M79671 | M79679 |
| M79663 | M79672 | M79680 |
| M79664 | M79673 | M79681 |
| M79665 | M79674 | M79682 |
| M79666 | M79675 | M79683 |
| M79667 | M79676 | M79684 |
| M79668 | | |

---

### NOTE

For reasons of clarity the 4-wheel units below are not in strict numerical order.

Some of these vehicles are now used by the L.M. Engineers Dept. and are not in public service.

---

## Motor Second
### (FOUR-WHEEL UNITS)

*Built by:* **British United Traction Co.**
*Engine:* B.U.T. (A.E.C.) 6-cyl. horizontal type of 125 b.h.p.
*Transmission:* **Mechanical.** Cardan shaft and freewheel to four-speed epicyclic gearbox and further cardan shaft to final drive.
Body: 37′ 6″ × 9′ 0″. Non-gangwayed. Driving compartment at each end.
Weight: 15 tons 0 cwt.
Seats 2nd: 34.

| | | |
|---|---|---|
| M79740 | M79745 | M79748 |

## Motor Brake Second
### (FOUR-WHEEL UNITS)

*Built by:* **British United Traction Co.**
*Engine:* B.U.T. (A.E.C.) 6-cyl. horizontal type of 125 b.h.p.
*Transmission:* **Mechanical.** Cardan shaft and freewheel to four-speed epicyclic gearbox and further cardan shaft to final drive.
Body: 37′ 6″ × 9′ 0″. Non-gangwayed. Driving compartment at each end.
Weight: 15 tons 0 cwt.
Seats 2nd: 28.

| | | |
|---|---|---|
| M79742 | M79744 | M79750 |
| M79743 | | |

## Trailer Second
### (FOUR-WHEEL UNITS)
*Built by:* **British United Traction Co.**
*Body:* 37′ 6″ × 9′ 0″. Non-gangwayed.
*Weight:* 10 tons 10 cwt.
*Seats 2nd:* 48.

M79741     M79747     M79749
M79746

## Motor Brake Second
### (SINGLE UNITS)
*Built by:* **Derby Works, B.R.**
*Engine:* Two B.U.T. (A.E.C.) 6-cyl. horizontal type of 150 b.h.p.
*Transmission:* **Mechanical.** Cardan shaft and freewheel to four-speed epicyclic gearbox and further cardan shaft to final drive.
*Body:* 57′ 6″ × 9′ 2″. Driving compartment at each end. Non-gangwayed.
*Weight:* 27 tons.
*Seats 2nd:* 52.

M79900     M79901

## Four-Wheel Railbus
*Built by:* **Bristol/E.C.W.**
*Engine:* Gardner 6.H.L.W. 6-cyl. type of 112 b.h.p. at 1,700 r.p.m.
*Transmission:* **Mechanical.** Cardan shaft and freewheel to Self-Changing Gears Ltd. five-speed epicyclic gearbox and further cardan shaft to final drive.
*Body:* 42′ 4″ × 9′ 3″. Non-gangwayed.
*Weight:* 13 tons 10 cwt.
*Seats 2nd:* 56.

SC79958     SC79959

## Four-Wheel Railbus
*Built by:* **Waggon und Maschinenbau.**
*Engine:* Buessing 150 b.h.p. at 1,900 r.p.m.
*Transmission:* **Mechanical.** Cardan shaft to ZF electro-magnetic six-speed gearbox.
*Body:* 41′ 10″ × 8′ 8⅝″. Non-gangwayed.
*Weight:* 15 tons.
*Seats 2nd:* 56.

| | | |
|---|---|---|
| E79960 | E79962 | E79964 |
| E79661 | E79963 | |

## Four-Wheel Railbus
*Built by:* **D. Wickham & Co.**
*Engine:* Meadows 6-cyl. type 6HDT500 of 105 b.h.p. at 1,800 r.p.m.
*Transmission:* **Mechanical.** Freeborn-Wickham disc-and-ring coupling driving Self-Changing Gears Ltd. four-speed epicyclic gearbox and cardan shaft to final drive.
*Body:* 38′ 0″ × 9′ 0″. Non-gangwayed.
*Weight:* 11 tons 5 cwt.
*Seats 2nd:* 44.

| | | |
|---|---|---|
| SC79965 | SC79967 | SC79969 |
| SC79966 | SC79968 | |

## Four-Wheel Railbus
*Built by:* **Park Royal Vehicles.**
*Engine:* B.U.T. (A.E.C.) 6-cyl. horizontal type of 150 b.h.p.
*Transmission:* **Mechanical.** Cardan shaft and freewheel to Self-Changing Gears Ltd. four-speed epicyclic gearbox and further cardan shaft to final drive.
*Body:* 42′ 0″ × 9′ 3″. Non-gangwayed.
*Weight:* 15 tons.
*Seats 2nd:* 50.

| | | |
|---|---|---|
| SC79970 | SC79972 | SC79974 |
| SC79971 | SC79973 | |

## Four-Wheel Railbus
*Built by:* **A.C. Cars Ltd.**
*Engine:* B.U.T. (A.E.C.) 6-cyl. horizontal type of 150 b.h.p.
*Transmission:* **Mechanical.** Cardan shaft and freewheel to four-speed epicyclic gearbox and further cardan shaft to final drive.
*Body:* 36′ 0″ × 8′ 11″.
*Weight:* 11 tons.
*Seats 2nd:* 46.

| | | |
|---|---|---|
| W79975 | W79977 | W79979 |
| W79976 | W79978 | |

## G.W.R. Railcars

| Car No. | Date | Engines | Total b.h.p. | Seats 2nd. |
|---------|------|---------|--------------|------------|
| 5/7 | 1935 | 2 | 242 | 70 |
| 8 | 1936 | 2 | 242 | 70 |
| 13/4§ | 1936 | 2 | 242 | — |
| 15* | 1936 | 2 | 242 | 70 |
| 17* | 1936 | 2 | 242 | — |
| 19-26/9-32† | 1940 | 2 | 210 | 48 |
| 33, 38‡ | 1942 | 4 | 420 | 92 |
| ‖1096 | — | — | — | 64 |

*Parcels cars.

‡Twin-coach unit with buffet facilities. Adjoining statistics apply per 2-car unit. These cars work as a three-car set with corridor second W1096W.

†These cars may work in pairs with an additional ordinary coach between.

§Rebuilt as Parcels Cars.

‖This is an ordinary 60 ft. ex-G.W. corridor second adapted for use between two diesel railcars, and is painted green.

| | | | |
|-------|-------|-------|-------|
| W5W | W17W | W23W | W30W |
| W7W | W19W | W24W | W31W |
| W8W | W20W | W25W | W32W |
| W13W | W21W | W26W | W33W |
| W14W | W22W | W29W | W38W |
| W15W | | W1096W | |

## Battery Electric Railcar Motor Brake Second
### (TWIN UNIT)

*Built by:* **Derby/Cowlairs Works, B.R.**

*Electrical Equipment:* Two 100 kW Siemens-Schuckert nose-suspended traction motors powered by 216 lead-acid cell batteries of 1070 amp/hour capacity.

*Body:* 57′ 6″ × 9′ 2″.
*Weight:* 37 tons 10 cwt.
*Seats 2nd:* 52.

SC79998

## Battery Electric Railcar Driving Trailer Composite
### (TWIN UNIT)

*Built by:* **Derby/Cowlairs Works, B.R.**

*Body:* 57′ 6″ × 9′ 2″.
*Weight:* 32 tons 10 cwt.
*Seats 1st:* 12.  *2nd:* 53.

SC79999

# NUMERICAL LIST OF ELECTRIC MULTIPLE UNITS

*The dimensions shown are length and width over body and width overall.*

*The letter "L" in the headings indicates an open vehicle fitted with toilet facilities*
*"K" indicates a side corridor vehicle with toilet.*

## London Midland Region

SYSTEM: 630 VOLTS D.C.
3rd & 4th RAIL

### LONDON DISTRICT THREE-CAR COMPARTMENT SETS

#### Motor Brake Second

Body: 59' 0" × 8' 11" & 9' 6".
Weight: 56 tons.
Seats 2nd: 84.
Equipment: Four 280 h.p. G.E.C. or M.V traction motors.

| | | |
|---|---|---|
| M28001M | M28010M | M28018M |
| M28002M | M28011M | M28019M |
| M28003M | M28012M | M28020M |
| M28004M | M28013M | M28021M |
| M28005M | M28014M | M28022M |
| M28006M | M28015M | M28023M |
| M28007M | M28016M | M28024M |
| M28008M | M28017M | M28025M |
| M28009M | | |

### Trailer Second

Body: 57' 0" × 8' 11" & 9' 6".
Weight: 28 tons.
Seats 2nd: 108.

| | | |
|---|---|---|
| M29401M | M29604M | M29615M |
| M29402M | M29605M | M29616M |
| M29403M | M29606M | M29617M |
| M29404M | M29607M | M29618M |
| M29405M | M29608M | M29619M |
| M29406M | M29609M | M29620M |
| M29409M | M29610M | M29621M |
| M29600M | M29611M | M29622M |
| M29601M | M29612M | M29624M |
| M29602M | M29613M | M29625M |
| M29603M | M29614M | |

### Driving Trailer Brake Second

Body: 57' 0" × 8' 11" & 9' 6".
Weight: 30 tons.
Seats 2nd: 96.

| | | |
|---|---|---|
| M28800M | M28809M | M28817M |
| M28801M | M28810M | M28818M |
| M28802M | M28811M | M28819M |
| M28803M | M28812M | M28820M |
| M28804M | M28813M | M28821M |
| M28805M | M28814M | M28822M |
| M28806M | M28815M | M28823M |
| M28807M | M28816M | M28824M |
| M28808M | | |

### LONDON DISTRICT THREE-CAR B.R. SETS

*B.R. Standard design*

#### Motor Open Brake Second

Body: 57' 5" × 9' 0" & 9' 6"
Weight: 47 tons.
Seats 2nd: 74.
Equipment: Four 185 h.p. G.E.C. traction motors.

| | | |
|---|---|---|
| M61133 | M61147 | M61161 |
| M61134 | M61148 | M61162 |
| M61135 | M61149 | M61163 |
| M61136 | M61150 | M61164 |
| M61137 | M61151 | M61165 |
| M61138 | M61152 | M61166 |
| M61139 | M61153 | M61167 |
| M61140 | M61154 | M61168 |
| M61141 | M61155 | M61169 |
| M61142 | M61156 | M61170 |
| M61143 | M61157 | M61171 |
| M61144 | M61158 | M61172 |
| M61145 | M61159 | M61173 |
| M61146 | M61160 | M61174 |

| M61175 | M61180 | M61185 |
|--------|--------|--------|
| M61176 | M61181 | M61186 |
| M61177 | M61182 | M61187 |
| M61178 | M61183 | M61188 |
| M61179 | M61184 | M61189 |

| M75160 | M75170 | M75180 |
|--------|--------|--------|
| M75161 | M75171 | M75181 |
| M75162 | M75172 | M75182 |
| M75163 | M75173 | M75183 |
| M75164 | M75174 | M75184 |
| M75165 | M75175 | M75185 |
| M75166 | M75176 | M75186 |
| M75167 | M75177 | M75187 |
| M75168 | M75178 | M75188 |
| M75169 | M75179 | M75189 |

### Trailer Second

*Body:* 57' 1" × 9' 0" & 9' 6".
*Weight:* 29 tons.
*Seats 2nd:* 108.

| M70133 | M70152 | M70171 |
|--------|--------|--------|
| M70134 | M70153 | M70172 |
| M70135 | M70154 | M70173 |
| M70136 | M70155 | M70174 |
| M70137 | M70156 | M70175 |
| M70138 | M70157 | M70176 |
| M70139 | M70158 | M70177 |
| M70140 | M70159 | M70178 |
| M70141 | M70160 | M70179 |
| M70142 | M70161 | M70180 |
| M70143 | M70162 | M70181 |
| M70144 | M70163 | M70182 |
| M70145 | M70164 | M70183 |
| M70146 | M70165 | M70184 |
| M70147 | M70166 | M70185 |
| M70148 | M70167 | M70186 |
| M70149 | M70168 | M70187 |
| M70150 | M70169 | M70188 |
| M70151 | M70170 | M70189 |

### Driving Trailer
### Open Brake Second

*Body:* 57' 5" × 9' 0" & 9' 6".
*Weight:* 30 tons.
*Seats 2nd:* 74.

| M75133 | M75142 | M75151 |
|--------|--------|--------|
| M75134 | M75143 | M75152 |
| M75135 | M75144 | M75153 |
| M75136 | M75145 | M75154 |
| M75137 | M75146 | M75155 |
| M75138 | M75147 | M75156 |
| M75139 | M75148 | M75157 |
| M75140 | M75149 | M75158 |
| M75141 | M75150 | M75159 |

*SYSTEM: 630 VOLTS D.C. 3rd RAIL*

## LIVERPOOL-SOUTHPORT
## TWO- AND THREE-CAR COMPARTMENT SETS

### Motor Brake Second

*Body:* 59' 0" × 8' 11" & 9' 3".
*Weight:* 56 tons.
*Seats 2nd:* 84.
*Equipment:* Four 265 h.p. Metropolitan Vickers traction motors.

| M28301M | M28305M | M28308M |
|---------|---------|---------|
| M28302M | M28306M | M28309M |
| M28303M | M28307M | M28310M |
| M28304M |         |         |

### Trailer Composite

*Body:* 57' 0" × 8' 11" & 9' 3".
*Weight:* 28 tons.
*Seats 1st:* 24.
*2nd:* 72.

| M29800M | M29804M | M29808M |
|---------|---------|---------|
| M29801M | M29805M | M29809M |
| M29802M | M29806M | M29810M |
| M29803M | M29807M | M29811M |

## Driving Trailer Brake Second

*Body:* 57′ 0″ × 8′ 11″ & 9′ 3″.
*Weight:* 28 tons.
*Seats 2nd:* 96.

| | | |
|---|---|---|
| M29100M | M29104M | M29108M |
| M29101M | M29105M | M29109M |
| M29102M | M29106M | M29110M |
| M29103M | M29107M | |

# LIVERPOOL-SOUTHPORT
## TWO- AND THREE-CAR OPEN SETS
### Motor Open Brake Second

*Body:* 66′ 6″ × 9′ 3″ & 9′ 5″.
*Weight:* 41 tons.
*Seats 2nd:* 88.
*Equipment:* Four 235 h.p. English Electric traction motors.

| | | |
|---|---|---|
| M28311M | M28331M | M28351M |
| M28312M | M28332M | M28352M |
| M28313M | M28333M | M28353M |
| M28314M | M28334M | M28354M |
| M28315M | M28335M | M28355M |
| M28316M | M28336M | M28356M |
| M28317M | M28337M | M28357M |
| M28318M | M28338M | M28358M |
| M28319M | M28339M | M28359M |
| M28321M | M28340M | M28360M |
| M28322M | M28341M | M28361M |
| M28323M | M28342M | M28362M |
| M28324M | M28343M | M28363M |
| M28325M | M28344M | M28364M |
| M28326M | M28345M | M28365M |
| M28327M | M28347M | M28366M |
| M28328M | M28348M | M28367M |
| M28329M | M28349M | M28368M |
| M28330M | M28350M | M28369M |

### Trailer Open Second

*Body:* 66′ 6″ × 9′ 3″ & 9′ 5″.
*Weight:* 24 tons.
*Seats 2nd:* 102.

| | | |
|---|---|---|
| M29545M | M29562M | M29579M |
| M29546M | M29563M | M29580M |
| M29547M | M29564M | M29581M |
| M29548M | M29565M | M29582M |
| M29549M | M29566M | M29583M |
| M29550M | M29567M | M29584M |
| M29551M | M29568M | M29585M |
| M29552M | M29569M | M29586M |
| M29553M | M29570M | M29587M |
| M29554M | M29571M | M29588M |
| M29555M | M29572M | M29589M |
| M29556M | M29573M | M29590M |
| M29557M | M29574M | M29591M |
| M29558M | M29575M | M29592M |
| M29559M | M29576M | M29593M |
| M29560M | M29577M | M29594M |
| M29561M | M29578M | |

### Trailer Open Second
### (Built as Composite)

*Body:* 66′ 6″ × 9′ 3″ & 9′ 5″.
*Weight:* 24 tons.
*Seats 2nd:* 82.

| | | |
|---|---|---|
| M29812M | M29815M | M29818M |
| M29813M | M29816M | M29819M |
| M29814M | M29817M | M29820M |

### Driving Trailer Open Composite

*Body:* 66′ 6″ × 9′ 3″ & 9′ 5″.
*Weight:* 25 tons.
*Seats 1st:* 53.
   *2nd:* 25.

| | | |
|---|---|---|
| M29866M | M29878M | M29889M |
| M29867M | M29879M | M29890M |
| M29868M | M29880M | M29891M |
| M29869M | M29881M | M29892M |
| M29870M | M29882M | M29893M |
| M29871M | M29883M | M29894M |
| M29872M | M29884M | M29895M |
| M29873M | M29885M | M29896M |
| M29874M | M29886M | M29897M |
| M29875M | M29887M | M29898M |
| M29876M | M29888M | M29899M |
| M29877M | | |

## LIVERPOOL-SOUTHPORT
### Motor Parcels Van

Body: {57' 0" × 8' 11" & 9' 3"\*.
{59' 0" × 8' 11" & 9' 3".
Weight:
Equipment: Two 265 h.p. Metropolitan-Vickers nose-suspended traction motors.

M28496M    \*M28497M


*SYSTEM: 650 VOLTS D.C. 3rd RAIL*

## WIRRAL & MERSEY
### THREE-CAR OPEN SETS
### Motor Open Brake Second

Body: 58' 0" × 8' 8" & 9' 11".
Weight: 36 tons.
Seats 2nd: 58.
Equipment: Four 135 h.p. B.T.H. traction motors.

| | | |
|---|---|---|
| M28371M | M28386M | M28677M |
| M28372M | M28387M | M28678M |
| M28373M | M28388M | M28679M |
| M28374M | M28389M | M28680M |
| M28375M | M28390M | M28681M |
| M28376M | M28391M | M28682M |
| M28377M | M28392M | M28683M |
| M28378M | M28393M | M28684M |
| M28379M | M28394M | M28685M |
| M28380M | | M28686M |
| M28381M | M28672M | M28687M |
| M28382M | M28673M | M28688M |
| M28383M | M28674M | M28689M |
| M28384M | M28675M | M28690M |
| M28385M | M28676M | |


### Trailer Open Composite

Body: 56' 0" × 8' 8" & 9' 11".
Weight: 20 tons.
Seats 1st: 40.
2nd: 15.

| | | |
|---|---|---|
| M29702M | M29718M | M29833M |
| M29703M | M29719M | M29834M |
| M29704M | M29720M | M29835M |
| M29705M | | M29836M |
| M29706M | M29821M | M29837M |
| M29707M | M29822M | M29838M |
| M29708M | M29823M | M29839M |
| M29709M | M29824M | M29840M |
| M29710M | M29825M | M29841M |
| M29711M | M29826M | M29842M |
| M29712M | M29827M | M29843M |
| M29713M | M29828M | M29844M |
| M29714M | M29829M | M29845M |
| M29715M | M29830M | M29846M |
| M29716M | M29831M | |
| M29717M | M29832M | |


### Driving Trailer Open Second

Body: 58' 0" × 8' 8" & 9' 11".
Weight: 21 tons.
Seats 2nd: 68.

| | | |
|---|---|---|
| M29131M | M29147M | M29275M |
| M29132M | M29148M | M29276M |
| M29133M | M29149M | M29277M |
| M29134M | M29150M | M29278M |
| M29135M | M29151M | M29279M |
| M29136M | M29152M | M29280M |
| M29137M | M29153M | M29281M |
| M29138M | M29154M | M29282M |
| M29139M | M29155M | M29283M |
| M29140M | M29156M | M29284M |
| M29141M | | M29285M |
| M29142M | M29271M | M29286M |
| M29143M | M29272M | M29287M |
| M29144M | M29273M | M29288M |
| M29145M | M29274M | M29289M |
| M29146M | | |

## MANCHESTER-BURY
## TWO-CAR B.R. SETS
*B.R. Standard design*
### Motor Open Brake Second

Body: 63′ 11¼″ × 9′ 0″ & 9′ 3″.
Weight:
Seats 2nd: 84.
Equipment: Two 141 h.p. English Electric
traction motors.

| | | |
|---|---|---|
| M65436 | M65445 | M65454 |
| M65437 | M65446 | M65455 |
| M65438 | M65447 | M65456 |
| M65439 | M65448 | M65457 |
| M65440 | M65449 | M65458 |
| M65441 | M65450 | M65459 |
| M65442 | M65451 | M65460 |
| M65443 | M65452 | M65461 |
| M65444 | M65453 | |

### Driving Trailer Composite

Body: 63′ 11¼″ × 9′ 0″ & 9′ 3″.
Weight:
Seats 1st: 16.
    2nd: 78.

| | | |
|---|---|---|
| M77157 | M77166 | M77175 |
| M77158 | M77167 | M77176 |
| M77159 | M77168 | M77177 |
| M77160 | M77169 | M77178 |
| M77161 | M77170 | M77179 |
| M77162 | M77171 | M77180 |
| M77163 | M77172 | M77181 |
| M77164 | M77173 | M77182 |
| M77165 | M77174 | |

## MANCHESTER–
## ALTRINCHAM
## THREE-CAR SETS
### Motor Brake Second

Body: 58′ 1″ × 8′ 11″ & 9′ 3″.
Weight: 57 tons.
Seats 2nd: 72.
Equipment: Four 330 h.p. traction
motors.

| | | |
|---|---|---|
| M28571M | M28579M | M28587M |
| M28572M | M28580M | M28588M |
| M28573M | M28581M | M28589M |
| M28574M | M28582M | M28590M |
| M28575M | M28583M | M28591M |
| M28576M | M28584M | M28592M |
| M28577M | M28585M | M28593M |
| M28578M | M28586M | M28594M |

### Trailer Composite

Body: 57′ 1″ × 8′ 11″ & 9′ 3″.
Weight: 30 tons.
Seats 1st: 24.
    2nd: 72.

| | | |
|---|---|---|
| M29396M | M29656M | M29664M |
| | M29657M | M29665M |
| M29650M | M29658M | M29666M |
| M29651M | M29659M | M29667M |
| M29652M | M29660M | M29668M |
| M29653M | M29661M | M29669M |
| M29654M | M29662M | M29670M |
| M29655M | M29663M | M29671M |

### Driving Trailer Second

Body: 58′ 1″ × 8′ 11″ & 9′ 3″.
Weight: 31 tons.
Seats 2nd: 108.

| | | |
|---|---|---|
| M29231M | M29239M | M29246M |
| M29232M | M29240M | M29247M |
| M29233M | M29241M | M29248M |
| M29234M | M29242M | M29249M |
| M29235M | M29243M | M29250M |
| M29236M | M29244M | M29251M |
| M29237M | M29245M | M29252M |
| M29238M | | |

## LANCASTER-
## MORECAMBE–HEYSHAM
## THREE-CAR OPEN SETS
### Motor Open Brake Second

Body: 57′ 0″ × 8′ 11″ & 9′ 6″.
Weight: 57 tons.
Seats 2nd: { 28
           { 38*.

*Equipment:* Four 215 h.p. English Electric traction motors.
*Four 215 h.p. Metropolitan-Vickers traction motors.

M28219M | M28221M | M28222M*
M28220M

## Trailer Open Second

*Body:* 57′ 0″ × 8′ 11″ & 9′ 6″.
*Weight:* 26 tons.
*Seats 2nd:* 62.

M29721M | M29723M | M29724M
M29722M

## Driving Trailer Open Second

*Body:* 57′ 0″ × 8′ 11″ & 9′ 6″.
*Weight:*
*Seats 2nd:* 56.

M29021M | M29023M | M29024M
M29022M

*SYSTEM: 1500 VOLTS D.C. OVERHEAD*

## MANCHESTER–GLOSSOP–HADFIELD THREE-CAR OPEN SETS

## Motor Open Brake Second

*Body:* 60′ 4½″ × 9′ 0″ & 9′ 3″.
*Weight:* 50 tons 12 cwt.
*Seats 2nd:* 52.
*Equipment:* Four 185 h.p. GEC traction motors.

| | | |
|---|---|---|
| M59401 | M59404 | M59407 |
| M59402 | M59405 | M59408 |
| M59403 | M59406 | |

## Trailer Open Second

*Body:* 55′ 0½″ × 9′ 0″ & 9′ 3″.
*Weight:* 26 tons 8 cwt.
*Seats 2nd:*

| | | |
|---|---|---|
| M59501 | M59504 | M59507 |
| M59502 | M59505 | M59508 |
| M59503 | M59506 | |

## Driving Trailer Open Second

*Body:* 55′ 4½″ × 9′ 0″ & 9′ 3″.
*Weight:* 27 tons 9 cwt.
*Seats 2nd:* 60.

| | | |
|---|---|---|
| M59601 | M59604 | M59607 |
| M59602 | M59605 | M59608 |
| M59603 | M59606 | |

*SYSTEM: 25 kV. A.C. 50 CYCLES OVERHEAD*

## MANCHESTER-CREWE LIVERPOOL-CREWE FOUR-CAR SETS

*B.R. Standard design*

## Driving Trailer Open Brake Second

*Body:* 64′ 0⅝″ × 9′ 0″ & 9′ 3″.
*Weight:* 31 tons 8 cwt.
*Seats 2nd:* 82.

## Trailer Composite (L)

*Body:* 63′ 6¼″ × 9′ 0″ & 9′ 3″.
*Weight:* 31 tons 5 cwt.
*Seats 1st:* 19.
*2nd:* 60.

## Motor Brake Second (Open *)

*Body:* 63′ 6¼″ × 9′ 0″ & 9′ 3″.
*Weight:* 53 tons 12 cwt.
*Seats 2nd:* {96.
{72*.
*Equipment:* Four A.E.I. 207 h.p. axle-hung nose-suspended d.c. traction motors.

## Driving Trailer Open Second (L)

*Body:* 64′ 0⅝″ × 9′ 0″ & 9′ 3″.
*Weight:* 35 tons 12 cwt.
*Seats 2nd:* 80.

### UNIT Nos.

| | | | |
|---|---|---|---|
| 001 | 010 | 019* | 028* |
| 002 | 011 | 020* | 029* |
| 003 | 012 | 021* | 030* |
| 004 | 013 | 022* | 031* |
| 005 | 014 | 023* | 032* |
| 006 | 015 | 024* | 033* |
| 007 | 016* | 025* | 034* |
| 008 | 017* | 026* | 035* |
| 009 | 018* | 027* | |

# Eastern Region

## LIVERPOOL ST.– SHENFIELD

### THREE-CAR OPEN UNITS

These sets were converted for working on 25,000 volts a.c. from 1,500 volts d.c. The centre trailers were altered to include the guards compartment and pantograph and part of the passenger saloon thus displaced transferred to the existing motor coach. The centre trailer now carries the transformer and rectifier to feed the existing d.c. control equipment and traction motors on the original motor coach.

### Motor Open Second

*Body:* 60′ 4¼″ × 9′ 0″ & 9′ 6″.
*Weight:* 50 tons 17 cwt.
*Seats* 2nd: 62.
*Equipment:* Four 157 h.p. nose-suspended d.c. traction motors.

### Trailer Open Brake Second

*Body:* 55′ 0¼″ × 9′ 0″ & 9′ 6″.
*Weight:* 26 tons.
*Seats* 2nd: 46.

### Driving Trailer Open Second

*Body:* 55′ 4″ × 9′ 0″ & 9′ 6″.
*Weight:* 27 tons 10 cwt.
*Seats* 2nd: 60.

#### UNIT Nos.

| | | | |
|---|---|---|---|
| 001 | 012 | 023 | 034 |
| 002 | 013 | 024 | 035 |
| 003 | 014 | 025 | 036 |
| 004 | 015 | 026 | 037 |
| 005 | 016 | 027 | 038 |
| 006 | 017 | 028 | 039 |
| 007 | 018 | 029 | 040 |
| 008 | 019 | 030 | 041 |
| 009 | 020 | 031 | 042 |
| 010 | 021 | 032 | 043 |
| 011 | 022 | 033 | 044 |

| | | | |
|---|---|---|---|
| 045 | 057 | 069 | 081 |
| 046 | 058 | 070 | 082 |
| 047 | 059 | 071 | 083 |
| 048 | 060 | 072 | 084 |
| 049 | 061 | 073 | 085 |
| 050 | 062 | 074 | 086 |
| 051 | 063 | 075 | 087 |
| 052 | 064 | 076 | 088 |
| 053 | 065 | 077 | 089 |
| 054 | 066 | 078 | 090 |
| 055 | 067 | 079 | 091 |
| 056 | 068 | 080 | 092 |

## LIVERPOOL ST.– SOUTHEND

### FOUR-CAR UNITS

These sets have been converted for working on 25,000 volts a.c. from 1,500 volts d.c. A new pantograph, transformer and rectifier mounted on one of the original driving trailers feeds the existing d.c. control and traction equipment on the motor coach.

*B.R. Standard design*

### Driving Trailer Second

*Body:* 63′ 11¼″ × 9′ 0″ & 9′ 3″.
*Weight:* 30 tons 5 cwt.
*Seats* 2nd: 108.

### Trailer Composite (L)

*Body:* 63′ 6″ × 9′ 0″ & 9′ 3″.
*Weight:* 30 tons.
*Seats* 1st: 19.
2nd: 60.

### Motor Brake Second

*Body:* 63′ 6″ × 9′ 0″ & 9′ 3″.
*Weight:* 48 tons 6 cwt.
*Seats* 2nd: 96.
*Equipment:* Four GEC 174 h.p. axle-hung nose-suspended d.c. traction motors.

### Driving Trailer Open Second (L)

*Body:* 63′ 11¼″ × 9′ 0″ & 9′ 3″.
*Weight:*
*Seats* 2nd: 80.

| | | | |
|---|---|---|---|
| 101 | 109 | 117 | 125 |
| 102 | 110 | 118 | 126 |
| 103 | 111 | 119 | 127 |
| 104 | 112 | 120 | 128 |
| 105 | 113 | 121 | 129 |
| 106 | 114 | 122 | 130 |
| 107 | 115 | 123 | 131 |
| 108 | 116 | 124 | 132 |

## COLCHESTER–CLACTON FOUR-CAR UNITS

*B.R. Standard design*

(for details see Liverpool St., Bishops Stortford/Hertford units 501—19.)

| | | | |
|---|---|---|---|
| 133 | 136 | 138 | 140 |
| 134 | 137 | 139 | 141 |
| 135 | | | |

## FENCHURCH ST.– SHOEBURYNESS FOUR-CAR UNITS

*B.R. Standard design*

### Driving Trailer Second

*Body:* 63′ 11¾″ × 9′ 0″ & 9′ 3″.
*Weight:* 32 tons.
*Seats 2nd:* 108.

### Trailer Composite (L)

*Body:* 63′ 6″ × 9′ 0″ & 9′ 3″.
*Weight:* 31 tons.
*Seats 1st:* 19.
     *2nd:* 60.

### Motor Brake Second

*Body:* 63′ 6″ × 9′ 0″ & 9′ 3″.
*Weight:* 56 tons 10 cwt.
*Seats 2nd:* 96.
*Equipment:* Four 192 h.p. English Electric nose-suspended traction motors.

### Driving Trailer Open Second (L)

*Body:* 63′ 11½″ × 9′ 0″ & 9′ 3″.

*Weight:* 36 tons.

*Seats 2nd:* 80.

| | | | |
|---|---|---|---|
| 201 | 229 | 257 | 285 |
| 202 | 230 | 258 | 286 |
| 203 | 231 | 259 | 287 |
| 204 | 232 | 260 | 288 |
| 205 | 233 | 261 | 289 |
| 206 | 234 | 262 | 290 |
| 207 | 235 | 263 | 291 |
| 208 | 236 | 264 | 292 |
| 209 | 237 | 265 | 293 |
| 210 | 238 | 266 | 294 |
| 211 | 239 | 267 | 295 |
| 212 | 240 | 268 | 296 |
| 213 | 241 | 269 | 297 |
| 214 | 242 | 270 | 298 |
| 215 | 243 | 271 | 299 |
| 216 | 244 | 272 | 300 |
| 217 | 245 | 273 | 301 |
| 218 | 246 | 274 | 302 |
| 219 | 247 | 275 | 303 |
| 220 | 248 | 276 | 304 |
| 221 | 249 | 277 | 305 |
| 222 | 250 | 278 | 306 |
| 223 | 251 | 279 | 307 |
| 224 | 252 | 280 | 308 |
| 225 | 253 | 281 | 309 |
| 226 | 254 | 282 | 310 |
| 227 | 255 | 283 | 311 |
| 228 | 256 | 284 | 312 |

## LIVERPOOL ST.–ENFIELD AND CHINGFORD THREE-CAR UNITS

*B.R. Standard design*

### Driving Trailer Open Second

*Body:* 63′ 11½ in × 9′ 0″ & 9′ 3″.
*Weight:*
*Seats 2nd:* 94.

### Motor Brake Open Second

*Body:* 63′ 6″ × 9′ 0″ & 9′ 3″.
*Weight:*
*Seats 2nd:* 84.
*Equipment:* Four G.E.C. 200 h.p. axle-hung nose-suspended d.c. traction motors.

**Driving Trailer Open Second**

*Body:* 63′ 11¼″ × 9′ 0″ & 9′ 3″.
*Weight:*
*Seats 2nd:* 94.

UNIT Nos.

| | | | |
|---|---|---|---|
| 401 | 414 | 427 | 440 |
| 402 | 415 | 428 | 441 |
| 403 | 416 | 429 | 442 |
| 404 | 417 | 430 | 443 |
| 405 | 418 | 431 | 444 |
| 406 | 419 | 432 | 445 |
| 407 | 420 | 433 | 446 |
| 408* | 421 | 434 | 447 |
| 409 | 422 | 435 | 448 |
| 410 | 423 | 436 | 449 |
| 411 | 424 | 437 | 450 |
| 412 | 425 | 438 | 451 |
| 413 | 426 | 439 | 452 |

Unit 408; interior fittings temporarily removed, set converted to mobile test unit.

## LIVERPOOL ST.-BISHOPS STORTFORD AND HERTFORD EAST FOUR-CAR UNITS

*B.R. Standard design*

**Driving Trailer Second**

*Body:* 63′ 11¼″ × 9′ 0″ & 9′ 3″.
*Weight:* 32 tons.
*Seats 2nd:* 108.

**Trailer Composite (L)**

*Body:* 63′ 6″ × 9′ 0″ & 9′ 3″.
*Weight:* 31 tons.
*Seats 1st:* 19.
*2nd:* 60.

## North Eastern Region

*SYSTEM: 600 VOLTS D.C. 3rd RAIL*

### SOUTH TYNESIDE TWO-CAR SETS

*B.R. Standard design*

**Motor Open Brake Second**

*Body:* 63′ 11¼″ × 9′ 0″ & 9′ 3″.

**Motor Brake Second**

*Body:* 63′ 6″ × 9′ 0″ & 9′ 3″.
*Weight:* 54 tons.
*Seats 2nd:* 96.
*Equipment:* Four G.E.C. 200 h.p. axle-hung nose-suspended d.c. traction motors.

### Driving Trailer Open Second (L)

*Body:* 63′ 11¼″ × 9′ 0″ & 9′ 3″.
*Weight:* 36 tons.
*Seats 2nd:* 80.

UNIT Nos.

| | | | |
|---|---|---|---|
| 501 | 506 | 511 | 516 |
| 502 | 507 | 512 | 517 |
| 503 | 508 | 513 | 518 |
| 504 | 509 | 514 | 519 |
| 505 | 510 | 515 | |

*SYSTEM: 575 VOLTS D.C. OVERHEAD*

### GRIMSBY-IMMINGHAM ELECTRIC TRAMS

| | | | | |
|---|---|---|---|---|
| 1 | 14 | 19 | 24 | 29 |
| 3 | 15 | 20 | 25 | 30 |
| 4 | 16 | 21 | 26 | 31 |
| 5 | 17 | 22 | 27 | 32 |
| 11 | 18 | 23 | 28 | 33 |
| 12 | | | | |

*Weight:* 40 tons.
*Seats 2nd:* 74.
*Equipment:* Two 250 h.p. English Electric traction motors.

| | | |
|---|---|---|
| E65311 | E65316 | E65321 |
| E65312 | E65317 | E65322 |
| E65313 | E65318 | E65323 |
| E65314 | E65319 | E65324 |
| E65315 | E65320 | E65325 |

## Driving Trailer Second

*Body:* 63' 11½" × 9' 0" & 9' 3".
*Weight:* 30 tons.
*Seats 2nd:*

| | | |
|---|---|---|
| E77100 | E77105 | E77110 |
| E77101 | E77106 | E77111 |
| E77102 | E77107 | E77112 |
| E77103 | E77108 | E77113 |
| E77104 | E77109 | E77114 |

## SOUTH TYNESIDE
## Motor Parcels Van

*Body:* 64' 5" × 9' 0" & 9' 3".
*Weight:* 49 tons.
*Equipment:* Four 250 h.p. English Electric traction motors.

E68000

## NORTH TYNESIDE
## ARTICULATED TWIN UNITS

### Motor Open Brake Second

*Body:* 55' 0" × 9' 0½" & 9' 3".
*Combined weight with trailer:* 54 tons 19 cwt.
*Seats 2nd:* 52.
*Equipment:* Two 154 h.p. Crompton Parkinson traction motors.

### Driving Trailer Open Second

*Body:* 55' 0" × 9' 0½" & 9' 3".
*Seats 2nd:* 76.

| Motor Coaches | Driving Trailers |
|---|---|
| E29101E | E29301E |
| E29102E | E29302E |
| E29103E | E29303E |
| E29104E | E29304E |
| E29105E | E29305E |
| E29106E | E29306E |
| E29107E | E29307E |
| E29108E | E29308E |
| E29109E | E29309E |
| E29110E | E29310E |
| E29111E | E29311E |

## Motor Open Brake Second

*Body:* 55' 0" × 9' 0½" & 9' 3".
*Combined weight with trailer:* 55 tons 7 cwt.
*Seats 2nd:* 52.
*Equipment:* Two 154 h.p. Crompton Parkinson traction motors.

### Driving Trailer Open Second

*Body:* 55' 0" × 9' 0½" & 9' 3".
*Seats 2nd:* 60.

| Motor Coaches | Driving Trailers |
|---|---|
| E29113E | E29313E |
| E29114E | E29314E |
| E29115E | E29315E |
| E29116E | E29316E |
| E29117E | E29317E |
| E29118E | E29318E |
| E29119E | E29319E |
| E29120E | E29320E |
| E29121E | E29321E |
| E29122E | E29322E |
| E29123E | E29323E |
| E29124E | E29324E |
| E29125E | E29325E |
| E29126E | E29326E |
| E29127E | E29327E |
| E29128E | E29328E |

## Motor Open Brake Second

*Body:* 55' 0" × 9' 0½" & 9' 3".
*Combined weight with trailer:* 53 tons 12 cwt.
*Seats 2nd:* 52.
*Equipment:* Two 154 h.p. Crompton Parkinson traction motors.

### Trailer Open Second

*Body:* 55' 0" × 9' 0½" & 9' 3".
*Seats 2nd:* 80.

| Motor Coaches | Driving Trailers |
| --- | --- |
| E29129E | E29229E |
| E29130E | E29230E |
| E29131E | E29231E |
| E29132E | E29232E |
| E29133E | E29233E |
| E29134E | E29234E |
| E29135E | E29235E |
| E29136E | E29236E |
| E29137E | E29237E |
| E29138E | E29238E |
| E29139E | E29239E |
| E29140E | E29240E |
| E29141E | E29241E |
| E29142E | E29242E |
| E29143E | E29243E |
| E29144E | E29244E |
| E29145E | E29245E |
| E29146E | E29246E |

## Motor Open Brake Second

*Body:* 55′ 0″ × 9′ 0½″ & 9′ 3″.
*Combined weight with trailer:* 54 tons 6 cwt.
*Seats 2nd :* 52.
*Equipment:* Two 154 h.p. Crompton Parkinson traction motors.

## Trailer Open Second

*Body:* 55′ 0″ × 9′ 0½″ & 9′ 3″.
*Seats 2nd:* 64.

| Motor Coaches | Driving Trailers |
| --- | --- |
| E29147E | E29247E |
| E29148E | E29248E |
| E29149E | E29249E |
| E29150E | E29250E |
| E29151E | E29251E |
| E29152E | E29252E |
| E29153E | E29253E |

| | |
| --- | --- |
| E29154E | E29254E |
| E29155E | E29255E |
| E29156E | E29256E |
| E29157E | E29257E |
| E29158E | E29258E |
| E29159E | E29259E |
| E29160E | E29260E |
| E29161E | E29261E |
| E29162E | E29262E |
| E29163E | E29263E |
| E29164E | E29264E |

## Single Motor Open Brake Second

*Body:* 59′ 0″ × 9′ 0½″ & 9′ 3″.
*Weight:* 47 tons 5 cwt.
*Seats 2nd:* 52.
*Equipment:* Two 154 h.p. Crompton Parkinson traction motors.

| | |
| --- | --- |
| E29165E | E29166E |

## Single Driving Trailer Open Second

*Body:* 56′ 6″ × 9′ 0¾″ & 9′ 3″.
*Weight:* 26 tons 10 cwt.
*Seats 2nd:* 68.

| | |
| --- | --- |
| E29376E | E29388E |
| E29387E | E29390E |

## Motor Parcels Van

*Body:* 59′ 0″ × 9′ 0½″ & 9′ 3″.
*Weight:* 38 tons 15 cwt.
*Equipment:* Four 154 h.p. Crompton Parkinson traction motors.

| | |
| --- | --- |
| E29467E | E29468E |

# Scottish Region

SYSTEM: 25 kV. A.C. 50 CYCLES OVERHEAD

## GLASGOW SUBURBAN THREE-CAR SETS

*B.R. Standard design*

### Driving Trailer Open Second
Body: 63′ 11⅝″ × 9′ 3″ & 9′ 3″
Weight: 34 tons.
Seats 2nd: 83.

### Motor Open Brake Second

Body: 63′ 6⅝″ × 9′ 3″ & 9′ 3″.
Weight: 56 tons.
Seats 2nd: 70.
Equipment: Four AEI (MV) 207 h.p. axle-hung nose-suspended d.c. traction motors.

### Driving Trailer Open Second

Body: 63′ 11⅝″ × 9′ 3″ & 9′ 3″.
Weight: 38 tons.
Seats 2nd: 83.

UNIT Nos.

| | | | |
|---|---|---|---|
| 001 | 024 | 047 | 070 |
| 002 | 025 | 048 | 071 |
| 003 | 026 | 049 | 072 |
| 004 | 027 | 050 | 073 |
| 005 | 028 | 051 | 074 |
| 006 | 029 | 052 | 075 |
| 007 | 030 | 053 | 076 |
| 008 | 031 | 054 | 077 |
| 009 | 032 | 055 | 078 |
| 010 | 033 | 056 | 079 |
| 011 | 034 | 057 | 080 |
| 012 | 035 | 058 | 081 |
| 013 | 036 | 059 | 082 |
| 014 | 037 | 060 | 083 |
| 015 | 038 | 061 | 084 |
| 016 | 039 | 062 | 085 |
| 017 | 040 | 063 | 086 |
| 018 | 041 | 064 | 087 |
| 019 | 042 | 065 | 088 |
| 020 | 043 | 066 | 089 |
| 021 | 044 | 067 | 090 |
| 022 | 045 | 068 | 091 |
| 023 | 046 | 069 | |

# Southern Region

*(Unit numbers to be seen on front and rear of each set)*
SYSTEM: 750 VOLTS D.C. 3rd RAIL

## TWO-CAR SETS
### (2-BIL.)
### Motor Brake Second (K)
Body: 62′ 6″ × 9′ 0″ & 9′ 3″.
Weight: 43 tons 10 cwt.
Seats 2nd: 56†.
          52.
Equipment: Two 275 h.p. English Electric traction motors.

## Driving Trailer
## Composite (K)

Body: 62′ 6″ × 9′ 0″ & 9′ 3″.
Weight: 31 tons 5 cwt.
Seats 1st: 24.
      2nd: 32.

| | | | |
|---|---|---|---|
| 2001† | 2039 | 2076 | 2114 |
| 2002† | 2040 | 2077 | 2115 |
| 2003† | 2041 | 2078 | 2116 |
| 2004† | 2042 | 2079 | 2117 |
| 2005† | 2043 | 2080 | 2118 |
| 2006† | 2044 | 2081 | 2120 |
| 2007† | 2045 | 2082 | 2121 |
| 2008† | 2046 | 2083 | 2122 |
| 2009† | 2047 | 2084 | 2123 |
| 2010† | 2048 | 2085 | 2124 |
| 2011 | 2049 | 2086 | 2125 |
| 2012 | 2050 | 2087 | 2126 |
| 2013 | 2051 | 2088* | 2127 |
| 2015 | 2052 | 2089 | 2128 |
| 2016 | 2053 | 2090 | 2129 |
| 2017 | 2054 | 2091 | 2130 |
| 2018 | 2055 | 2092 | 2132 |
| 2019 | 2056* | 2093 | 2133‡ |
| 2020 | 2057 | 2094 | 2134 |
| 2021 | 2058 | 2095 | 2135 |
| 2022 | 2059 | 2096 | 2136 |
| 2023 | 2060 | 2097 | 2137 |
| 2024 | 2061 | 2098 | 2138 |
| 2025 | 2062 | 2099 | 2139 |
| 2026 | 2063 | 2100‡ | 2140 |
| 2027 | 2064 | 2101 | 2141 |
| 2028 | 2065 | 2103 | 2142 |
| 2029 | 2066 | 2104 | 2143 |
| 2030 | 2067 | 2105 | 2144 |
| 2031 | 2068 | 2106 | 2145 |
| 2032 | 2069*‡ | 2107 | 2146 |
| 2033 | 2070 | 2108 | 2147 |
| 2034 | 2071 | 2109 | 2148 |
| 2035 | 2072 | 2110 | 2149 |
| 2036 | 2073 | 2111 | 2150 |
| 2037 | 2074 | 2112 | 2151 |
| 2038 | 2075 | 2113 | 2152 |

*BIL Motor Coach and 1939 type HAL Trailer.
‡BIL Motor Coach and post-war all steel HAL Trailer.

---

## TWO-CAR SETS (2-HAL.)
### 1939-type
### Motor Brake Second

Body: 62' 6" × 9' 0" & 9' 3".
Weight: 44 tons.
Seats 2nd: 70.
Equipment: Two 275 h.p. English Electric nose-suspended traction motors.

## Driving Trailer Composite (K)

Body: 62' 6" × 9' 0" & 9' 3".
Weight: 32 tons.
Seats 1st: 18 or 24. 2nd: 40 or 32.

| | | | |
|---|---|---|---|
| 2601 | 2624 | 2648 | 2671 |
| 2602 | 2625 | 2649 | 2672 |
| 2603 | 2626 | 2650 | 2673 |
| 2604 | 2627 | 2651 | 2674 |
| 2605 | 2628 | 2652 | 2675 |
| 2606 | 2629 | 2653* | 2676 |
| 2607 | 2630 | 2654 | 2677 |
| 2608 | 2631 | 2655 | 2678 |
| 2609 | 2632 | 2656 | 2679 |
| 2610 | 2633 | 2657 | 2681 |
| 2611 | 2634 | 2658 | 2682 |
| 2612 | 2635 | 2659 | 2683 |
| 2613 | 2636 | 2660 | 2684 |
| 2614 | 2637 | 2661 | 2685 |
| 2615 | 2638 | 2662 | 2686 |
| 2616 | 2639 | 2663 | 2687 |
| 2617 | 2640 | 2664 | 2688 |
| 2618 | 2641 | 2665 | 2689 |
| 2619 | 2642 | 2666 | 2690 |
| 2620 | 2643 | 2667 | 2691 |
| 2621 | 2644 | 2668 | 2692 |
| 2622 | 2645 | 2669 | |
| 2623 | 2647 | 2670 | |

*Post-war all steel Trailer.

---

## TWO-CAR SETS (2-HAL.)
### Post War all-steel type.
### Motor Brake Second

Body: 62' 6" × 9' 0" & 9' 3".
Weight: 42 tons.
Seats 2nd: 84.
Equipment: Two 275 h.p. English Electric nose-suspended traction motors.

### Driving Trailer
### Composite (K)

*Body:* 62′ 6″ × 9′ 0″ & 9′ 3″

*Weight:* 31 tons.
*Seats 1st:* 18.
    2nd: 40.

| 2693 | 2695 | 2697 | 2699 |
| 2694 | 2696 | 2698 | |

---

## TWO-CAR SETS
## (2-HAL.)
*Post War all-steel type.*
### Motor Brake Saloon Second

*Body:* 62′ 6″ × 9′ 0″ & 9′ 3″.
*Weight:* 39 tons.
*Seats 2nd:* 82.
*Equipment:* Two 275 h.p. English Electric
  traction motors.

### Driving Trailer
### Composite (K)
*Body:* 62′ 6″ × 9′ 0″ & 9′ 3″.
*Weight:* 31 tons.
*Seats 1st:* 24.
    2nd: 32.

2700

---

## FOUR-CAR SETS
## (4-LAV.)
### Motor Brake Second
*Body:* 62′ 6″ × 9′ 0″ & 9′ 3″.
*Weight:* 41 tons.
    44 tons*.
    45 tons†.
*Seats 2nd:* 70
*Equipment:* Two 275 h.p. Metropolitan-
  Vickers traction motors.
†*Two 275 h.p. English Electric traction
  motors.

### Trailer Composite
*Body:* 62′ 0″ × 9′ 0″ & 9′ 3″.
*Weight:* 28 tons.
    29 tons*.
*Seats 1st:* 16.
    2nd: 70.

### Trailer Composite (K)
*Body:* 62′ 0″ × 9′ 0″ & 9′ 3″.
*Weight:* 29 tons.
    30 tons*.
*Seats 1st:* 30.
    2nd: 24.

### Motor Brake Second
(As Above)

| 2921 | 2930 | 2939 | 2948 |
| 2922 | 2931 | 2940 | 2949 |
| 2923 | 2932 | 2941 | 2950 |
| 2924 | 2933 | 2942 | 2951 |
| 2925 | 2934 | 2943 | 2952 |
| 2926† | 2935 | 2944 | 2953 |
| 2927 | 2936 | 2945 | 2954* |
| 2928 | 2937 | 2946 | 2955* |
| 2929 | 2938 | 2947 | |

†One motor coach of 1939 2-HAL type.
* 1939 Bulleid units.

---

## SIX-CAR SETS
## (6-PUL.)
*Gangwayed within set*
### Motor Saloon Brake Second
*Body:* 63′ 6″ × 9′ 0″ & 9′ 5″.
*Weight:* 59 tons.
*Seats 2nd:* 52.
*Equipment:* Four 225 h.p. B.T.H. traction
  motors.

### Trailer Second (K)
*Body:* 63′ 6″ × 9′ 0″ & 9′ 3″.
*Weight:* 35 tons.
*Seats 2nd:* 68.

### Trailer Composite (K)
*Body:* 63′ 6″ × 9′ 0″ & 9′ 3″.
*Weight:* 35 tons.
*Seats 1st:* 30.
    2nd: 24.

### Trailer Composite
### Pullman (L)
*Body:* 66′ 0″ × 8′ 11½″ & 8′ 11½″.
*Weight:* 43 tons.
*Seats 1st:* 12.
    2nd: 16.

### Trailer Composite (K)
(As Above)

## Motor Saloon Brake Second

(As Above)

| | | | |
|------|------|-------|------|
| 3001 | 3006 | 3011 | 3016 |
| 3002 | 3007 | 3012 | 3017 |
| 3003* | 3008 | 3013 | 3018 |
| 3004 | 3009 | 3014* | 3019 |
| 3005 | 3010 | 3015 | 3020 |

*One PAN motor coach.

---

## SIX-CAR SETS
## (6-PAN.)

*Gangwayed within set*

### Motor Saloon Brake Second

*Body:* 63′ 6″ × 9′ 0″ & 9′ 5″.
*Weight:* 59 tons.
*Seats 2nd:* 52.
*Equipment:* Four 225 h.p. English Electric traction motors.

### Trailer Second (K)

*Body:* 63′ 6″ × 9′ 0″ & 9′ 3″.
*Weight:* 31 tons 10 cwt.
*Seats 2nd:* 68.

### Trailer First (K)

*Body:* 59′ 0″ × 9′ 0″ & 9′ 3″.
*Weight:* 31 tons.
*Seats 1st:* 42.

### Trailer Pantry First (K)

*Body:* 63′ 6″ × 9′ 0″ & 9′ 3″.
*Weight:* 32 tons.
*Seats 1st:* 30.

### Trailer Second (K)

(As Above)

### Motor Saloon Brake Second

(As Above)

| | | | |
|------|-------|------|------|
| 3021 | 3025 | 3029 | 3034 |
| 3022 | 3026† | 3030 | 3035 |
| 3023 | 3027 | 3031 | 3036 |
| 3024 | 3028 | 3033 | 3037 |

† One PUL motor coach.

## SIX-CAR SETS
## (6-PUL.)

*Gangwayed within set*

### Motor Saloon Brake Second

*Body:* 63′ 6″ × 9′ 0″ & 9′ 5″.
*Weight:* 57 tons.
   59 tons*.
*Seats 2nd:* { 56.
       52*.
*Equipment:* Four 225 h.p. B.T.H. traction motors.

### Trailer Second (K)

*Body:* 59′ 0″ × 9′ 0″ & 9′ 3″.
*Weight:* 34 tons.
*Seats 2nd:* 56.

### Trailer Composite (K)

*Body:* 59′ 0″ × 9′ 0″ & 9′ 3″.
*Weight:* 34 tons.
*Seats 1st:* 30.
   2nd: 16.

### Trailer Composite Pullman (L)

*Body:* 66′ 0″ × 8′ 11½″ & 8′ 11½″.
*Weight:* 43 tons.
*Seats 1st:* 12.
   2nd: 16.

### Trailer Composite

(As Above)

### Motor Saloon Brake Second

*Body:* 63′ 6″ × 9′ 0″ & 9′ 5″.
*Weight:* 59 tons.
*Seats 2nd:* 52.
*Equipment:* Four 225 h.p. B.T.H. traction motors.

| | | |
|------|------|-------|
| 3041 | 3042 | 3043* |

## FIVE-CAR PULLMAN SETS
## (5-BEL.)

*All-Pullman;*
*Gangwayed within set*

### Motor Brake Second Pullman (L)

*Body:* 66′ 0″ × 8′ 11½″ & 8′ 11½″.
*Weight:* 62 tons.
*Seats 2nd:* 48.
*Equipment:* Four 225 h.p. B.T.H. traction motors.

## Trailer Second Pullman (L)

*Body:* 66′ 0″ × 8′ 11¼″ & 8′ 11½″.
*Weight:* 39 tons.
*Seats 2nd:* 56.

## Trailer Kitchen First Pullman (L)

*Body:* 66′ 0″ × 8′ 11¼″ & 8′ 11½″
*Weight:* 43 tons.
*Seats 1st:* 20.

## Trailer Kitchen First Pullman (L)

### (As Above)

## Motor Brake Second Pullman (L)

### (As Above)

| 3051 | 3052 | 3053 |
|------|------|------|

---

## FOUR-CAR SETS
### (4-RES.)
*Gangwayed throughout*
## Motor Saloon Brake Second

*Body:* 63′ 6″ × 9′ 0″ & 9′ 4½″.
*Weight:* 46 tons 10 cwt.
*Seats 2nd:* 52.
*Equipment:* Two 225 h.p. English Electric traction motors.

## Trailer First (K)

*Body:* 63′ 6″ × 9′ 0″ & 9′ 3″.
*Weight:* 33 tons.
*Seats 1st:* 30.
   *1st Dining:* 12.

## Trailer Kitchen Second (K)

*Body:* 63′ 6″ × 9′ 0″ & 9′ 4½″.
*Weight:* 35 tons.
*Seats 2nd Dining:* 36.

## Motor Saloon Brake Second
### (As Above)

| 3054 | 3059 | 3065 | 3069 |
|------|------|------|------|
| 3055 | 3061 | 3066 | 3070 |
| 3056 | 3062 | 3067 | 3071 |
| 3057 | 3064 | 3068 | 3072* |

*Kitchen Second in this unit converted to Buffet Car, weight 35 tons.

## FOUR-CAR SETS
### (4-BUF.)
*Gangwayed throughout*
## Motor Saloon Brake Second

*Body:* 63′ 6″ × 9′ 0″ & 9′ 4½″.
*Weight:* 46 tons 10 cwt.
*Seats 2nd:* 52.
*Equipment:* Two 225 h.p. English Electric traction motors.

## Trailer Composite (K)

*Body:* 63′ 6″ × 9′ 0″ & 9′ 3″.
*Weight:* 32 tons 12 cwt.
*Seats 1st:* 30.
   *2nd:* 24.

## Trailer Buffet (L)

*Body:* 63′ 6″ × 9′ 0″ & 9′ 3″.
*Weight:* 37 tons.
*Seats Buffet:* 26.

## Motor Saloon Brake Second
### (As Above)

| 3073 | 3077 | 3080 | 3083 |
|------|------|------|------|
| 3074 | 3078 | 3081 | 3084 |
| 3075 | 3079 | 3082 | 3085 |
| 3076 |      |      |      |

---

## FOUR-CAR SETS
### (4-COR.)
*Gangwayed throughout*
## Motor Saloon Brake Second

*Body:* 63′ 6″ × 9′ 0″ & 9′ 4½″.
*Weight:* 46 tons 10 cwt.
*Seats 2nd:* 52.
*Equipment:* Two 225 h.p. English Electric traction motors.

## Trailer Second (K)

*Body:* 63′ 6″ × 9′ 0″ & 9′ 3″.
*Weight:* 32 tons 13 cwt.
*Seats 2nd:* 68.

## Trailer Composite (K)

*Body:* 63′ 6″ × 9′ 0″ & 9′ 3″.
*Weight:* 32 tons 12 cwt.
   *33 tons.
*Seats 1st:* 30.
   *2nd:* 24
      16.*

## Motor Saloon Brake Second
### (As Above)

| | | | |
|---|---|---|---|
| 3101 | 3116 | 3131 | 3146 |
| 3102 | 3117 | 3132 | 3147 |
| 3103 | 3118 | 3133 | 3148 |
| 3104 | 3119 | 3134 | 3149 |
| 3105 | 3120 | 3135 | 3150 |
| 3106 | 3121 | 3136 | 3151 |
| 3107 | 3122 | 3137 | 3152 |
| 3108 | 3123 | 3138 | 3153 |
| 3109 | 3124 | 3139 | 3154 |
| 3110 | 3125 | 3140 | 3155 |
| 3111 | 3126 | 3141 | 3156 |
| 3112 | 3127 | 3142 | 3157 |
| 3113 | 3128 | 3143 | 3158* |
| 3114 | 3129 | 3144 | |
| 3115 | 3130 | 3145 | |

---

## FOUR-CAR SUBURBAN SETS (DOUBLE DECK) (4-DD.)

### Motor Brake Second

*Body:* 62' 6" × 9' 0" & 9' 3".
*Weight:* 39 tons.
*Seats 2nd:* Lower deck 55
        Upper deck 55 (*plus* 10 tip-up)
*Equipment:* Two 250 h.p. English Electric traction motors.

### Trailer Second

*Body:* 62' 0" × 9' 0" & 9' 3".
*Weight:* 28 tons.
*Seats 2nd:* Lower deck 78
        Upper deck 66 (*plus* 12 tip-up)

### Trailer Second
(As Above)

### Motor Brake Second
(As Above)

| | |
|---|---|
| 4001 | 4002 |

---

## FOUR-CAR SUBURBAN SETS (4-SUB.)

### Motor Brake Second

*Body:* 62' 6" × 9' 0" & 9' 3".
*Weight:* 43 tons.
*Seats 2nd:* 102.
*Equipment:* Two 275 h.p. English Electric traction motors.

### Trailer Second

*Body:* 62' 0" × 9' 0" & 9' 3".
*Weight:* 29 tons'
*Seats 2nd:* 132.

### Trailer Second

*Body:* 62' 0" × 9' 0" & 9' 3"
*Weight:* 29 tons.
*Seats 2nd:* 120.

### Motor Brake Second
(As Above)

| | | | |
|---|---|---|---|
| 4101 | 4104 | 4107 | 4110 |
| 4102 | 4105 | 4108 | |
| 4103 | 4106 | 4109 | |

---

### Motor Brake Second

*Body:* 62' 6" × 9' 0" & 9' 3".
*Weight:* 43 tons.
*Seats 2nd:* 96.
*Equipment:* Two 275 h.p. English Electric traction motors.

### Trailer Second

*Body:* 62' 0" × 9' 0" & 9' 3".
*Weight:* 28 tons.
*Seats 2nd:* 108.

### Trailer Second

*Body:* 62' 0" × 9' 0" & 9' 3".
*Weight:* 28 tons.
*Seats 2nd:* 120.

### Motor Brake Second
(As Above)

| | | | |
|---|---|---|---|
| 4111 | 4114 | 4117 | 4120 |
| 4112 | 4115 | 4118 | |
| 4113 | 4116 | 4119 | |

---

### Motor Brake Second (Semi-Saloon)

*Body:* 62' 6" × 9' 0" & 9' 3".
*Weight:* 43 tons.
*Seats 2nd:* 84.
*Equipment:* Two 275 h.p. English Electric traction motors.

### Trailer Second

*Body:* 62' 0" × 9' 0" & 9' 3"
*Weight:* 28 tons.
*Seats 2nd:* 108.

## Trailer Second
### (Semi-Saloon)
*Body:* 62' 0" × 9' 0" & 9' 3".
*Weight:* 28 tons.
*Seats 2nd:* 106.

## Motor Brake Second
### (Semi-Saloon)
#### (As Above)

| | | | |
|---|---|---|---|
| 4121 | 4124 | 4127 | 4130 |
| 4122 | 4125 | 4128 | |
| 4123 | 4126 | 4129 | |

---

## Motor Saloon Brake Second
*Body:* 62' 6" × 9' 0" & 9' 3".
*Weight:* 39 tons.
*Seats 2nd:* 82.
*Equipment:* Two 250 h.p. English Electric traction motors.

## Trailer Second
*Body:* 62' 0" × 9' 0" & 9' 3".
*Weight:* 28 tons.
*Seats 2nd:* 120.

## Trailer Saloon Second
*Body:* 62' 0" × 9' 0" & 9' 3".
*Weight:* 28 tons.
*Seats 2nd:* 102.

## Motor Saloon Brake Second
#### (As Above)

| | | | |
|---|---|---|---|
| 4277 | 4283 | 4289 | 4295 |
| 4278 | 4284 | 4290 | 4296 |
| 4279 | 4285 | 4291 | 4297 |
| 4280 | 4286 | 4292 | 4298 |
| 4281 | 4287 | 4293 | 4299 |
| 4282 | 4288 | 4294 | |

## Motor Brake Second
*Body:* 56' 11" × 8' 6" & 9' 0".
*Weight:* 39 tons.
*Seats 2nd:* 90.
*Equipment:* Two 275 h.p. Metropolitan-Vickers traction motors.

## Trailer Second
*Body:* 60' 0" × 8' 6" & 9' 0".
*Weight:* 27 tons.
*Seats 2nd:* 90.

## Trailer Second
*Body:* 62' 0" × 9' 0" & 9' 3".
*Weight:* 28 tons.
*Seats 2nd:* 120.

## Motor Brake Second
#### (As Above)

| | | | |
|---|---|---|---|
| 4305 | 4311 | 4322* | 4324 |
| 4308* | 4314 | 4323 | 4325 |
| 4310† | 4319 | | |

\* Units 4308/22 have two 62-ft. post-war 120 seat all-steel trailers.

† Unit 4310 has two 60-ft. 90-seat trailers.

---

## Motor Brake Second
*Body:* 62' 6" × 8' 6" & 9' 0".
*Weight:*
*Seats 2nd:* 80.
*Equipment:* Two 275 h.p. English Electric traction motors.

## Trailer Second
*Body:* 62' 0" × 8' 6" & 9' 0".
*Weight:*
*Seats 2nd:* 90.

## Trailer Second
*Body:* 62' 0" × 9' 0" & 9' 3".
*Weight:*
*Seats 2nd:* 120.

## Motor Brake Second
#### (As Above)

| | | | |
|---|---|---|---|
| 4326 | 4335* | 4343 | 4348* |
| 4329 | 4337 | 4346 | 4352 |
| 4330 | 4338 | 4347 | 4353 |
| 4333 | 4341 | | |

\* Units 4335/48 have two 62-ft. post-war 120-seat all-steel trailers.

---

## Motor Brake Second
*Body:* 62' 6" × 9' 0" & 9' 3".
*Weight:* 43 tons.
*Seats 2nd:* 96.
*Equipment:* Two 275 h.p. English Electric traction motors.

## Trailer Second

*Body:* 62' 0" × 9' 0" & 9' 3"
*Weight:* 28 tons.
*Seats* 2nd: 120.

## Trailer Second

(As Above)

## Motor Brake Second

(As Above)

| 4355 | 4358 | 4360 | 4362 |
| 4356 | 4359 | 4361 | 4363 |
| 4357 |      |      |      |

---

## Motor Brake Second

*Body:* 62' 6" × 9' 0" & 9' 3".
*Weight:* 43 tons.
*Seats* 2nd: 96.
*Equipment:* Two 275 h.p. English Electric traction motors.

## Trailer Second

*Body:* 62' 0" × 9' 0" & 9' 3".
*Weight:* 28 tons.
*Seats* 2nd: 108

## Trailer Second

*Body:* 62' 0" × 9' 0" & 9' 3".
*Weight:* 28 tons.
*Seats* 2nd: 120.

## Motor Brake Second

(As Above)

| 4364 | 4368 | 4371 | 4374 |
| 4365 | 4369 | 4372 | 4375 |
| 4366 | 4370 | 4373 | 4376 |
| 4367 |      |      |      |

## Motor Brake Second

*Body:* 62' 6" × 9' 0" & 9' 3".
*Weight:*
*Seats* 2nd: 96.
*Equipment:* Two 275 h.p. English Electric traction motors.

## Trailer Second

*Body:* 62' 0" × 9' 0" & 9' 3".
*Weight:*
*Seats* 2nd: 108.

## Trailer Saloon Second

*Body:* 62' 0" × 9' 0" & 9' 3".
*Weight:*
*Seats* 2nd: 102.

## Motor Brake Second

(As Above)

4377

---

## Motor Saloon Brake Second

*Body:* 62' 6" × 9' 0" & 9' 3".
*Weight:* 42 tons.
*Seats* 2nd: 82.
*Equipment:* Two 275 h.p. English Electric traction motors.

## Trailer Second

*Body:* 62' 0" × 9' 0" & 9' 3".
*Weight:* 28 tons.
*Seats* 2nd: 120.

## Trailer Saloon Second

*Body:* 62' 0" × 9' 0" & 9' 3".
*Weight:* 28 tons.
*Seats* 2nd: 102.

## Motor Saloon Brake Second

(As Above)

| 4378 | 4381 | 4384 | 4387 |
| 4379 | 4382 | 4385 |      |
| 4380 | 4383 | 4386 |      |

---

## Motor Saloon Brake Second

*Body:* 62' 6" × 9' 0" & 9' 3".
*Weight:* 39 tons.
*Seats* 2nd: 82.
*Equipment:* Two 250 h.p. English Electric traction motors.

## Trailer Second

*Body:* 62' 6" × 9' 0" & 9' 3".
*Weight:* 28 tons.
*Seats* 2nd: 120.

## Trailer Second

(As Above)

## Motor Saloon Brake Second

(As Above)

| | | | |
|------|------|------|------|
| 4601 | 4603 | 4605 | 4607 |
| 4602 | 4604 | 4606 | |

---

## Motor Saloon Brake Second

*Body:* 62′ 6″ × 9′ 0″ & 9′ 3″.
*Weight:* 39 tons.
*Seats 2nd:* 82.
*Equipment:* Two 250 h.p. English
Electric traction motors.

### Trailer Second

*Body:* 62′ 0″ × 9′ 0″ & 9′ 3′.
*Weight:* 28 tons.
    27 tons. *
*Seats 2nd:* 120.
    108*.

### Trailer Saloon Second

*Body:* 62′ 0″ × 9′ 0″ & 9′ 3″.
*Weight:* 26 tons.
    28 tons.
*Seats 2nd:* 102.

## Motor Brake Saloon Second

(As Above)

| | | | |
|------|------|------|-------|
| 4621 | 4643 | 4665 | 4687 |
| 4622 | 4644 | 4666 | 4688* |
| 4623 | 4645 | 4667 | 4689 |
| 4624 | 4646 | 4668 | 4690 |
| 4625 | 4647 | 4669 | 4691 |
| 4626 | 4648 | 4670 | 4692 |
| 4627 | 4649 | 4671 | 4693 |
| 4628 | 4650 | 4672 | 4694 |
| 4629 | 4651 | 4673 | 4695 |
| 4630 | 4652 | 4674 | 4696* |
| 4631 | 4653 | 4675 | 4697 |
| 4632 | 4654 | 4676 | 4698 |
| 4633 | 4655 | 4677 | 4699 |
| 4634 | 4656 | 4678 | 4700 |
| 4635 | 4657 | 4679 | 4701 |
| 4636 | 4658 | 4680 | 4702 |
| 4637 | 4659 | 4681 | 4703 |
| 4638 | 4660 | 4682 | 4704 |
| 4639 | 4661 | 4683 | 4705 |
| 4640 | 4662 | 4684 | 4706 |
| 4641 | 4663 | 4685 | 4707 |
| 4642 | 4664 | 4686 | 4708 |

| | | | |
|------|------|-------|------|
| 4709 | 4721 | 4733* | 4744 |
| 4710 | 4722 | 4734 | 4745 |
| 4711 | 4723* | 4735 | 4746 |
| 4712 | 4724 | 4736 | 4747 |
| 4713 | 4725 | 4737 | 4748 |
| 4714 | 4726 | 4738 | 4749 |
| 4715 | 4727 | 4739* | 4750 |
| 4716 | 4728* | 4740 | 4751 |
| 4717 | 4729 | 4741 | 4752 |
| 4718 | 4730 | 4742 | 4753 |
| 4719 | 4731 | 4743 | 4754 |
| 4720 | 4732 | | |

## FOUR-CAR SUBURBAN SETS (4-EPB.)

### Motor Saloon Brake Second

*Body:* 62′ 6″ × 9′ 0″ & 9′ 3″.
*Weight:* 40 tons.
*Seats 2nd:* 82.
*Equipment:* Two 250 h.p. English
Electric traction motors.

### Trailer Second

*Body:* 62′ 0″ × 9′ 0″ & 9′ 3″.
*Weight:* 28 tons.
*Seats 2nd:* 120.
    108*.

### Trailer Saloon Second

*Body:* 62′ 0″ × 9′ 0″ & 9′ 3″.
*Weight:* 27 tons.
*Seats 2nd:* 102.

### Motor Saloon Brake Second

(As Above)

| | | | |
|-------|------|------|------|
| 5001 | 5013 | 5025 | 5036 |
| 5002 | 5014 | 5026 | 5037 |
| 5003 | 5015 | 5027 | 5038 |
| 5004 | 5016 | 5028 | 5039 |
| 5005* | 5017 | 5029 | 5040 |
| 5006 | 5018 | 5030 | 5041 |
| 5007 | 5019 | 5031 | 5042 |
| 5009 | 5020 | 5032 | 5043 |
| 5010 | 5021 | 5033 | 5044 |
| 5011 | 5022 | 5034 | 5045 |
| 5012 | 5024 | 5035 | 5046 |

| | | | |
|---|---|---|---|
| 5047 | 5136 | 5178 | 5220* |
| 5048 | 5137 | 5179 | 5221 |
| 5049 | 5138 | 5180 | 5222 |
| 5050 | 5139 | 5181 | 5223 |
| 5051 | 5140 | 5182 | 5224 |
| 5052 | 5141 | 5183 | 5225 |
| 5053 | 5142 | 5184 | 5226 |
| 5101 | 5143 | 5185 | 5227 |
| 5102 | 5144 | 5186 | 5228 |
| 5103 | 5145 | 5187 | 5229 |
| 5104 | 5146 | 5188 | 5230 |
| 5105 | 5147 | 5189 | 5231 |
| 5106 | 5148 | 5190 | 5232 |
| 5107 | 5149 | 5191 | 5233 |
| 5108 | 5150 | 5192 | 5234 |
| 5109 | 5151 | 5193 | 5235 |
| 5110 | 5152 | 5194 | 5236 |
| 5111 | 5153 | 5195 | 5237 |
| 5112 | 5154 | 5196 | 5238 |
| 5113 | 5155 | 5197 | 5239 |
| 5114 | 5156 | 5198 | 5240 |
| 5115 | 5157 | 5199 | 5241 |
| 5116 | 5158 | 5200 | 5242 |
| 5117 | 5159 | 5201 | 5243 |
| 5118 | 5160 | 5202 | 5244 |
| 5119 | 5161 | 5203 | 5245 |
| 5120 | 5162 | 5205 | 5246 |
| 5121 | 5163 | 5206 | 5247 |
| 5122 | 5164 | 5207 | 5248 |
| 5123 | 5165 | 5208 | 5249 |
| 5124 | 5166 | 5209 | 5250 |
| 5125 | 5167 | 5210 | 5251 |
| 5126 | 5168 | 5211 | 5252 |
| 5127 | 5169 | 5212 | 5253 |
| 5128 | 5170 | 5213 | 5254 |
| 5129 | 5171 | 5214 | 5255 |
| 5130 | 5172 | 5215 | 5256 |
| 5131 | 5173 | 5216 | 5257 |
| 5132 | 5174 | 5217 | 5258 |
| 5133 | 5175 | 5218 | 5259 |
| 5134 | 5176 | 5219 | 5260 |
| 5135 | 5177 | | |

## FOUR-CAR SUBURBAN SETS (4-EPB.)

*B.R. Standard design*

### Motor Saloon Brake Second

*Body:* 63' 11½" × 9' 0" & 9' 3".
*Weight:* 39 tons.
        40 tons.
*Seats 2nd:* 82.
*Equipment:* Two 250 h.p. English Electric traction motors.

### Trailer Second (Semi-Compartment)

*Body:* 63' 6" × 9' 0" & 9' 3".
*Weight:* 29 tons.
*Seats 2nd:* 112.

### Trailer Second (Semi-Compartment)

(As Above)

### Motor Saloon Brake Second

(As Above)

| | | | |
|---|---|---|---|
| 5301* | 5315 | 5329 | 5343 |
| 5302* | 5316 | 5330 | 5344 |
| 5303 | 5317 | 5331 | 5345 |
| 5304 | 5318 | 5332 | 5346 |
| 5305 | 5319 | 5333 | 5347 |
| 5306 | 5320 | 5334 | 5348 |
| 5307 | 5321 | 5335 | 5349 |
| 5308 | 5322 | 5336 | 5350 |
| 5309 | 5323 | 5337 | 5351 |
| 5310 | 5324 | 5338 | 5352 |
| 5311 | 5325 | 5339 | 5353 |
| 5312 | 5326 | 5340 | 5354 |
| 5313 | 5327 | 5341 | 5355 |
| 5314 | 5328 | 5342 | 5356 |

*Formed partly of S.R. type vehicles on 62' underframes weights as 5001–5260.

## TWO-CAR SETS (2-HAP.)

### Motor Brake Second (Semi-Saloon)

*Body:* 62' 6" × 9' 0" & 9' 3".
*Weight:* 40. tons.
*Seats 2nd:* 84.
*Equipment:* Two 250 h.p. English Electric traction motors.

### Driving Trailer Composite (K)

Body· 62' 6" × 9' 0" & 9' 3".
Weight: 32 tons.
Seats 1st  18.
2nd:  36.

| | | | |
|---|---|---|---|
| 5601 | 5610 | 5619 | 5628 |
| 5602 | 5611 | 5620 | 5629 |
| 5603 | 5612 | 5621 | 5630 |
| 5604 | 5613 | 5622 | 5631 |
| 5605 | 5614 | 5623 | 5632 |
| 5606 | 5615 | 5624 | 5633 |
| 5607 | 5616 | 5625 | 5634 |
| 5608 | 5617 | 5626 | 5635 |
| 5609 | 5618 | 5627 | 5636 |

## TWO-CAR
## SUBURBAN SETS
## (2-NOP.)

### Motor Brake Second
### (Semi-Saloon)

Body: 62' 6" × 9' 0" & 9' 3".
Weight: 40 tons.
Seats 2nd: 84.
Equipment:  Two  250  h.p.  English
Electric traction motors.

### Driving Trailer Second
### (Semi-Saloon)

Body: 62' 6" × 9' 0" & 9' 3"
Weight: 30 tons.
Seats 2nd: 94.

| | | | |
|---|---|---|---|
| 5651 | 5660 | 5669 | 5677 |
| 5652 | 5661 | 5670 | 5678 |
| 5653 | 5662 | 5671 | 5679 |
| 5654 | 5663 | 5672 | 5680 |
| 5655 | 5664 | 5673 | 5681 |
| 5656 | 5665 | 5674 | 5682 |
| 5657 | 5666 | 5675 | 5683 |
| 5658 | 5667 | 5676 | 5684 |
| 5659 | 5668 | | |

## TWO-CAR
## SUBURBAN SETS
## (2-EPB.)

B.R. Standard design

### Motor Brake Second
### (Semi-Saloon)

Body: 63' 11½" × 9' 0" & 9' 3".
Weight: 40 tons.
Seats 2nd: 84.
Equipment:  Two  250  h.p.  English
Electric traction motors.

### Driving Trailer Second
### (Semi-Compartment)

Body: 63' 11½" × 9' 0" & 9' 3".
Weight: 30 tons.
31 tons*.
Seats 2nd: 102.

| | | | |
|---|---|---|---|
| 5701 | 5721 | 5741 | 5761 |
| 5702 | 5722 | 5742 | 5762 |
| 5703 | 5723 | 5743 | 5763 |
| 5704 | 5724 | 5744 | 5764 |
| 5705 | 5725 | 5745 | 5765 |
| 5706 | 5726 | 5746 | 5767 |
| 5707 | 5727 | 5747 | 5768 |
| 5708 | 5728 | 5748 | 5769 |
| 5709 | 5729 | 5749 | 5770 |
| 5710 | 5730 | 5750 | 5771 |
| 5711 | 5731 | 5751 | 5772 |
| 5712 | 5732 | 5752 | 5773 |
| 5713 | 5733 | 5753 | 5774 |
| 5714 | 5734 | 5754 | 5775 |
| 5715 | 5735 | 5755 | 5776 |
| 5716 | 5736 | 5756 | 5777 |
| 5717 | 5737 | 5757 | 5778 |
| 5718 | 5738 | 5758 | 5779 |
| 5719 | 5739 | 5759 | 5800* |
| 5720 | 5740 | 5760 | |

## TWO-CAR SETS
## (2-HAP.)

B.R. Standard design

### Motor Brake Second
### (Semi-Saloon)

Body: 63' 11½" × 9' 0" & 9' 3"
Weight: 40 tons.
Seats 2nd: 84.
Equipment:  Two  250  h.p.  English
Electric traction motors.

## Driving Trailer Composite (L)

*Body:* 63' 11½" × 9' 0" & 9' 3".
*Weight:* 30 tons.
*Seats 1st:* 19.
2nd: 50.

| | | | |
|---|---|---|---|
| 6001 | 6028 | 6054 | 6080 |
| 6002 | 6029 | 6055 | 6081 |
| 6003 | 6030 | 6056 | 6082 |
| 6004 | 6031 | 6057 | 6083 |
| 6005 | 6032 | 6058 | 6084 |
| 6006 | 6033 | 6059 | 6085 |
| 6007 | 6034 | 6060 | 6086 |
| 6008 | 6035 | 6061 | 6087 |
| 6009 | 6036 | 6062 | 6088 |
| 6010 | 6037 | 6063 | 6089 |
| 6011 | 6038 | 6064 | 6090 |
| 6012 | 6039 | 6065 | 6091 |
| 6013 | 6040 | 6066 | 6092 |
| 6014 | 6041 | 6067 | 6093 |
| 6015 | 6042 | 6068 | 6094 |
| 6016 | 6043 | 6069 | 6095 |
| 6017 | 6044 | 6070 | 6096 |
| 6018 | 6045 | 6071 | 6097 |
| 6019 | 6046 | 6072 | 6098 |
| 6020 | 6047 | 6073 | 6099 |
| 6021 | 6048 | 6074 | 6100 |
| 6022 | 6049 | 6075 | 6101 |
| 6023 | 6050 | 6076 | 6102 |
| 6024 | 6051 | 6077 | 6103 |
| 6025 | 6052 | 6078 | 6104 |
| 6026 | 6053 | 6079 | 6105 |
| 6027 | | | |

---

## FOUR-CAR SETS (4-BEP.)

*B.R. Standard design*

*Gangwayed throughout*

### Motor Saloon Brake Second

*Body:* 64' 6" × 9' 0" & 9' 3".
*Weight:* 40 tons*.
41 tons.
*Seats 2nd:* 56.
*Equipment:* Two 250 h.p. English Electric traction motors.

## Trailer Composite (K)

*Body:* 64' 6" × 9' 0" & 9' 3".
*Weight:* 31 tons*.
33 tons.
*Seats 1st :* 24
2nd: 24

## Trailer Buffet

*Body:* 64' 6" × 9' 0" & 9' 3".
*Weight:* 35 tons*.
36 tons.
*Seats Buffet:* 21.

## Motor Saloon Brake Second

(As Above)

| | | | |
|---|---|---|---|
| 7001* | 7007 | 7013 | 7018 |
| 7002* | 7008 | 7014 | 7019 |
| 7003 | 7009 | 7015 | 7020 |
| 7004 | 7010 | 7016 | 7021 |
| 7005 | 7011 | 7017 | 7022 |
| 7006 | 7012 | | |

---

## FOUR-CAR SETS (4-CEP.)

*B.R. Standard design*

*Gangwayed throughout*

## Motor Saloon Brake Second

*Body:* 64' 6" × 9' 0" & 9' 3".
*Weight:* 40 tons*.
41 tons.
*Seats 2nd:* 56.
*Equipment:* Two 250 h.p. English Electric traction motors.

## Trailer Composite (K)

*Body:* 64' 6" × 9' 0" & 9' 3".
*Weight:* 31 tons*.
33 tons.
*Seats 1st:* 24.
2nd: 24.

## Trailer Second (K)

*Body:* 64' 6" × 9' 0" & 9' 3".
*Weight:* 31 tons*.
32 tons.
*Seats 2nd:* 64.

## Motor Saloon Brake Second

(As Above)

| | | | |
|---|---|---|---|
| 7101* | 7127 | 7153 | 7179 |
| 7102* | 7128 | 7154 | 7180 |
| 7103* | 7129 | 7155 | 7181 |
| 7104* | 7130 | 7156 | 7182 |
| 7105 | 7131 | 7157 | 7183 |
| 7106 | 7132 | 7158 | 7184 |
| 7107 | 7133 | 7159 | 7185 |
| 7108 | 7134 | 7160 | 7186 |
| 7109 | 7135 | 7161 | 7187 |
| 7110 | 7136 | 7162 | 7188 |
| 7111 | 7137 | 7163 | 7189 |
| 7112 | 7138 | 7164 | 7190 |
| 7113 | 7139 | 7165 | 7191 |
| 7114 | 7140 | 7166 | 7192 |
| 7115 | 7141 | 7167 | 7193 |
| 7116 | 7142 | 7168 | 7194 |
| 7117 | 7143 | 7169 | 7195 |
| 7118 | 7144 | 7170 | 7196 |
| 7119 | 7145 | 7171 | 7197 |
| 7120 | 7146 | 7172 | 7198 |
| 7121 | 7147 | 7173 | 7199 |
| 7122 | 7148 | 7174 | 7200 |
| 7123 | 7149 | 7175 | 7201 |
| 7124 | 7150 | 7176 | 7202 |
| 7125 | 7151 | 7177 | 7203 |
| 7126 | 7152 | 7178 | 7204 |

---

## Motor Luggage Van

Body: 64' 6" × 9' 0" & 9' 3".
Weight: 45 tons.
Equipment: Two 250 h.p. English
Electric traction motors.

*Note:* These vehicles can work singly, hauling a limited load, or in multiple with EP-type stock. They are equipped with traction batteries for working on non-electrified quay lines at Dover and Folkestone.

### COACH Nos.

| | |
|---|---|
| S68001 | S68004 |
| S68002 | S68005 |
| S68003 | S68006 |

## WATERLOO & CITY
## ONE- OR FIVE-CAR SETS

### Motor Saloon Brake Second

Body: 47' 0" × 8' 7¾".
Weight:
Seats 2nd: 40.
Equipment: Two 190 h.p. English
Electric traction motors.

| | | | |
|---|---|---|---|
| 51 | 54 | 57 | 60 |
| 52 | 55 | 58 | 61 |
| 53 | 56 | 59 | 62 |

### Trailer Saloon Second

Body: 47' 0" × 8' 7¾".
Weight: 18 tons 14 cwt.
Seats 2nd: 52.

| | | | |
|---|---|---|---|
| 71 | 75 | 79 | 83 |
| 72 | 76 | 80 | 84 |
| 73 | 77 | 81 | 85 |
| 74 | 78 | 82 | 86 |

Trains are formed of a single motor car or up to five-car units comprising two motor cars and three trailers.

---

## S.R. DEPARTMENTAL ELECTRIC UNITS

Two-car motor de-icing units formed from the Motor Coaches of withdrawn 1925 units.

| | | | |
|---|---|---|---|
| 92 | 95 | 98 | 101 |
| 93 | 96 | 99 | |
| 94 | 97 | 100 | |

First published 1961
Reprinted 2012

ISBN 978 0 7110 3735 9

Published by Ian Allan Publishing

an imprint of Ian Allan Publishing Ltd, Hersham, Surrey, KT12 4RG.

Printed by Ian Allan Printing Ltd, Hersham, Surrey, KT12 4RG.

Code: 1209/B

This is a facsimilie reprint of an original edition first published in 1961,
and as such, all advertisements are no longer valid.

Distributed in the United States of America and Canada by
BookMasters Distribution Services.

Visit the Ian Allan Publishing website at www.ianallanpublishing.com

*Front cover:*
Somerset & Dorset Joint Railway Class 7F No 53803 is seen near
Wellow with a down freight in March 1961. *G. H. Hunt / Colour-Rail*

*Back cover:*
A Swindon-built Class 124 unit forms the 9.45am Leeds–Manchester
service near Spen Valley junction in January 1961. *D. J. Lane*